Places, Streets and Movement

A companion guide to Design Bulletin 32

Residential roads and footpaths

September 1998

Department of the Environment, Transport and the Regions: London

Department of the Environment, Transport and the Regions
Eland House
Bressenden Place
London SW1E 5DU
Telephone 020 7944 3000
Internet service http://www.detr.gov.uk/

Further copies of this report are available from:

Department of the Environment, Transport and the Regions
Publications Sale Centre
Unit 8
Goldthorpe Industrial Estate
Goldthorpe
Rotherham S63 9BL
Tel: 01709 891318
Fax: 01709 881673
and branches of The Stationery Office

ISBN 1-85112-113-7

Published by the DETR. Reprinted in the UK March 2001 on paper comprising 75% post consumer waste and 25% ECF pulp. Product code 00PD1421

This guide was compiled by Alan Baxter & Associates (David Taylor, Robert Thorne, Andrew Cameron, Lynne Armishaw, Tariq Yahiadui) on behalf of the Department of the Environment, Transport and the Regions. Consultant: Peter Phippen, PRP Architects. Designed by Thomas Manss & Company (Thomas Manss, David Law, Annet Hilgersom). 1998

Sounding board members
During the preparation of this guide, advice was received from a Sounding Board consisting of the following people: David R. Beales, Director of Planning, East Hertfordshire District Council; Mrs Susan Bridge, Regional Planning Manager (Midlands), Bellway Estates Plc; Kelvin Campbell, Urban Initiatives; Ian Chatten, Team Leader, Traffic Management Group, Dept of Planning & Development, Knowsley Metropolitan Borough Council; Paul Cooke, D. J. Higgins & Son; Paul Davis, Group Strategic Land & Planning Manager, Beazer Homes Plc; Paul Garber, Wimpey Homes; Trisha Gupta, Countryside Properties Plc; Peter Hardy, Community Safety Department, Sussex Police; Stephen Heathcote, Head of Environmental Design, Wokingham District Council; Alan Hedges (Consultant in Social & Business Planning & Research); Dr Mayer Hillman, Policy Studies Institute; Peter Knowles, Force Architectural Liaison Officer, Bedfordshire Police; Ian Madgewick, Highways Development Liaison Engineer, Dorset County Council; John Noble; David Oliver, ex-District Architect, West Dorset District Council; Graham Pye, J. A. Pye (Oxford) Ltd; David Richards, Senior Partner, Barton Willmore Planning; John Simpson, John Simpson Partners Architects; Paul Smith, Architectural Technical Director, Wilson Bowden Plc; Les Sparks, Director of Planning & Architecture, Birmingham City Council; Mike Stanley, Head of Traffic Mangement, Bristol City Council; Alan Stones, Planning Department, Essex County Council; Alun Trott, Chief Engineer, County Surveyors Dept., Hampshire County Council; The nominated officers for Department of the Environment, Transport & the Regions were Richard Pullen, Fred Offen OBE, Eric Wyatt and Steve Batey.

Contents

This guide was compiled by Alan Baxter & Associates
(David Taylor, Robert Thorne, Andrew Cameron,
Lynne Armishaw, Tariq Yahiadui) on behalf of the
Department of the Environment, Transport and the Regions.
Consultant: Peter Phippen, PRP Architects.
Designed by Thomas Manss & Company
(Thomas Manss, David Law, Annet Hilgersom).
1998

Introduction

In the debate about our built environment the design of new housing development and the improvement of existing housing areas feature high on the agenda. The quality of where we live depends not just on our houses but also how they relate to their surroundings. Roads help to determine that quality. They are essential, yet too often in the immediate past it seems that roads have dominated housing areas, without regard to the overall quality of the locality.

This guide has been prepared to help reverse that tendency. It reasserts the need to create places which serve the needs of all, not just car drivers. The layout of housing areas should be based on the nature of the local place, rather than the rigid requirements of vehicle movement. Plans should provide for travel by foot, cycle and public transport just as they should for travel by car.

A number of developments in recent years have successfully accomplished these aims using the advice in Design Bulletin 32. This guide summarises what has been learned from them. It is based on the practical experience of those involved in every aspect of housebuilding and development, and on ideas which have been adopted and built.

This guide encourages a greater emphasis on place, community and context in the design of housing layouts. It promotes:

- *A flexible interpretation of DB32, involving more responsiveness to site and setting in the layout of new development to achieve a better balance between highway requirements and other factors.*

- *Developments designed to emphasise a sense of place and community, with movement networks to enhance those qualities.*

- *The reduction of car use through the provision of local facilities and public transport within walking distance of housing.*

- *The detailed design of roads, footpaths and cycle routes to avoid dominance by the car; and finally*

- *A move away from overly prescriptive standards.*

The advice presented here follows on the guidance given in Design Bulletin 32, Residential Roads and Footpaths (1977; 2nd edition 1992), which remains the principal technical source for the subject. This guide complements DB32, and is intended to ensure that DB32 is used more imaginatively than has previously been the case. It should be fully taken into account in the design of new housing areas and the upgrading of existing ones.

This work is intended for use by all those involved in the design of new housing developments and the rejuvenation of existing areas – primarily house builders, architects and urban designers, planners and traffic engineers. It is intentionally not slanted towards any one profession or group, in the belief that what is said here is relevant to all those who have an interest in the design of the places where we live. Unsatisfactory developments are usually the result of a blinkered approach, which can best be avoided by taking a broad view of the subject from the beginning. This guide explains:

- *The use of Design Bulletin 32 to create places which work well for everyone, and are not dominated by the car.*

- *What to take account of in a locality in designing a new development or improving an existing area.*

- *How to draw up a development framework, and what it should include.*

- *The qualities to aim for in creating developments which will be well loved and cared for.*

- *How the layout of areas, old and new, can contribute to the promotion of walking, cycling and public transport.*

The range of approaches described in this guide shows how the information in DB32 can be used to create high quality places. In addition, specific advice is given on the design of roads, footways and cycle tracks and their integration in different forms of development.

1

DB32 in context Current planning policies enable new residential areas to be developed which are as satisfying and cared for as the best existing areas

The policy framework

The Government is committed to planning land uses and infrastructure which reduce reliance on the private car, supported by complementary transport measures.

The advice given in this guide and in DB32 itself should be seen in the context of wider national Government policy and initiatives aimed at achieving attractive and sustainable residential areas and settlements through better design.

By means of its Sustainable Development Strategy, its developing Integrated Transport Strategy and national planning policy guidance, the Government wishes to promote:

- *more sustainable patterns of living, working and travelling;*
- *more effective integration between the land-use planning and transport; and*
- *the creation and maintenance of attractive successful places in which people are happy to live, work and take their leisure.*

The creation of attractive residential areas with a genuine sense of place is a prerequisite to achieving sustainability.

Sustainable Development Strategy

The emerging Sustainable Development Strategy seeks to ensure a better quality of life for everyone, now and for generations to come. To be sustainable, development must make good use of natural resources, protect the environment, promote social cohesion and contribute to local, regional and national prosperity. Building sustainable communities will be integral to achieving more sustainable development. Such communities should allow everyone to live in a clean and safe environment, be able to afford the basic services they need, and have the means to obtain a reasonable quality of life.

Planning has a key role to play in helping to achieve this more sustainable pattern of development. It seeks to integrate those economic, environmental and social factors, which are all important to sustainable development, in making decisions about where to put homes, jobs, shops and leisure facilities. By doing so, it can limit demands on land and the environment, and reduce the need to travel, especially by car.

The Government intends to publish the new Sustainable Development Strategy by the end of 1998.

Integrated Transport Strategy

The Government is committed to developing an integrated transport strategy which will provide the framework for the country's transport policy into the next millennium. The White Paper on the Future of Transport explains how a more integrated approach can be achieved.

A key objective of the Integrated Transport Strategy is to produce more sustainable transport patterns, in particular to reduce dependence on the car by providing genuine alternatives, and promoting greater use of more attractive public transport. By fostering forms of development which encourage walking, cycling and easy access to public transport, and by locating travel-generating development in existing centres, planning can complement other measures aimed at promoting greater use of public transport and reducing the environmental impact of transport.

The continuing need for more housing will also need to be considered in the context of the integrated transport policy. Whether new housing is located within existing urban areas or elsewhere, it will need to make the most of sites which are accessible to public transport, including sites close to town centres and local neighbourhood centres, to achieve more sustainable patterns of development.

These issues have been pursued further in the preparatory work for the Integrated Transport White Paper. The Government also fully supports the objectives of the National Cycling Strategy and encourages local authorities to take account of these objectives when considering new, and improvements to existing, developments. The National Walking Strategy, when published, should be given similar consideration.

Streets are places for meetings, socialising and exchange, not just for traffic.

Government policy favours an integrated approach to transport, not car-dominated streets.

Four out of five journeys under one mile are made on foot. Developments should be designed with walking (and cycling) in mind.

Urban Design

Good urban design, imaginatively used, helps to make places more attractive in which to live, and in the context of the need for more housing, may help them to accommodate more homes than was previously the case. To accommodate more development within urban areas, but more particularly to create more sustainable patterns of development, local planning authorities will need to explore the feasibility of an increase in the density of development around town and local centres and other areas well served by public transport. There may also be a need to achieve higher density development on greenfield sites, where that can be done in a high quality way.

As outlined in the Government's policy document 'Planning for the Communities of the Future', published in 1998, further advice will be issued both through a revision of PPG3 and good practice guidance on design in the planning system.

Planning Policy Guidance

Already the Government's Planning Policy Guidance promotes development which is of a more sustainable form and location, and which is well designed and fits in with its surroundings. Planning Policy Guidance Note 1 (Revised): General Policies and Principles sets out the Government's main aims and policies on different aspects of planning, including sustainable development, mixed use and good design, which local authorities must take into account in preparing their development plans. It advises that development plans should set out design policies against which development proposals are to be considered and emphasises the importance of such policies being based on a proper assessment of the character of the local area. It emphasises "the fact that a design or layout is appropriate for one area does not mean it is appropriate everywhere". PPG1 specifically identifies layout as one of the key factors that should be covered in plans in guiding the overall design of development. Mixed use development is promoted as a means of helping to create vitality and diversity and reducing the need to travel.

The revised PPG1 supports the key messages in PPG 13: Transport. PPG13, issued in 1994, sets out the planning framework for local authorities to integrate their transport programmes and land use policies. The aim is to help reduce growth in the length and number of motorised journeys and to encourage alternative means of travel which have less environmental impact.

On the location and development of housing, PPG13 recommends:

- *wherever possible, new housing should be located in existing urban areas, or in areas well served by public transport;*
- *conversely, development should be discouraged in places where it is likely to generate car commuting;*
- *local authorities should maintain existing housing densities and, where appropriate, increase them; and*
- *mixed-use development should be promoted to enable people to live near their work.*

PPG1: General Policies and Principles: Sets out the principles of sustainable development.

PPG3: Housing: Emphasises the importance of local context on the scale and shape of new developments.

PPG6: Town Centres and Retail Developments: Outlines policies to maintain a lively retail sector and other uses in existing town centres.

PPG7: The Countryside – Environment Quality and Economic and Social Development: Provides guidance on land use planning in rural areas, including policies for housing and new development.

PPG12: Development Plans and Regional Planning Guidance: Sets out the need to acknowledge local context and encourage alternative transport in development plans.

PPG13: Transport: Emphasises the need for integrated transport policies to help achieve sustainable developments. On housing its principal advice is that 'housing development should be located, wherever possible, so as to provide a choice of means of travel to other facilities.'

PPG15: Planning and the Historic Environment: Sets out the Government's policies on the conservation of the historic environment, including advice on the impact of new roads.

The role of design bulletin 32 and places streets and movement

In the context of these wider policies, DB32 and this guide have a major role to play. They can and should be used in the planning stages of development projects involving housing, in both new and existing areas, to help ensure that proposed development supports the aim of sustainable development. As the introduction to DB32 says, the first way to do this is to have a development brief which takes account of the characteristics of the site, the functions it is to have and varied access requirements of its users.

Local highways standards

Local highway standards should provide developers and others with information on the standards of design, layout and construction which local authorities would expect new developments to follow, particularly where roads are to be adopted. Design Bulletin 32 and this companion guide contain advice on layout and design which could be incorporated into local standards where appropriate.

It is strongly recommended that all local authorities have available information on the standards that they expect developers to follow, so that they can clearly understand what is required in preparing or interpreting a development brief.

Local plans and supplementary planning guidance

Local highway standards are not statutory; nor are DB32 and the many local design guides which reflect and interpret its precepts. However, all of these documents are vital to the design process because of the guidance they provide on the overall layout and design of residential roads and footpaths. PPG1 also advises that the weight accorded to supplementary design guidance in planning decisions will be expected to increase where it has been prepared in consultation with the public and with those whose work it may affect, and has been formally adopted by the local planning authority. PPG1 makes explicit reference to the fact that local design guides should explain how relevant general advice, including that relating to the design of roads and footways, is to be interpreted and applied at a local level in order to take account of the character of each area.

At the local level the key to achieving good design lies in the design policies contained in local plans and in the advice given in local design guides. Local authorities with a clear vision of their area's needs, and the kind of places that should accommodate them, can establish a framework for the creation of first-rate development. It is then for the developers and their designers to deliver them.

Houses adjacent to small workplaces

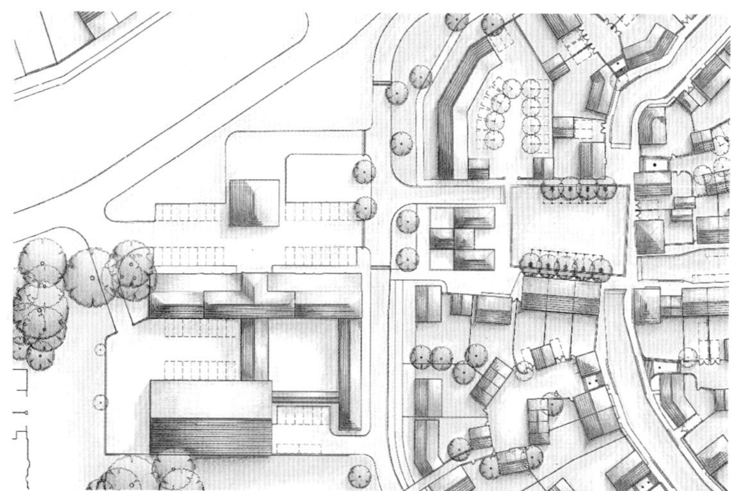

Mixed use developments can help reduce the need for travel: at the new community of Poundbury in Dorset workplaces (shown in blue on the map) are integrated with the housing.

The larger workplaces are accessed directly from the distributor roads.

The historical perspective

Communities of every size depend on movement. The main lesson from history is that high quality places are ones in which the provision for movement of every kind is integrated with the other functions of streets and spaces.

An understanding of how towns and villages have developed is an essential starting point for the design of new communities. The study of existing places helps establish an appreciation of local context and of the way traditional urban layouts can exert a calming effect on traffic.

The places where we live have been shaped by a wide range of influences; primarily by their location, function and patterns of ownership but also, over the last half century or more, by the requirements of our planning system. Most historic places owe their layout to their original function. Towns have grown up around a market place, a bridgehead or a harbour; villages have been formed according to the pattern of farming and the ownership of land.

In the long perspective of history, the deliberate planning of towns and other settlements is mostly a new phenomenon, whether it be the planned development of a new suburb on the outskirts of a town or the establishment of a totally new community. Alongside the planning of new development (whether by the landowner, the developer or the local authority) has gone the increasing regulation of the building and rebuilding of existing places.

Whether planned or not, all places rely on movement as their lifeblood. This is as true for the ordinary back street as it is for the crossroads in a major transport hub. At the most basic level housing cannot function without access and servicing, but the road or street is also a place where people meet and pass the time of day. In the past these functions were largely assumed and the laying out of roads can almost be said to have taken care of itself. But with the growth of planning by various agencies the making of roads and streets, particularly in new housing areas, has been subject to increasing regulation. This pattern of control in the shaping of development is something which we now take for granted.

Traditional towns often focus on their market place, as here at Beverley in Yorkshire.

Many inter-war suburbs, although not designed around the car, have been adapted to car ownership because of their generous road widths. The result is an environment dominated by cars.

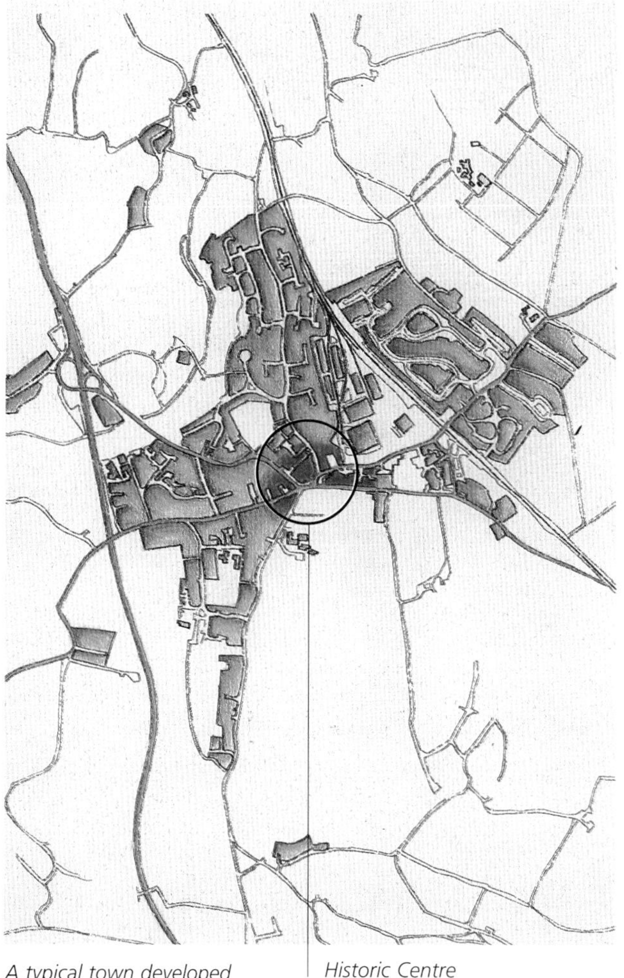

A typical town developed around a historic core. Recent additions have been designed to standard layouts regardless of local context, and are inadequately related to the centre.

When the regulation of roads and streets began it was the danger of fire that was uppermost in people's minds. Subsequently the issue of health came to the forefront and the classic 36ft wide bye-law street was devised as a means of ensuring the passage of air in densely built-up areas. Later still, the desire to guarantee that sunshine would get to every house produced the requirement for a 70ft separation between house fronts which shaped so many developments from the 1920s onwards.

It was not until after the Second World War, and particularly with the dramatic increase in car ownership from the 1960s onwards, that traffic considerations came to dominate the regulation of road design. Developers and house builders were obliged to follow the local highway requirements because if they failed to do so their roads might not be adopted by the local authority. The result was an over-rigid application of standards at the expense of other considerations that can contribute to the making of good places.

Market places such as this one at Chesterfield are still centres for buying, selling and sociability.

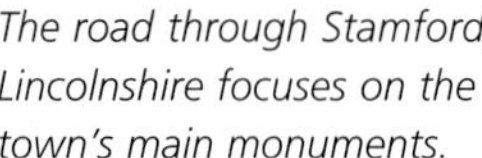

The road through Stamford, Lincolnshire focuses on the town's main monuments.

Historically the arrangement of buildings has shaped the street. At Colchester in Essex new buildings have helped maintain that traditional pattern.

Brindley Place, Birmingham is a mixed use development arranged around high quality public spaces.

Travel by Britons
by cycle, bus, train, car and plane

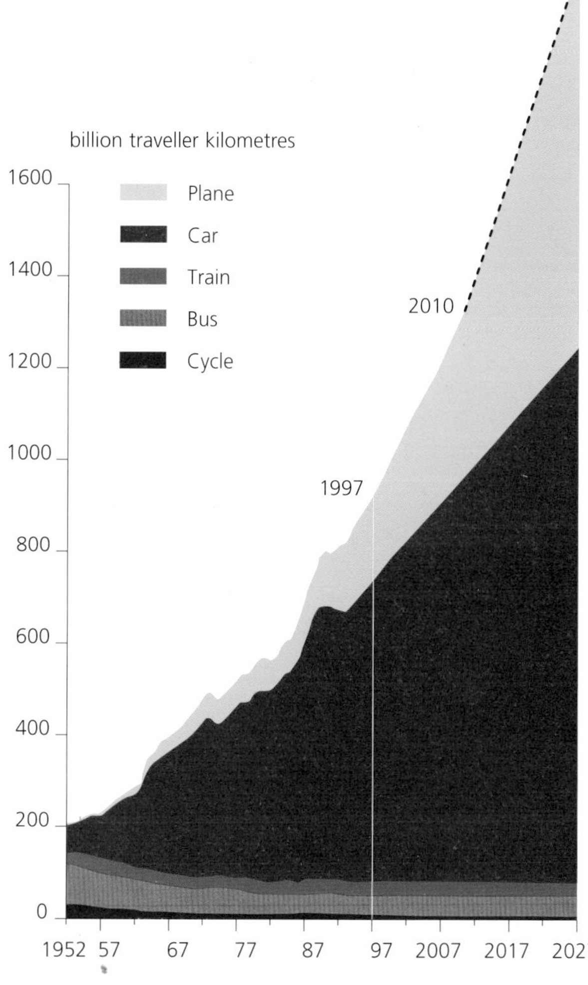

Over the years the way we use roads, streets and footpaths has changed significantly. The lesson from history is that such use will continue to change, and our response should be to accommodate change without over-reacting. When any one aspect of their use is singled out, and becomes the subject of the over-zealous application of a set of rules, their overall role becomes distorted.

The first edition of Design Bulletin 32 was published in 1977 to help promote a better balance between highway requirements and the other factors which need to be taken into account in designing new housing developments. It was revised fifteen years later to include more about traffic calming and the treatment of roads in existing areas. The second edition also included a more detailed consideration of security issues, which were not as high on the agenda in the 1970s as they have since become.

The broad aim of DB32, and thus of this guide, is to strike the right balance between the creation of a high quality environment and the role of the road as a means of movement and access. That balance has often been successfully achieved in the past and there is nothing to prevent its being achieved again now.

Actual and forecast growth in traffic – Great Britain (1952–2027). Many people take for granted an ever-increasing freedom of movement, especially by car. But an increase in car use on the scale predicted here will have unacceptable environmental consequences.

Historically the layout of English towns has been formed by the pattern of landholdings, and streets have obeyed that pattern. St John Street at Ashbourne, Derbyshire shows the kind of good quality street that resulted from that process.

Public spaces are traditionally marked by a square or a widening in the road. At Appleby in Cumbria the road widens to accommodate the Moot Hall.

The Garden Suburb Movement sought to replace the monotony of Victorian streets with a variety of streets and spaces.

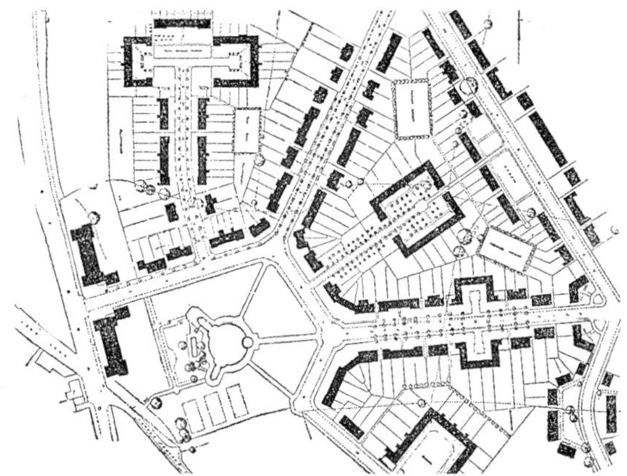

Inter-war council estates were designed with wide layouts to give houses the maximum light and sunshine.

Halton Brow at Runcorn, which was developed 1967-71, brought a breakthrough in thinking about the relationship between housing and roads. Narrow access roads were designed to create a traffic-calmed environment.

But more often than not, recent developments have adhered to standardised layouts, with the road as the dominant feature.

2

Key principles and issues Design Bulletin 32 enables the right balance to be struck between movement and the creation of good residential areas

Key principles and issues: Introduction

The design of housing areas has a major influence on people's transport movements. The creation of high quality places, with local facilities close at hand, will help reduce dependence on the car.

Too often new developments have been designed around the requirements of the car.

This chapter describes the underlying principles which should guide the development of new housing and the up-grading of existing housing areas. It is illustrated by examples of recent designs in which these principles have been successfully applied, plus a few examples of the kinds of development to be avoided.

The dramatic increase in car use during the last fifty years has transformed the way we live. For those with access to a car it has meant a fundamental change in the kinds of journey they make and in the choice of where to live, work and spend free time. The car has permitted freedom of movement on a scale never experienced before.

That freedom has had major consequences for the quality of movement of everyone in our society. What has benefited countless people has also disadvantaged many others, including children and the elderly. They often find themselves either isolated in places that are ill-served by public transport, or afraid to use traffic-dominated roads. The dramatic decline in the everyday experience of children walking or cycling to school is only one of many ways in which typical journeys have changed.

Congestion is harmful to everyone, not just motorists.

At a broader level, the increase in car use has altered the resources that are consumed in people's transport movements. Longer and more frequent journeys are made, and walking, cycling or using public transport have declined as the means of travel. With a view to achieving the best use of our limited resources, it is the Government's intention to reverse the most excessive tendencies of recent years and to develop a sustainable and integrated use of different means of transport. The Government proposes that pedestrians should be given greater priority especially in residential areas.

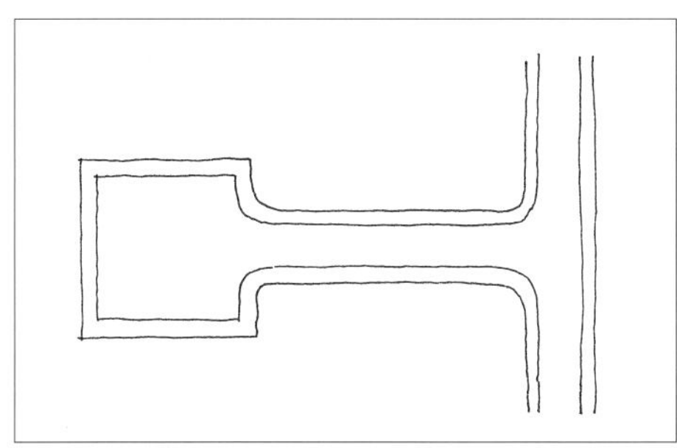

Roads first

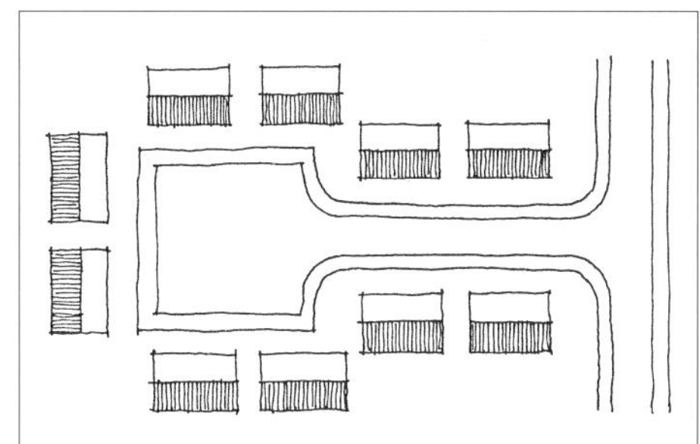

Houses later

Culs-de-sac are the classic form of road-dominated layout, with the road designed first and then the houses arranged around them. Though they have benefits (particularly as places where children can play in relative safety) they limit ease of movement, especially for pedestrians and cyclists.

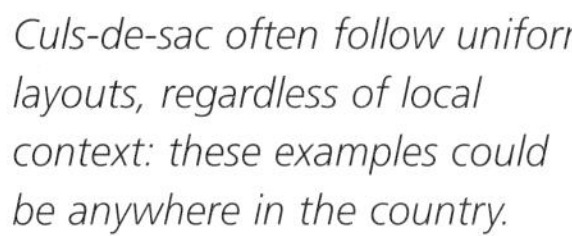

Culs-de-sac often follow uniform layouts, regardless of local context: these examples could be anywhere in the country.

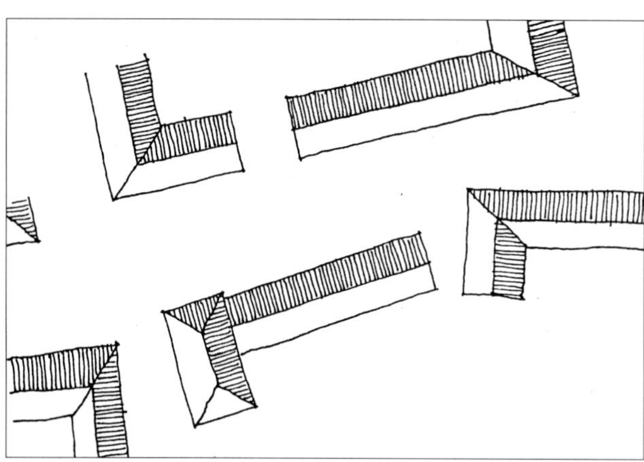

Arrange the buildings to fit the local context.

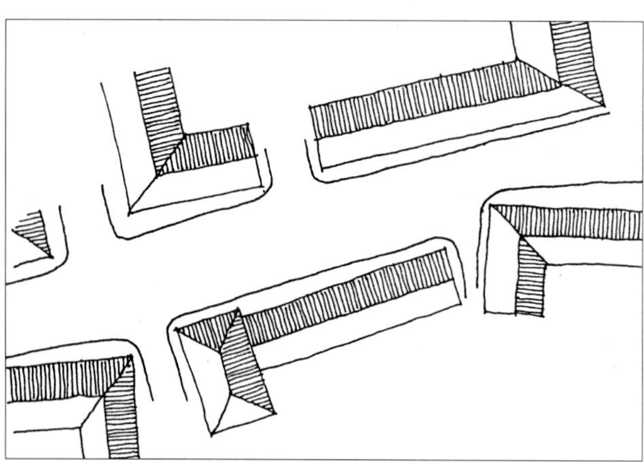

Then fit the roads in the spaces created.

How people travel is directly related to where they live. It is influenced by where their house is located – in a town centre, suburb or village – and also by the design and layout of their immediate surroundings. A family at the end of a long suburban cul-de-sac may have very different transport choices to one living in a city centre flat.

In most housing developments during recent decades, the response to increasing car use has been to focus layout design on the movement and parking of vehicles at the expense of other considerations. It is easy to understand how this has happened. Road design obeys certain engineering principles, devised primarily with safety and the convenience of motor traffic in mind. The universality of these principles has meant that all roads have been designed according to the same broad set of rules, regardless of the role a particular road has to play. By contrast, other considerations – of place, community and context – although equally important have frequently been overridden. They require a subtly different approach for every project, rather than the application of a standard set of formulae.

This reconciliation between the quality of place and the requirements of road design is never straightforward or easy, especially since no one place is quite like another. The key factors to take into account are:

- *The nature of the place where development is to occur.*
- *How that place relates to its surroundings, including movement routes.*
- *The framework of development, including the network of spaces and movement patterns.*

This approach is discussed in more detail in the sections that follow.

Dorchester is a typical medium-sized town, originally developed around a crossroads. The extension at Poundbury on the western outskirts has been designed to complement the historic core.

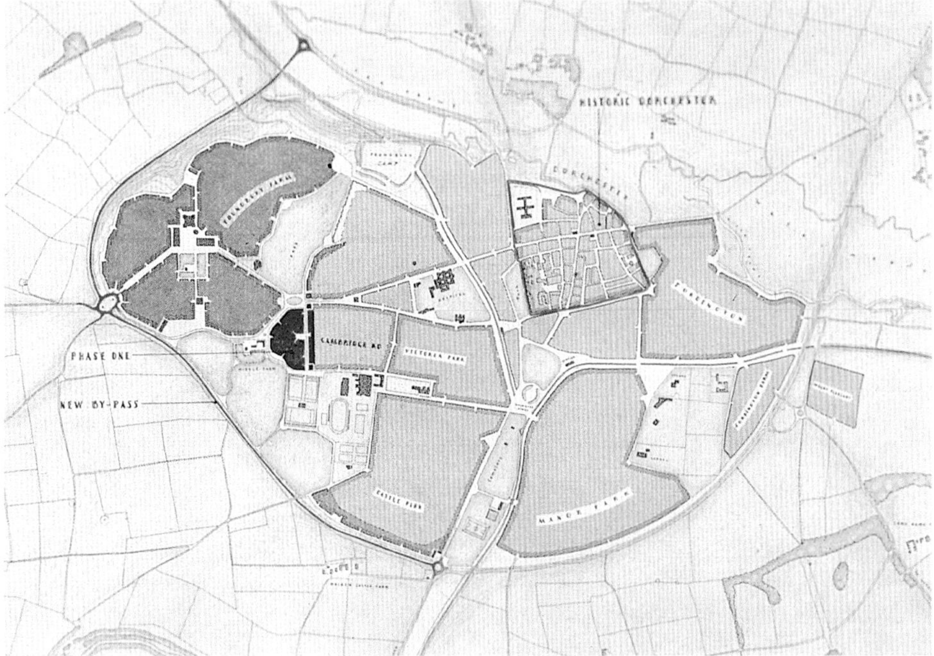

The framework for development allows each section to establish a life of its own, but still connected to the town as a whole.

Look at the place not the car

In the creation of housing areas the priority should be to establish a sense of place and community, with movement networks used to enhance those qualities.

The main result of the emphasis on the movement of cars and vehicles has been that in new developments the roads are designed first, and then the houses are fitted around them. The planning of housing layouts has been dictated first and foremost by the road hierarchy, from the distributor road down to the cul-de-sac or courtyard. The geometry of road design and the highway authority's adoption standards have frequently created places which relate badly to their locality and are indistinguishable one from another.

Within residential areas, new and old, it is the sense of place which should have priority. In the making of places it is not the road layout but the relationship of buildings to each other which should be paramount. Fortunately there are now a good number of developments around the country which demonstrate how buildings and roads can be integrated in a way that is sensitive to their locality: some are illustrated in this guide. They show that highway needs can be met, using the technical information in DB32, within developments which have a genuine sense of community and local context.

Ideally the design of new developments should be based on a network of spaces rather than a hierarchy of roads; a layout of development in which roads play their part but are not dominant.

Historically most places have had a network of spaces, whether they be a medieval market town, an eighteenth century spa, or a Victorian suburb. The hierarchy of such places can often be easily recognised, even by a first time visitor, and though the functions of the town may have changed the layout remains the key to people's understanding of where they are. The hierarchy inherent in the layout frequently has an effect in calming and filtering the traffic, even though that was not the main preoccupation of those who originally laid out the town.

By their nature, present-day housing developments have a more uniform function than most historic places, but that does not invalidate the need to create a clear network in their layout through the way the buildings and spaces are arranged. Density, building form and enclosure are the main ingredients in creating developments which have a clear sense of local identity.

In all schemes a development brief or framework should be established at the outset. This will define the basic layout of spaces (streets, squares and courtyards) and how movement relates to them. The framework should be flexible enough to accommodate change as the development progresses, yet robust enough to ensure that the clarity of the overall pattern is maintained from beginning to end.

The principal functions of the development brief will be:

- *To ensure that the key characteristics of the local context are taken into account from the outset.*
- *To establish the overall form of the development, based on the density and layout of buildings and spaces.*
- *To show how the layout of roads and streets will contribute to the spatial hierarchy, as well as linking the development to the rest of the locality.*

In most projects involving the upgrading of an existing housing area a hierarchy of spaces already exists, in which case the priority should be to maintain and enhance the layout pattern which has been inherited. Superimposing a new network on existing spaces generally produces unsatisfactory results.

The following pages illustrate four projects in different parts of the country which follow the principles outlined here.

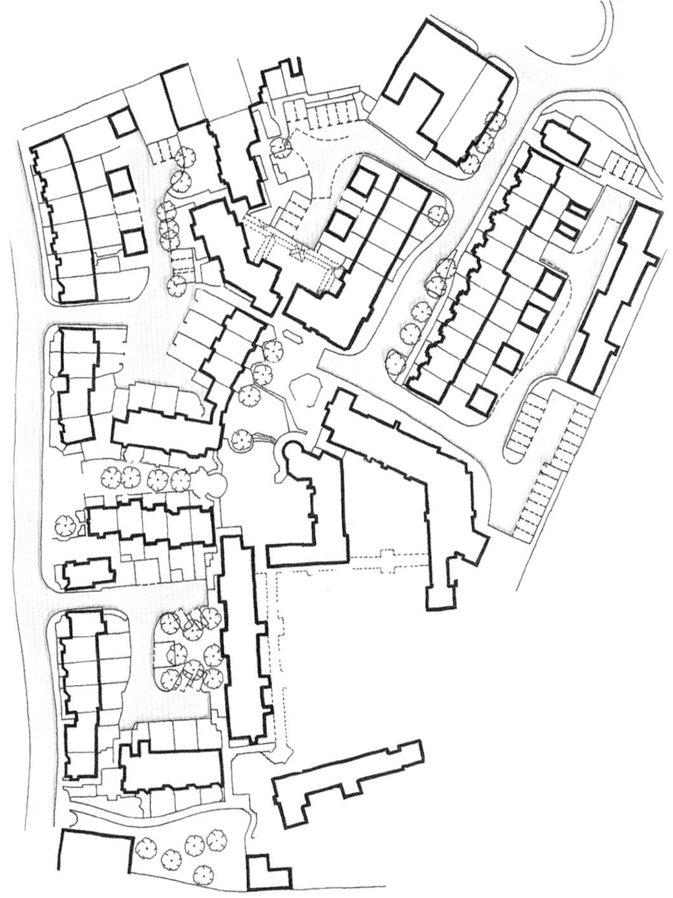

New developments at Beverley in Yorkshire respect the town's existing urban pattern and scale. The courtyard arrangement discourages vehicle access but helps create new pedestrian routes through the town.

At Wick Village in Hackney the layout of new housing makes a feature of its relationship to the canal. There is access from two adjacent roads, but no through routes for vehicles and the layout is designed so that parked cars never dominate the spaces.

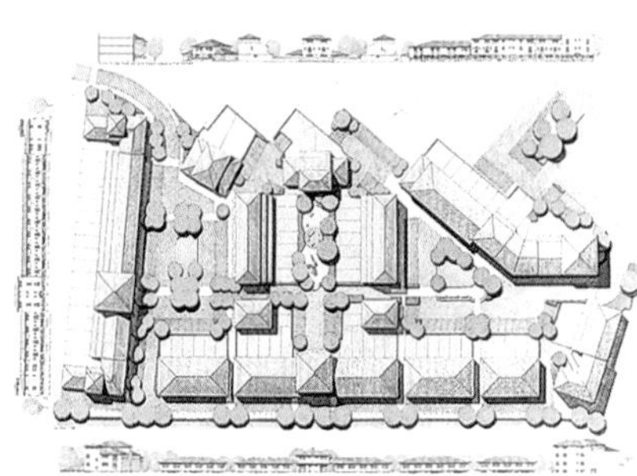

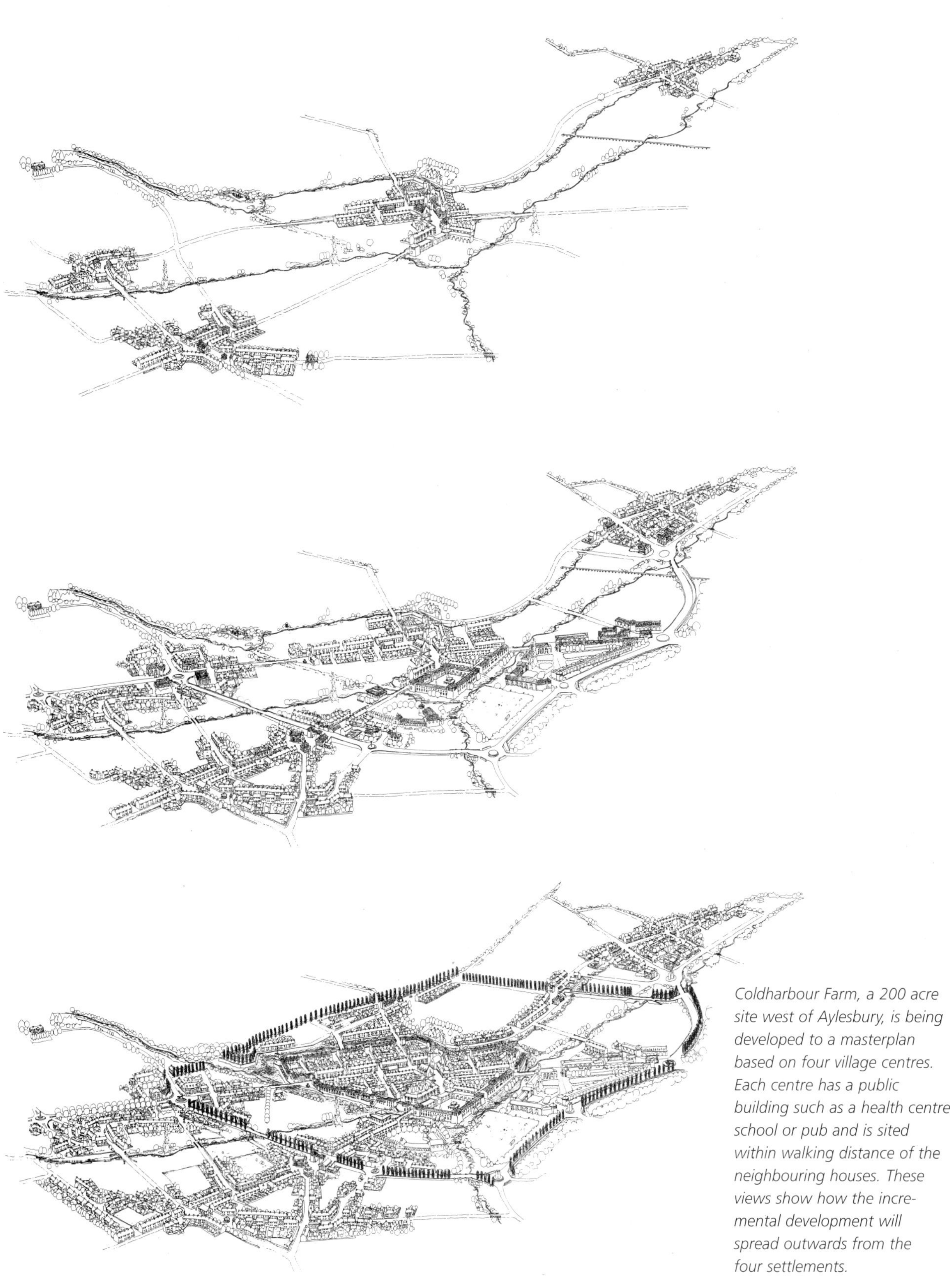

Coldharbour Farm, a 200 acre site west of Aylesbury, is being developed to a masterplan based on four village centres. Each centre has a public building such as a health centre, school or pub and is sited within walking distance of the neighbouring houses. These views show how the incremental development will spread outwards from the four settlements.

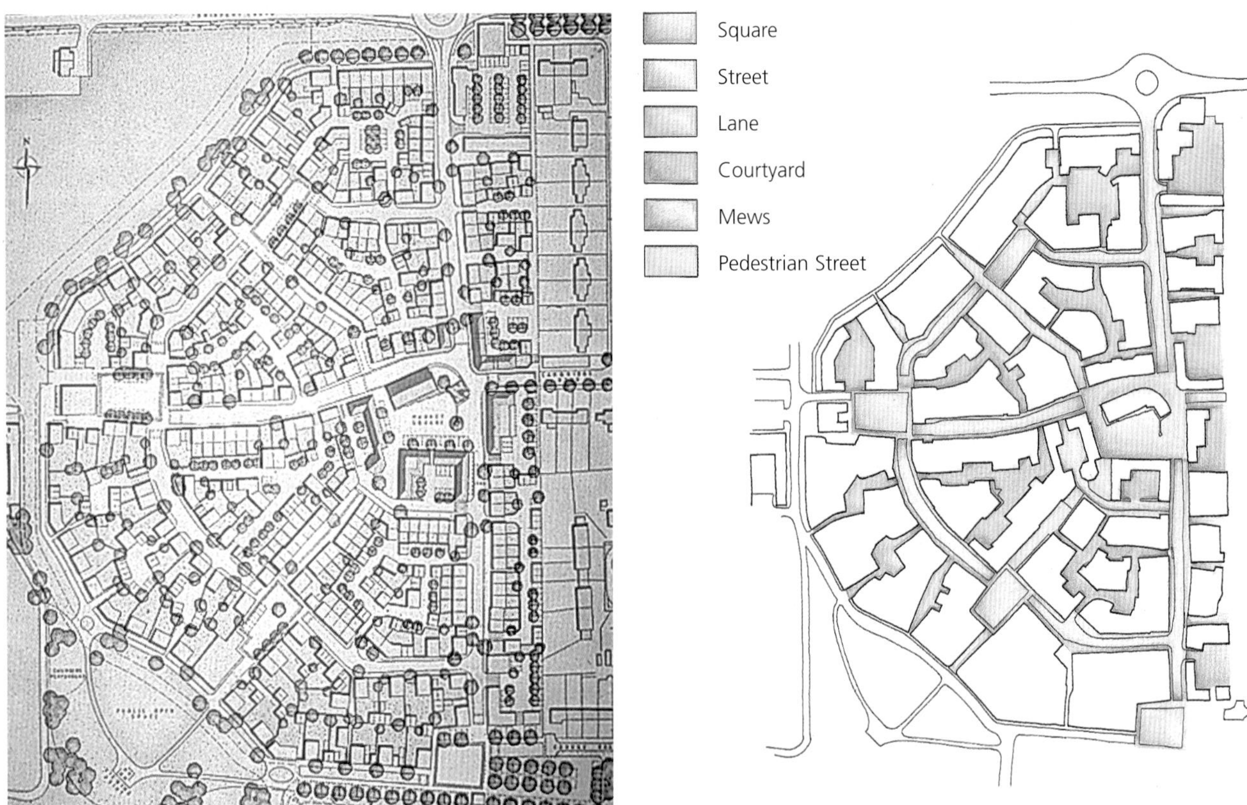

The first phase of development at Poundbury has been laid out around a network of spaces. Vehicles have full access but primacy is given to the creation of coherent, attractive neighbourhoods.

Square

The network of spaces at Poundbury give a clear identity to each part of the development. The layout provides effective traffic calming without the need for additional constraints.

Street

Courtyard

Mews

Pedestrian Street

The all too typical alternative: a development showing no regard to its setting and no clear hierarchy of spaces.

The movement framework

The design of a movement framework for new development is the best way to ensure that travel by foot, bicycle and public transport have priority.

To be successful, sustainable development needs to consider all forms of movement. Only if it does so will people be encouraged to forsake their reliance on the car in favour of travelling by foot, bicycle and public transport. In addition, a comprehensive strategy for movement has the virtue of providing room for change in the future.

With that in mind, the framework for a new development should take into account:

- *Priorities for movement; firstly by foot, also by bicycle, public transport and car. The needs of disabled people should receive particular attention.*

- *The relationship between movement and all forms of development.*

- *The links between new movement routes and existing infrastructure.*

One particular benefit of considering movement in all its facets at the outset is that routes for different forms of movement can be safeguarded during the course of the development. Occasionally the appropriate route for a footpath or a cycle track is not the same as for a road. Positive discrimination in favour of direct routes for pedestrians or cyclists has to be built into the plan from the outset because fitting them in later will be difficult, if not impossible.

The integration of pedestrian and cycle routes into the building fabric is as vital as the relationship between roads and buildings. It is particularly important to ensure that routes are safe, secure and convenient: if they are not, people will feel forced back onto the roads resulting in conflict over the use of roadspace.

In places where it is not appropriate to have separate routes for pedestrians and cyclists, it is all the more vital to ensure that the roads and streets are designed to be shared by all forms of movement with safety and convenience. In such cases, designing for speeds of 20mph or below should be a first priority.

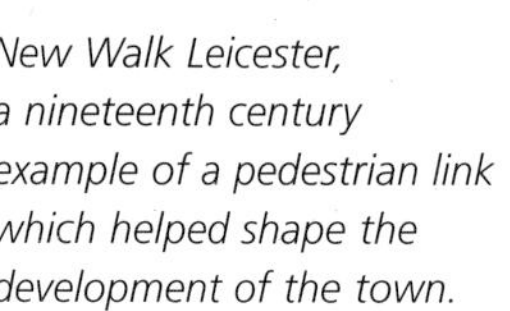

New Walk Leicester, a nineteenth century example of a pedestrian link which helped shape the development of the town.

Cycle routes should offer clear links through an area.

Framework for large scale development

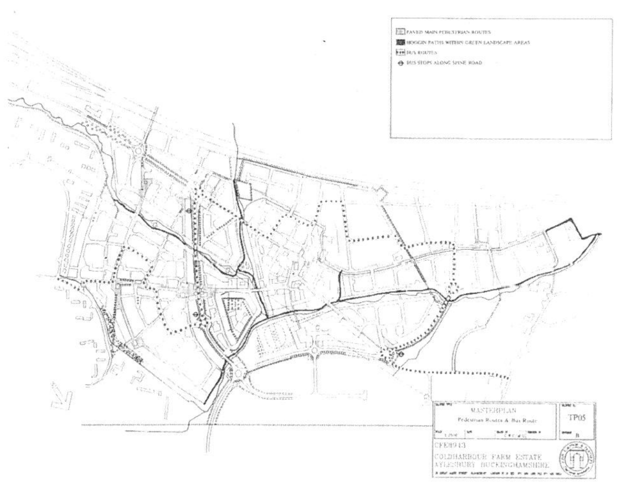

Coldharbour Farm is a development of over 1,500 houses, plus workplaces, shops and social facilities. The masterplan allows for all forms of movement. Shown here are the pedestrian routes (yellow) which link the village settlements, and the bus routes (purple) which connect the development to the wider world.

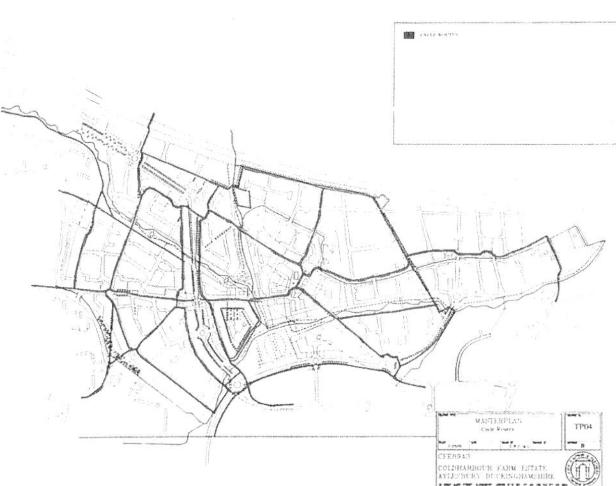

Priority is given to cycling as the way to get around the area.

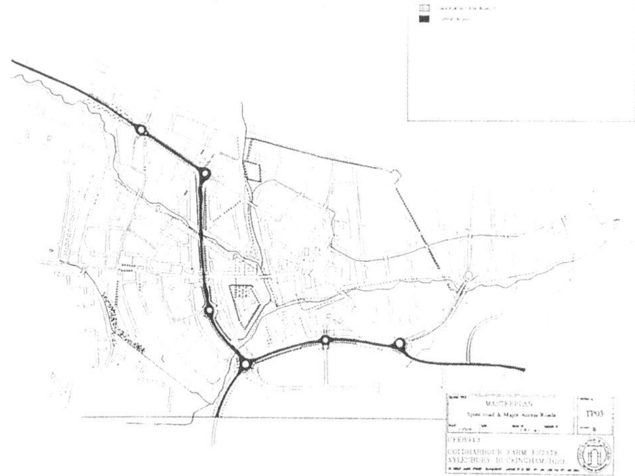

Vehicle access is based on a spine road through the area (red), linked to major access roads (yellow). The bird's-eye view overleaf shows how the development wlll appear when complete.

Neighbourhoods have a clear hierarchy of spaces – dense at the centre, less dense at the edges.

Short streets in housing areas keep traffic speeds low.

The masterplan for Coldharbour Farm shows how the movement framework is combined with the overall form of the development to create a set of distinctive places.

Framework for medium scale development

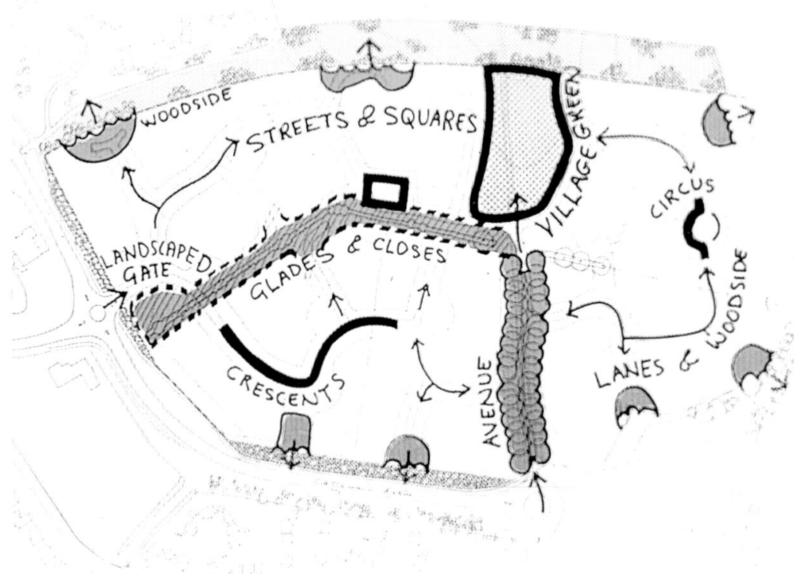

This is a site for about 300 houses east of Bury St. Edmunds. The development brief promotes the use of different densities and spaces to accord with the local topography. Cycle tracks and footpaths provide routes within the area and beyond.

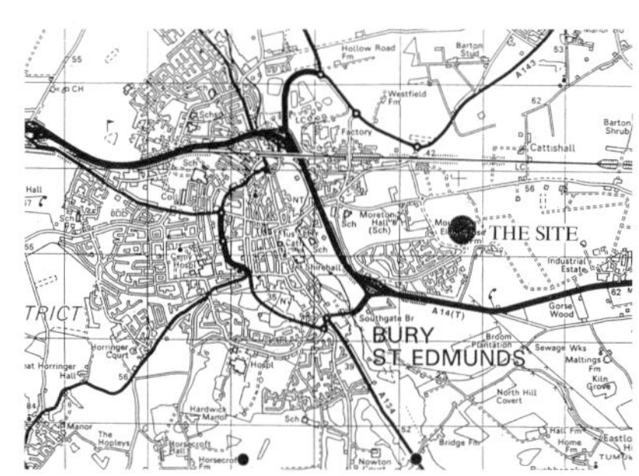

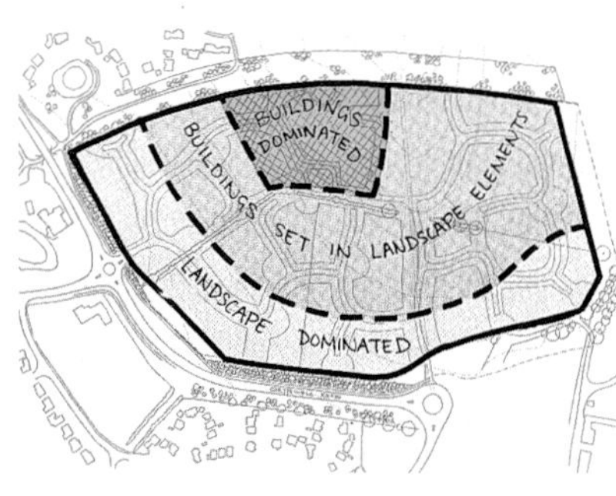

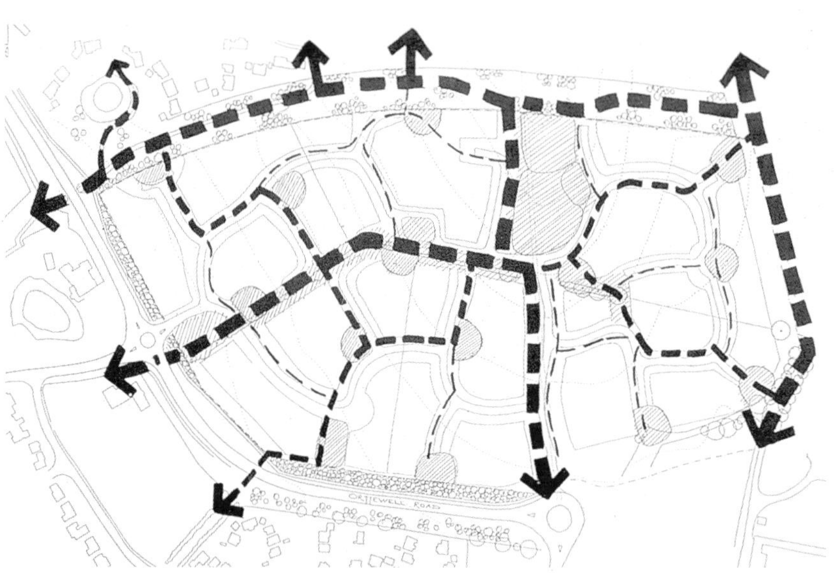

cycle track ▬ ▬ ▬ ▬ ▬
footpath — — — — —

Framework for small scale development

This extension of 40 houses to the village of Broadwindsor in Dorset is arranged around a loop road of the same character as the main village street. An orthodox cul-de-sac solution (though previously used in the village) was rejected at the outset, as being inappropriate to the area. By combining development sites it was possible to create a through street. In a rural location such as this, rat-running via the new street is not a problem.

The rejected cul-de-sac design.

The new street design reflects the traditional layout of the village.

Creating a high quality public realm

The design of development is crucial to the creation of successful communities. Amongst the factors discussed here the most important is the provision of basic local facilities within walking distance of people's homes.

Achieving a sense of community cannot be done by physical planning alone. However, it is possible through the careful planning of buildings and spaces to create places where it feels good to live and work. The key considerations are:

- *The balance between housing and other uses.*
- *The quality and maintenance of streets and public spaces.*
- *The integration of new development and old.*
- *The provision of convenient and safe pedestrian and cycle routes.*

Physical planning can help create a good community.

Play areas should be at the centre of a neighbourhood and well overlooked.

Children instinctively appreciate good meeting-places.

Well-planned streets and spaces are fundamental to good settlements. This means that streets should be designed to provide the forum for social interaction as well as to facilitate movement. They should have the types of spaces which can accommodate all sorts of activities, formal or informal, planned or spontaneous.

The way people use and experience places varies greatly:

- *Many women, carers and elderly people spend much of their time close to home and value local facilities which are safe and accessible.*
- *Children need safe and accessible streets. They should be able to walk or cycle to school near their homes, and to play without fear from vehicles.*
- *People with restricted mobility need streets which are safe, well lit and well maintained.*

Cycle tracks help knit places together.

Local centres should be accessible for everyone.

A priority for planners should be to enable people to have access to local facilities on foot or by bicycle. Ideally this means a local shop for daily needs within five to eight minutes' walk (400 metres) of home. If possible there should also be a mixture of shops, businesses and other uses within walking distance. The principle of the walkable neighbourhood is the key to creating a sociable, sustainable community.

Squares still work well in all forms of development, providing a local focus and a mix of communality and privacy.

If a place is well used it stands a better chance of being loved and cared for. It is more likely that rubbish will be tidied up and that trees and planting will be cared for. Above all, people will feel safer as they walk through the area.

Unfortunately it is rare for new developments not to generate some opposition in the local area. Therefore it is important to facilitate social connections at the earliest opportunity. Links from the heart of a new development into existing settlements encourage movement and contact between people in different neighbourhoods.

The public spaces in an area (streets, footpaths, parks and open spaces) give it an identity beyond that described by its architecture. The creation of a positive identity is the key to engendering a sense of pride in a place. There is no standard formula for endowing a new development with a clear, recognisable identity but, as described in the next section, the best starting-point is an appreciation of the local context.

Responding to the local context

The detailed understanding of topography, ecology and neighbouring settlements should be fundamental to the design of housing layouts.

New housing should relate to the density and scale of the existing place. Here the new housing on the right complements the layout of the existing village.

Suburban forms may be appropriate in some areas.

Over recent decades residential developments have become increasingly uniform across the country. In travelling through England it is often hard to detect major differences in new housing between one region and another. By contrast, older housing displays many local differences in overall layout, design and materials.

Local housing characteristics make an immense contribution to the quality of the places where we live. Wherever possible the design of new housing should respond to and enhance those characteristics.

There have been many reasons for the increasing standardisation of new housing developments, and some of the forces leading to uniformity have long been in existence. One of those forces has been the over-rigid application of formulae for road design, regardless of local differences. Whereas historically England has an immense variety of settlements and places, new housing built around those places tends, partly because of road design, to look increasingly the same.

The extent to which new housing responds to its local context depends not only on the design of the houses themselves but also on the design of the roads and footpaths. New residential roads should be designed to be safe and convenient, and existing roads improved, whilst maintaining a sense of local diversity. The basis of this reconciliation should be an understanding of the locality and the relationship of the new development to the existing place, whether it be town, village or suburb. In areas which have little existing distinctiveness developers should aim to create a new sense of place, drawing on elements from a wider context.

In the design of layouts for new housing four main factors should be taken into consideration:

The local topography, including existing boundaries. Almost every part of the English landscape has been shaped in the past by patterns of ownership and cultivation. New developments should always take account of these patterns and their physical evidence; the relationship of buildings to landscape, and the use of hedges, walls and fences.

The shape and character of existing development.
Much new house building occurs as the extension to existing settlements, whether on the outskirts of a country village or as part of the planned expansion of a major town. The starting point for the design of new development should be an understanding of the existing settlement patterns.

Existing routes and movement patterns.
The degree of connection and permeability in a new development is often the key to its success. Where established routes exist, whether a footpath, a short cut or a minor road, they can provide the clue to satisfactory and enduring linkages. The design of routes and connections should always take accountant of security issues.

Landscaping and trees should form an integral part of the settlement plan.

Trees and planting.
The preservation of mature trees, and new planting appropriate to the area, can do a great deal to help integrate old and new development. Planting can reinforce the hierarchy between one space and another.

Often in residential projects the response to local context is confined to architectural finishes – tile hanging in one place, knapped flints or patterned brickwork in another – but these are often less important than the design of layouts which reflect the fundamental anatomy of the local topography and building fabric.

These considerations should weigh even more heavily in the design of infill or "brown field" developments in existing towns, and in developments within conservation areas. In such cases special care should be taken to ensure that the design of roads and access routes contributes to the existing urban patterns.

There follow four examples of recent developments, each of which has been designed to respond to a very different locality.

Street pattern links to rest of local areas.

Posts limit through vehicles traffic.

On-street parking in front of houses.

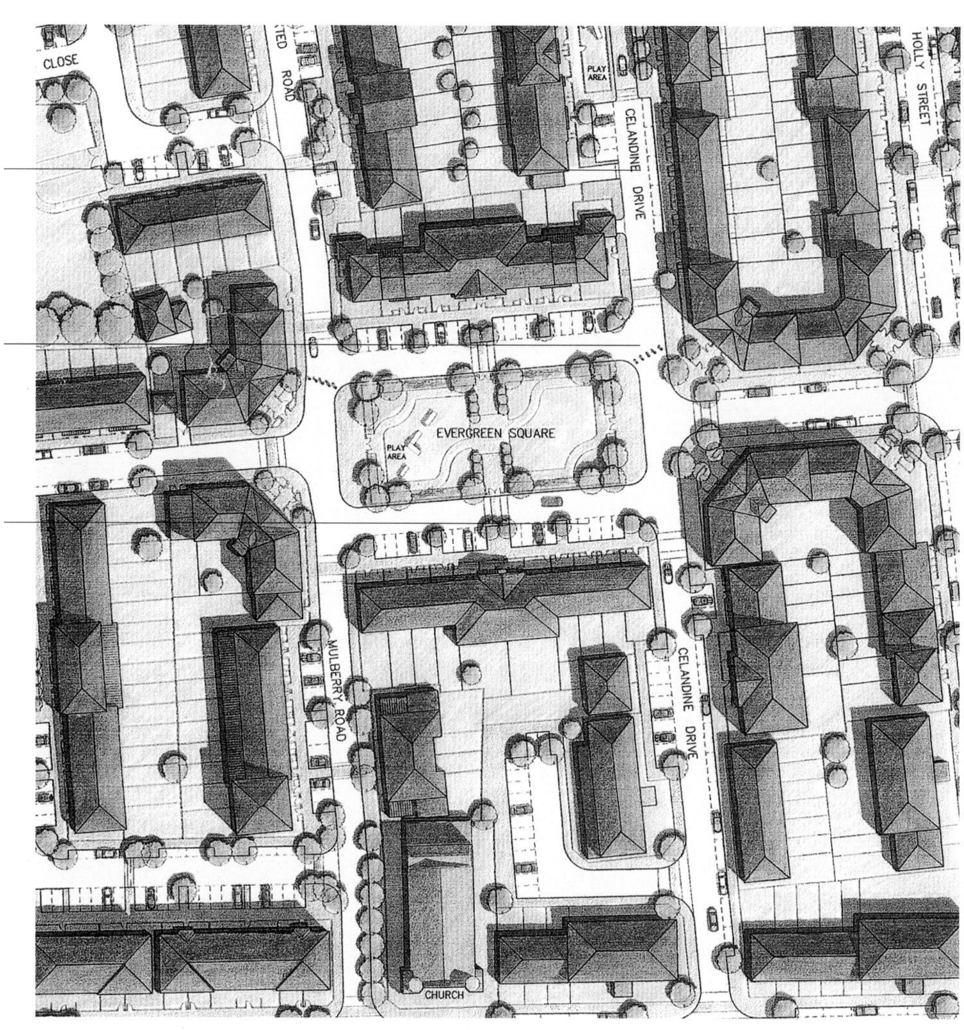

The Holly Street Estate in Hackney, a notorious example of 1960s comprehensive redevelopment, is being rebuilt to a plan which revives much of the original street pattern of the area. Houses and flats face onto streets in the traditional manner, and on-street parking is arranged so that people can see their cars from their homes.

Car parking is in courtyards, with only casual parking on the main frontages.

New triangle complements existing spaces in the village.

This extension of Abbotsbury in Dorset respects the rural informality of the existing village. The location of parking to the rear of houses maintains the street frontage.

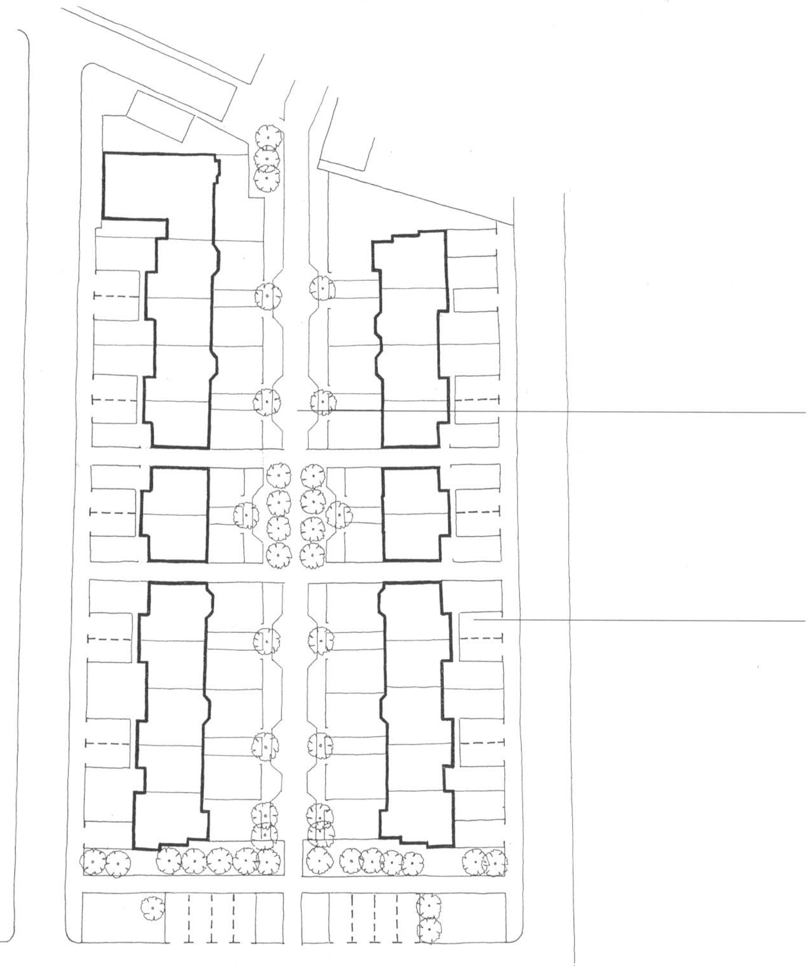

Central path provides well-used route from local shops. (see central illustration)

Rear parking bays (see righthand illustration)

Lumley Walk, Gateshead reinterprets the traditions of the Tyneside terrace in contemporary terms. The parking area at the back of each house can if desired be used as additional garden space.

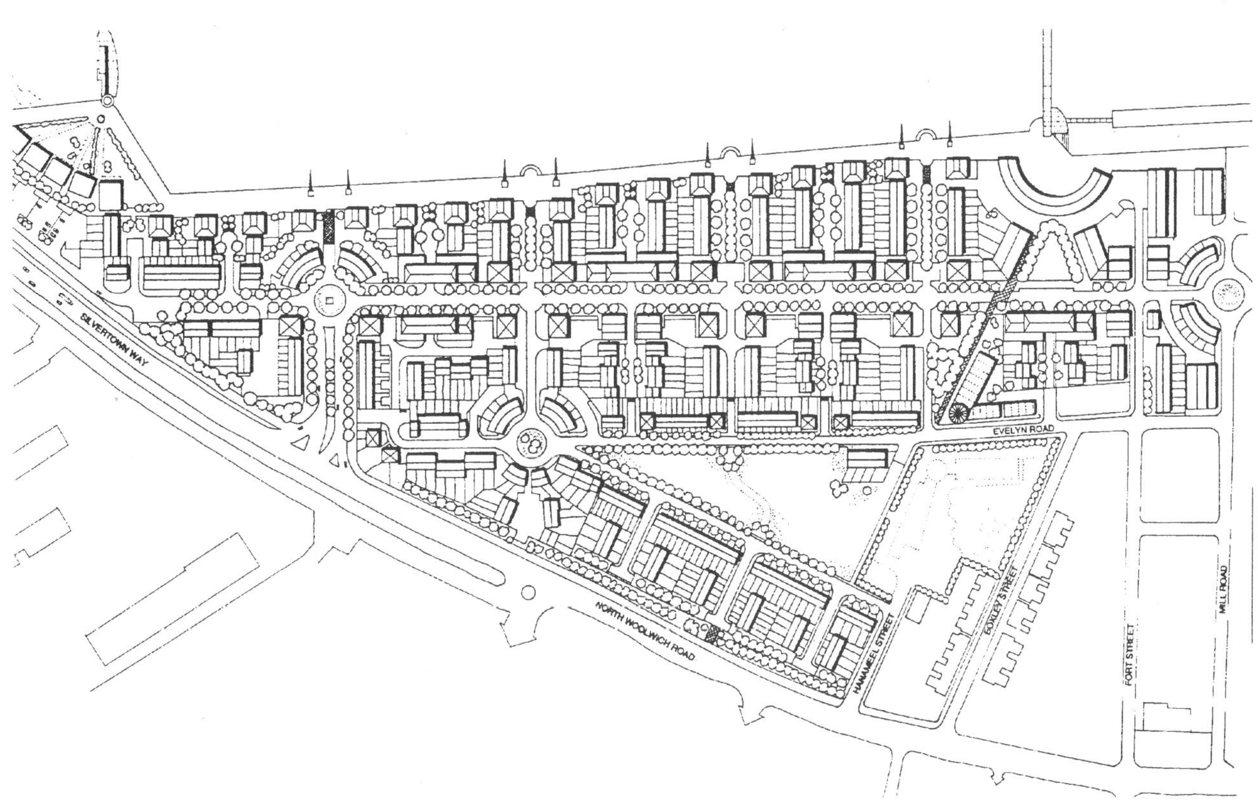

The development of West Silvertown in the London docks acknowledges the geometry and scale of the adjacent dock basin. The masterplan (above) shows an urban pattern of development based on a regular grid. Here is an instance where suburban informality would be wholly inappropriate.

Security

Analysis of the local context should take account of security issues. The broad principles of crime prevention through design are universally applicable, but the way they are implemented depends on the needs of the locality.

The design of housing layouts can make a major contribution to both the prevention of crime and alleviating the fear of crime. Most crime is opportunistic, and common sense measures can make an area secure for both people and property. The main points to be borne in mind are:

- *Crime depends upon concealment. Well used or overlooked streets and spaces make the criminal feel uncomfortable and exposed.*
- *Anonymous and uncared for spaces can cause long-term problems. The design of layouts should provide a clear definition of ownership and responsibility for every part of a development.*
- *Clear and direct routes through an area for all forms of movement are desirable, but should not undermine the "defensible space" of particular neighbourhoods.*

An assessment of potential risks should be made early in the development of the design, in consultation with the local police Architectural Liaison Officer (or in London, the Crime Prevention Design Advisor). There are significant local variations in the degree of risk. Crime prevention measures which are essential in one area may be less necessary elsewhere. The priority should be to understand the local context, and to achieve a balance between security and other issues. For instance, some provision of culs-de-sac may be appropriate to the character of a particular area, but totally inappropriate elswhere.

In terms of detailed design, the principal means of crime prevention are:

- *Natural surveillance: neighbours should be able to see each other's houses, and where cars are parked outside (at front or back), owners should be able to see them.*
- *Routes that are overlooked and busy. If separate footpaths or cycle tracks form part of a layout they should be on routes which generate high levels of movement and should be as short as possible. Long, indirect pedestrian and cycle links may feel threatening for users, and may provide escape routes for criminals.*
- *Play areas or communal space located where they are well-related to surrounding areas and are overlooked. They should not be regarded as just a use for parcels of land left over after the rest of the layout has been drawn up.*

The development of a good community spirit is the most obvious way of deterring crime, but that cannot be relied on as a solution on its own. Mutual support works best when the design of an area has taken account of security issues at the outset.

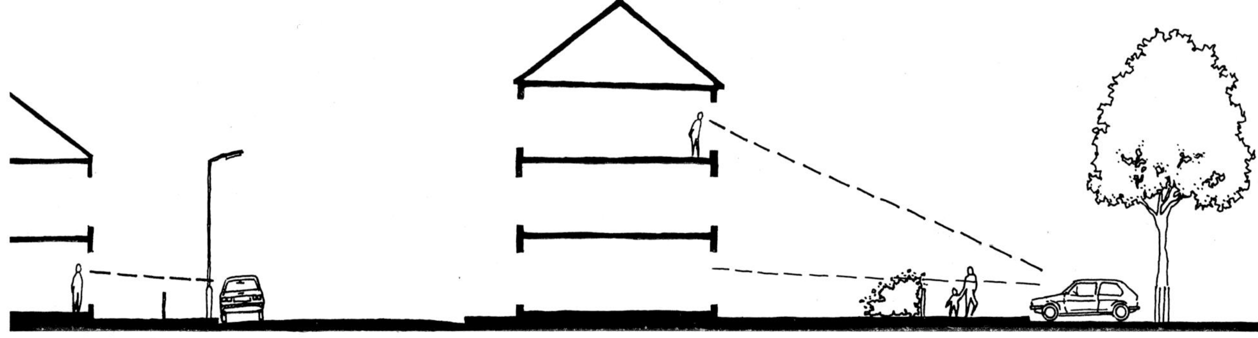

References: Association of Chief Police Officers Project Design Group, Secured by Design (1994)

Parking should be located where owners can see their cars.

Achieving a balanced approach

The preparation of a development brief should involve all those who will play a part in a new development or the improvement of an existing area. The planning system seeks to achieve a balance between a wide variety of interests and concerns.

Good neighbourhoods and settlements do not occur by chance. The prerequisite for successful development is detailed cooperation between all those involved, in particular the designer of the development and the local planning authority.

The worst that can happen is the development of a scheme to a standard formula with no active input from the local authority. By contrast what should happen is a detailed discussion from the outset of the overall concept for the development, including how it relates to the locality.

- *The production of a development brief is an essential process, even for small developments. Ideally this should be done by the developer in conjunction with the local authority. A well-prepared, realistic brief will help iron out disagreements and misunderstanding at an early stage.*

- *Section 17 of the Crime and Disorder Act 1998 imposes a new duty on a local planning authority to exercise its functions with due regard to both the likely effect on, and the need to do all it reasonably can to prevent, crime and disorder. The obligation to consider crime and security issues in formulating design policies and exercising development control functions is therefore placed more strongly upon planning authorities than has previously been the case. This does not mean that security considerations will always take precedence. Local authorities will need to use their judgement in weighing security factors against other considerations, such as the desirability of promoting ease of movement. The advice contained in DOE Circular 5/94 "Planning Out Crime" will continue to apply. Planning authorities should work with others to find suitable ways of achieving crime prevention objectives, allowing for flexibility of approach, and sensitivity to the particular local circumstances.*

When the planning application stage is reached it should be dealt with by a development team at the local planning authority to ensure a balanced consideration of all the factors involved. Cooperation within and between local authorities is just as important as liaison between the authority and the developer.

The same approach is equally valid for projects in existing areas. Proposals for new developments affecting existing streets and communities are likely to be regarded as contentious, and should be consulted on widely. The process of consultation can be the means to creating places which are well managed and cared for.

Penrith Road, Rochdale, part of a well-established area of traffic calmed streets.

In the Marlborough Road area of Bedford, traffic calming has been introduced to reduce accidents on residential roads used by through traffic.

3

Detailed aspects of layout The creation of good places requires attention to every aspect of movement and layout

The shape of the development: Introduction

Guidance is given in this section on how the design of roads, junctions and parking spaces can contribute to the creation of high quality areas.

The detailed design of roads and spaces is crucial to the shaping of all developments. Even quite modest differences in the design of a street or junction, or in the siting of a parking bay, can have a major impact on the quality of an area.

This section discusses some of the more important aspects of the relationship between roads and places. The main theme here is that the requirements for the use of cars need not be inimical to the creation of good places, but with care and commitment the requirements can be fitted to suit each particular locality.
The section opens with the masterplan drawings for Dickens Heath in the West Midlands, which illustrates well how a distinctive place can be developed which meets many of the contemporary demands for movement.

A well designed settlement will have a hierarchy of spaces rather than be dominated by a hierarchy of road types. Enclosed, well defined spaces and a variety of configurations should be the starting point. Landscaping can be used to reinforce the shape and identity of a place.

The shape of a place should reflect its unique location, scale and character.

Dickens Heath, Solihull

The proposed development at Dickens Heath in the West Midlands (shown here and on the previous page) is designed around traditional squares and greens. Commercial and public buildings have a building-line at the back edge of the pavement: it is they, rather than the roads, which define the different spaces.

Dickens Heath has a road hierarchy based on the principles in DB32

Road Type	Design Speed	Min Carriageway Width	Min Footway/Service Provision	Widening on Bends	Min Stopping Sight Distance	Traffic Calming Type
Main Traffic Routes	25mph	i) 6.75m ii) 6.1m iii) 5.5m	2 x 1.8m if not required then min 1m verge	Yes	45m	Horizontal & Vertical
Minor Access Road	20mph	5.5m	2 x 1.8m if frontage one side then 1 x 1.8m	Yes	33m	Horizontal & Vertical
Shared Surfaces	15mph	min 7m overall width		No	23m	Horizontal & Vertical
Country Lane	20mph	5.5m at entry 3.0m internally and passing bays	1 x 1.8m footway 1 x 1m verge	Yes	33m	Horizontal & Vertical

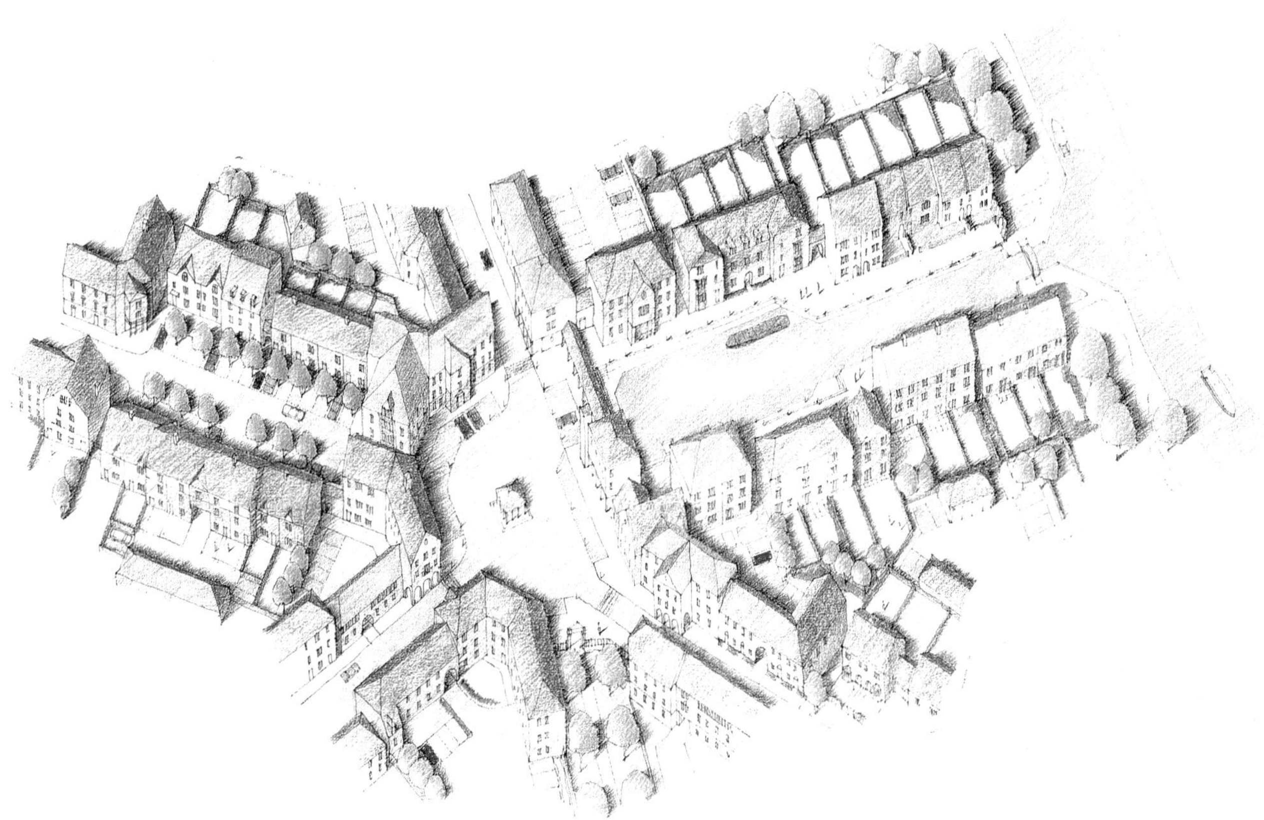

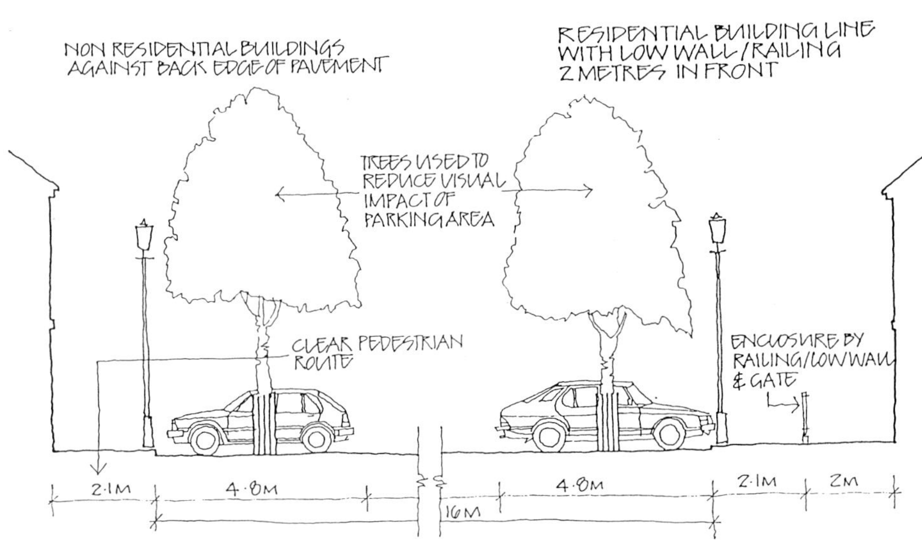

Residential and non-residential buildings are arranged slightly differently in relation to the roads. Cars are parked at right angles to the kerb: lamp posts and bollards prevent encroachment of cars over footway.

Types of road

In DB32 all streets have a designated road type with alternative carriageway widths related to different types of development. These road types can be varied according to the scale and location of a development.

Road types need to be used as a part of the overall concept and detailed design for development. In most cases they should not be the leading factor in determining the form of development. If used as the starting point in the design, in isolation from considerations of place and context, they can lead to developments where the layout is dictated solely by the geometry and size of the road.

The carriageway widths quoted in DB32 are the minimum needed for the free movement of traffic (some delay is acceptable if, for instance, two removal vans meet). Areas for other functions of the street, such as parking or cycle lanes, should be included as an addition to the minimum widths.

As a general guide it is suggested that the minimum width required for the free movement of traffic in residential areas be as follows:

	Around	Around	Up to around
No. dwellings served	50-300	25-50	25
Carriageway width (m)	5.5	4.8	4.1

This table applies mainly to the design of suburban housing areas. For urban areas reference should also be made to 'Transport in the Urban Environment' by the Institution of Highway and Transportation in Association with the then Department of Transport.

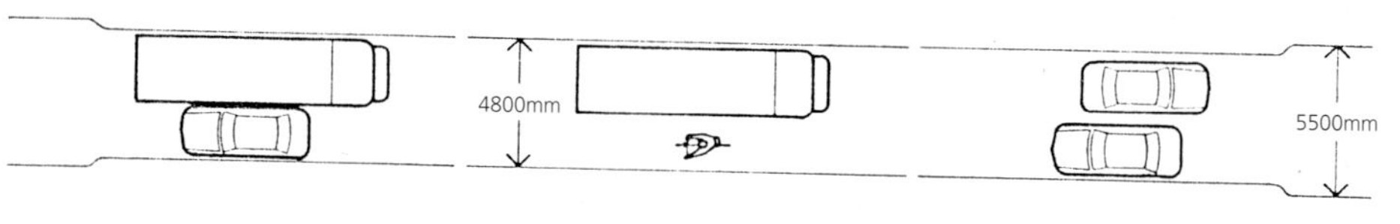

Typical example of minimum carriageway width.

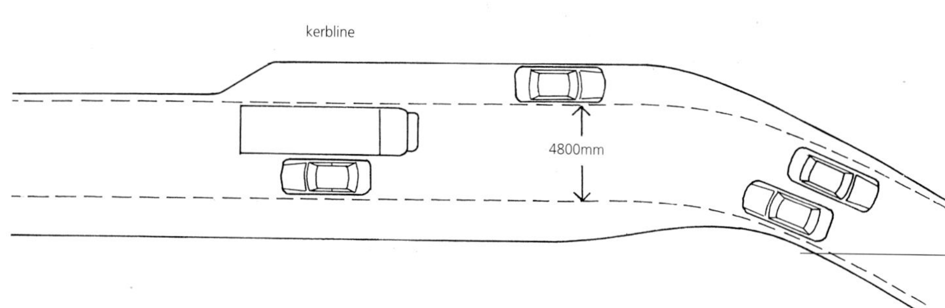

Zones for parking added to minimum width.

Line of kerb has traffic calming effect

Reference: DB32 p38 + p40

Tracking

Tracking is the provision of the required carriageway width for vehicle movement within the overall width of the street.

Instead of taking the highway engineering requirements as the starting-point for layout design, the arrangement of buildings and enclosure should be considered first. The demands they generate should then be checked against the highway engineering needs. With this approach buildings can be laid out to suit an urban form with pavements and kerbs helping to define and emphasise spaces. The space between kerbs will consequently vary. It will be used to contain all the functions of the street including parking and movement of vehicles. The areas needed for movement of vehicles can be checked using the minimum widths quoted in DB32 as zones for tracking. With this approach the kerbline need not follow the line of vehicle tracking if care is given to the combination of sightlines, parking and crossover points. There is no need for the tracking zone to be separately defined.

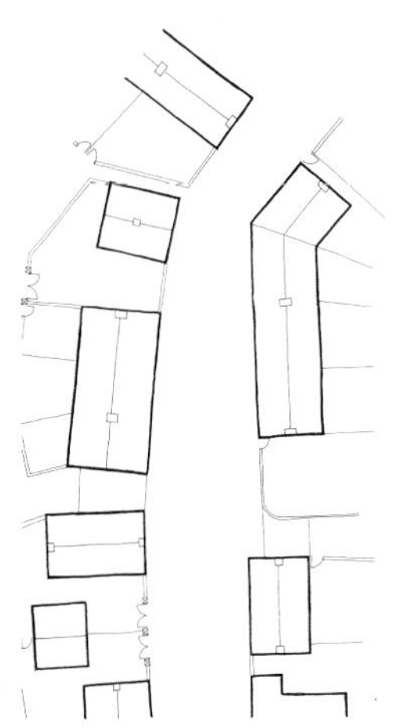

Buildings arranged to form street enclosure.

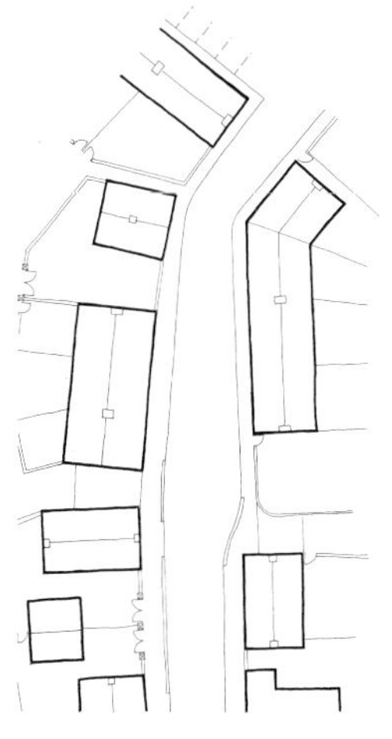

Footways laid out in front of buildings help to reinforce the space and enclosure.

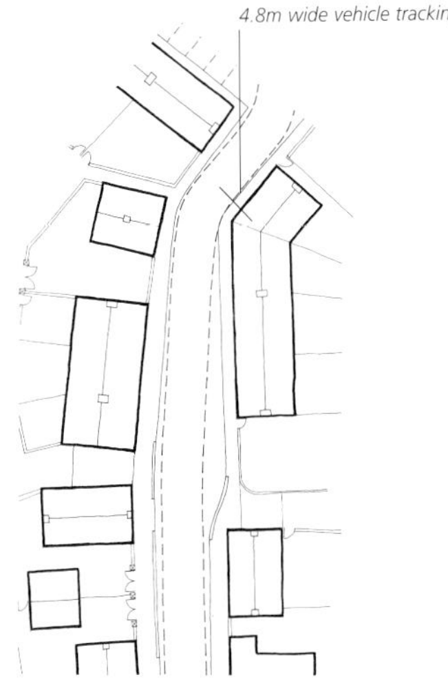

Carriageway width checked by plotting vehicle tracking paths, using minimum widths quoted in DB32.

A main street incorporating tracking wide enough for buses.

Footways with kerbs parallel to the building line help define the urban space.

At Great Notley in Essex a more suburban form of layout has been generated where buildings do not always form a tight enclave. A good quality development has been created through the use of conventional tracking, in which the overall road widths follow to the carriageway widths.
The layout has been greatly influenced by a main spine route with adjacent pedestrian and cycle routes within a landscaped corridor. Loop roads, access roads and culs de sac are served from the main road. The spine also provides the main public transport artery for the site. Through traffic avoids the area by using a by-pass.

Extensive use of landscaping and planting is made to help reduce the overall dominance of the car.

The main spine road with cycle and pedestrian routes alongside.

Adjacent areas formed around squares and culs-de-sac.

Junctions

Junctions are much more than just a way of handling traffic. They provide a point of entry which helps define a place, and they are landmarks on the route through an area. A well-designed junction is one which has a recognisable identity defined by the buildings or spaces around it.

Clearly there are many forms the space at a junction can take. With good design the highway engineering guidance in DB32 and PPG13 can be incorporated into places so they have a clear purpose and identity. But if used in isolation from the creation of place these standards can generate areas that work well for the car but have little relevance to people.

Manoeuvring at Junctions
Movement patterns of larger vehicles at junctions can have a dramatic effect on the nature of the space. They are the hardest to incorporate into a layout when trying to influence drivers to keep speeds low. Wide swept paths create traffic dominated areas since there is a tendency for cars to follow these curves easily with a greater freedom of movement and little speed restaint.

Typical geometrical requirements for refuse vehicles are indicated here. Varying radii permit the turning vehicle to remain entirely within its own carriageway half or swing out onto parts of the other carriageway. For most residential areas the frequency of larger vehicles is low. If this is the case they should be permitted to use the whole road area, particularly if vehicle speeds can be designed to 20mph.

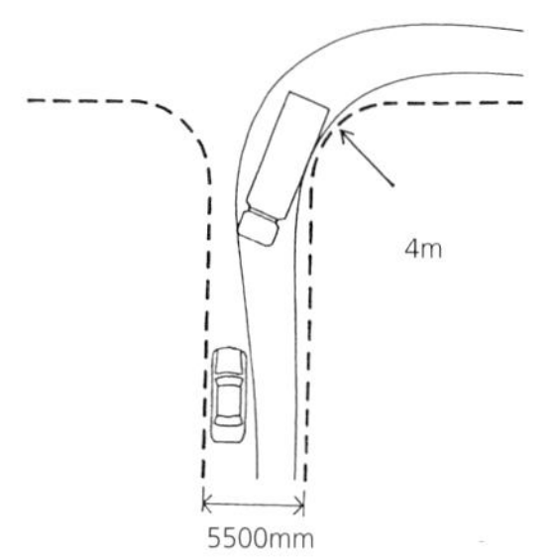

4m radius – refuse vehicle turning blocks movement for other vehicles on priority road and non-priority road.

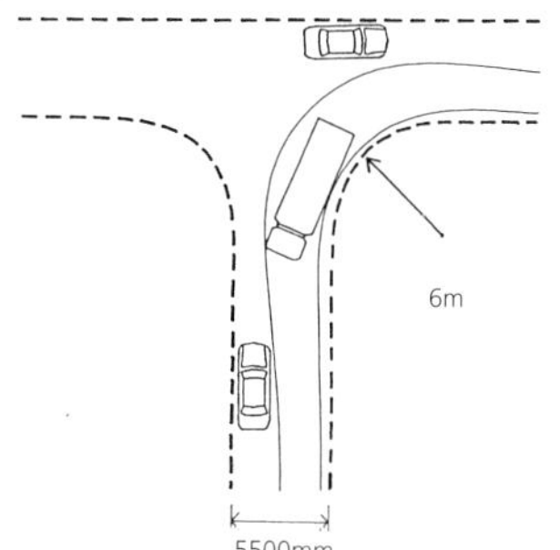

6m radius – refuse vehicle turning allows movement on priority road but blocks movement on non-priority road.

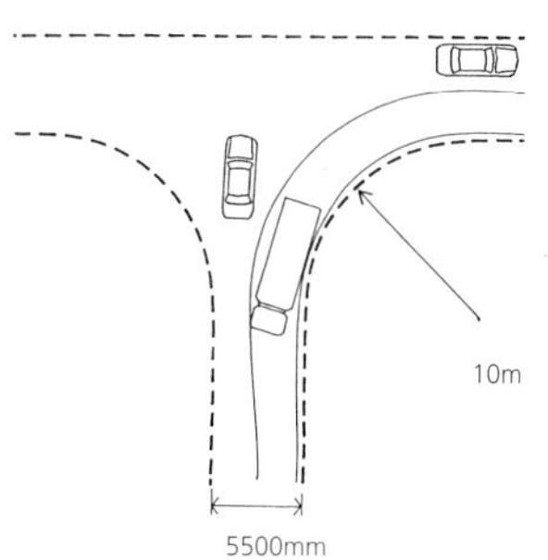

10 m radius – refuse vehicle turning does not block movement for other vehicles.*

** Removal vans will block traffic on all movements and roads except the traffic on priority roads with a 10m radius.*
NB: Removal vans are not common in residential areas.

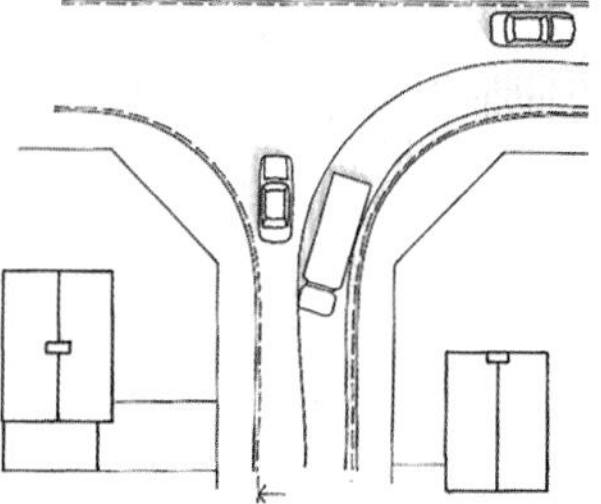

Footway edge follows wide swept path of refuse vehicles. This leads to a tendency for vehicles and vehicle speeds to dominate the space.

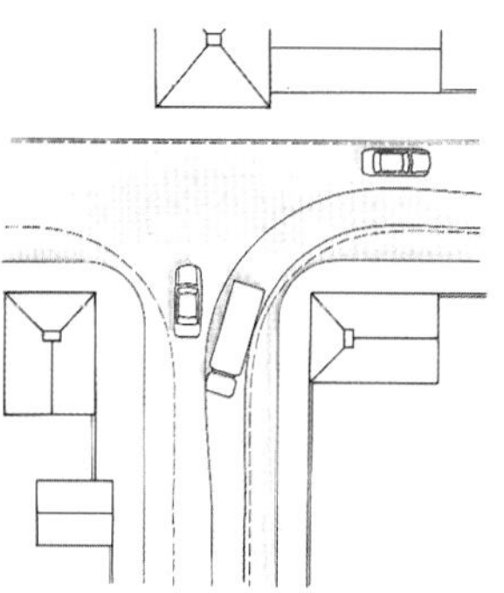

Tighter kerb radii can be used with a wider carriageway. The refuse vehicle turning requirement is still contained within the space, yet vehicles do not dominate.
By using the same concept of tracking, wider carriageways can be set out to generate tighter junctions. These have much better calming effect on traffic speed.

Reference: DB32 p48 + p49

Sightlines at Road Junctions

The design of sightlines at junctions is discussed in detail in both DB32 and PPG13, annex D. This section draws together the advice in those two documents. The guidance given here needs to be assessed in the circumstances of each case. Sightlines should never be reduced to a level where danger is likely to be caused.

Clear horizontal sightlines should take account of both what the driver can see and what pedestrians (especially children) can see. Sightlines need to be determined from an eye height of 1.05m – 2m, to an object height of 0.6m – 2m.

The diagrams and commentary given here describe the most salient points involved.

To enable drivers emerging from a minor road or access to see and be seen by drivers proceeding along the major road, unobstructed visibility is needed within the shaded area (x/y) in plan. Vertical visibility is also required as shown in the section.

Requirements for X and Y dimensions are summarised as:

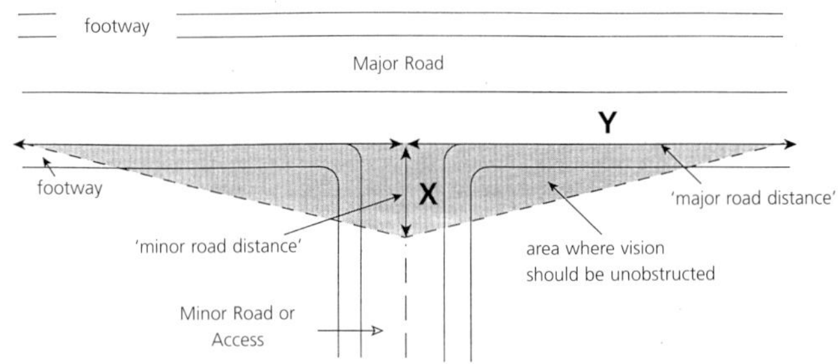

X dimension (minor road distance)

- 9m: The normal requirement for major new junctions and for the improvement of existing junctions between access roads and district or local distributor roads - for instances where the minor road is busy (ref. PPG13 annex D para. 2).
- 4.5m: For less busy minor roads and busy private access points.
- 2.4m: The minimum necessary for junctions within development to enable a driver who has stopped at a junction to see down the major road without encroaching onto it.
- 2.0m: For single dwellings or small groups of up to half a dozen dwellings or thereabouts.

Only in exceptional circumstances should a distance of less than 2.0m be considered.

The advice in this section supersedes that contained in both PPG13 and DB32.

Y dimension (major road distance)

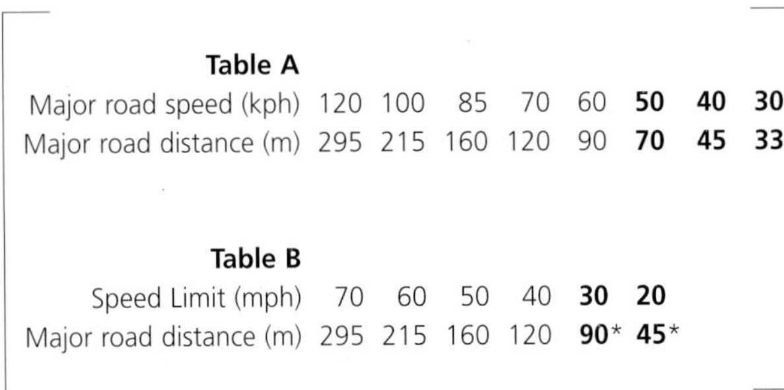

Table A

Major road speed (kph)	120	100	85	70	60	**50**	**40**	**30**
Major road distance (m)	295	215	160	120	90	**70**	**45**	**33**

Table B

Speed Limit (mph)	70	60	50	40	**30**	**20**
Major road distance (m)	295	215	160	120	**90***	**45***

Reference: DB32 pp.50–53 and PPG13 Annex D

** includes an allowance for motorists travelling at 10kph above the speed limit.*

Tables A and B are drawn from Annex D of PPG13 with the speeds for residential areas shown in bold. In addition to the dimension quoted, where it can be shown that vehicle speeds will be contained to either 30mph or 20mph the respective Y distances in table B can be amended to 60m and 33m respectively.

Sightlines for Cycle Tracks

When a new cycle track meets a local road the X and Y distances can be shorter than for road junctions. The relevant dimensions are given in Sustrans, *The National Cycle Network,* Issue 2 (1997), pp.142-3.

Sightlines at Access Ways

For vehicles crossing a footway at lightly-used access points (for example, entrances to courtyards of no more than 10 vehicles or driveways to individual dwellings) a splayed entrance is required. In such cases the minimum X and Y distances should both be 2.0m, with the Y distance measured along the back of the footway. There should be clear visibility at a level of 0.6m above road level for areas used by children.

Access way

In many places, where there are few vehicles involved, it may be appropriate to have a crossover at footway level with a drop kerb at the entrance to an access way. This has the clear effect of symbolising that priority should be given to pedestrians.

Arrangement of Junctions

Two alternative designs for junctions constructed within the last few years are described here by way of example.

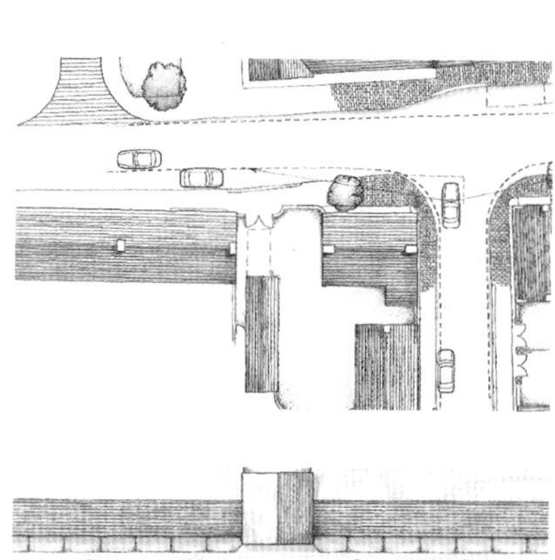

The junction of two streets, the minor with a designed vehicle speed of 20mph and the major a designed vehicle speed of 30mph. Buildings have been arranged to create an urban junction with a variable width carriageway. Casual parking in front of terrace housing is allowed for in increased carriageway widths, and the relevant sightlines are provided within added carriageway and footway space.

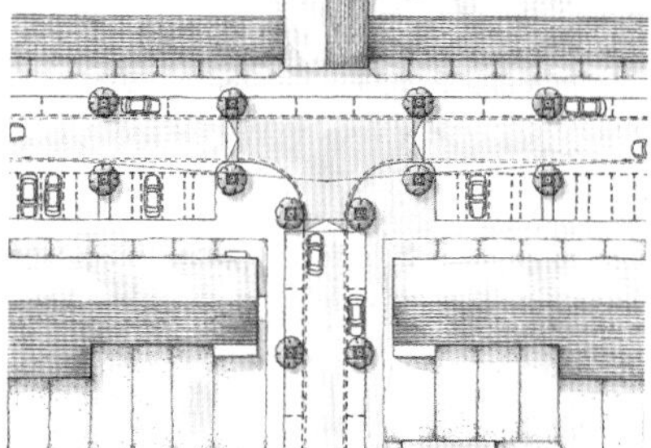

Terraced housing arranged in a linear form in keeping with local Victorian suburban streets. Car parking is provided on the street (within the adopted boundary) both parallel to and end on to the carriageway. Traffic calming in the form of raised tables at junctions and other points in the street is used to keep traffic speeds under 20mph. Parked cars do not interfere with the visibility splays.

Traffic calming

Wherever possible, traffic speeds should be managed by the arrangement of buildings and spaces. Physical traffic calming measures, such as speed humps and chicanes, should be regarded as back-up measures where the layout alone does not produce low speeds.

The aim should be to take account of traffic calming at the earliest stages in the design process, not to add it as an afterthought. The key considerations are:

- *Smaller corner radii rather than wide sweeping curves at junctions, to force slower and more careful movement by all vehicles.*
- *Junctions generally reduce vehicle speeds considerably. More frequent junctions mean slower movement through the development.*
- *The arrangement of parking on the street can contribute to traffic calming.*

Above all a combination of features, primarily in the arrangement of buildings and the design of junctions, can be used to create a low speed environment.

With existing areas, where the layout of streets is largely fixed, calming features should be appropriate to the location and context. The rigid application of standard solutions should be avoided.

- *Chicanes and pinch-points provide opportunities for planting and the creation of informal spaces.*
- *Raised junctions improve the opportunities for pedestrians to cross. However they should be designed so that children and visually impaired people do not presume they are part of the footway.*
- *Wherever possible cycle by-passes should be incorporated within traffic calming features.*
- *In an older streetscape or conservation area there are no standard solutions. Features should relate to the local context, using traditional materials wherever possible.*

The perception of a street contained by buildings is not the same as one which passes through a wide open space. The character of a street affects a driver's behaviour.

By changing the vertical (walls, fences and planting) or lateral (road shape) alignments, the perceived width of a street can be narrowed and views foreshortened. This constantly changing understanding of the street will affect the speed at which drivers feel it is safe to travel.

Retaining existing landscape features like hedgerows or attractive spaces, and configuring the streets around them, reinforces the image of a special place, and can encourage more careful driving.

round-topped speed humps

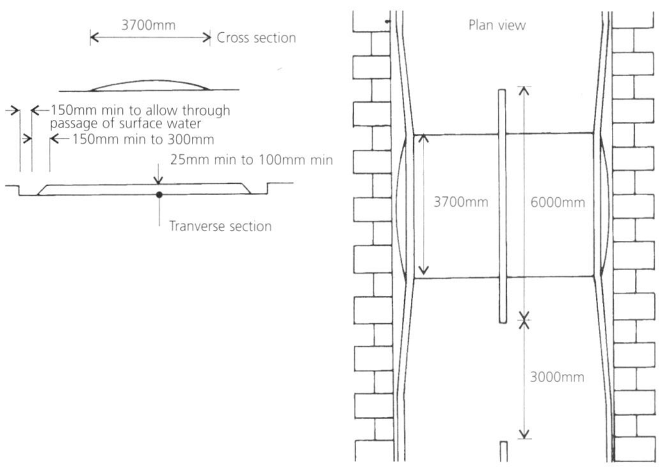

Round-topped and flat-topped speed humps can be effective in residential areas, (although they may sometimes be seen as visually intrusive). This example includes a cycle by-pass lane.

flat-topped speed humps

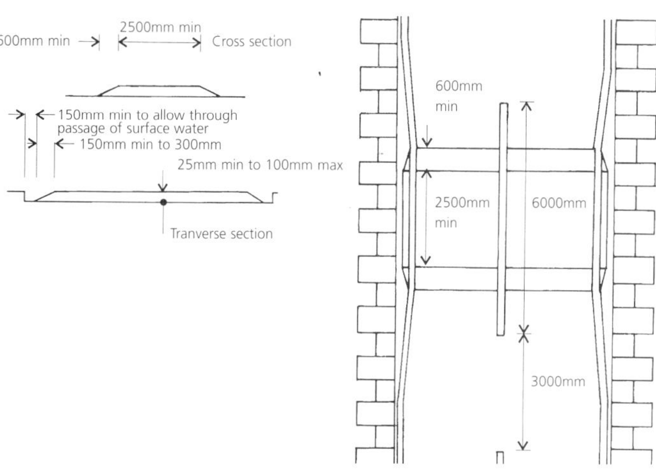

Speed cushions

Dimensional advice for speed cushions, to be used subject to local conditions.

Length	3700mm maximun. 3500mm for routes with mini-buses. 2000-3000mm on other routes.
Width	1600-1700mm for bus routes Up to 2000mm elsewhere.
Gradient	In the direction of vehicle travel: not steeper than 1 in 8.

Side ramps: not steeper than 1 in 4.

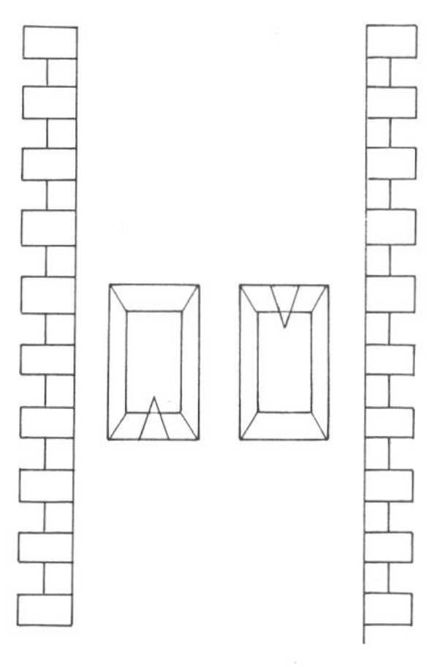

Speed cushions are more appropriate on roads used by buses.

Reference: 1 Traffic Advisory Leaflet 7/93: Traffic Calming Regulations
2 Traffic Advisory Leaflet 2/96: 75mm High Road Humps
3 Traffic Advisory Leaflet 7/96: Highways (Road Humps) Regulations 1996
4 Traffic Advisory Leaflet 1/98: Speed Cushion Schemes

raised junction

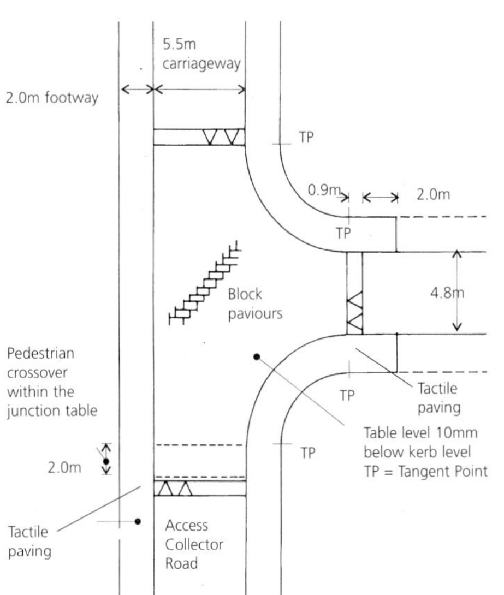

Raised junctions help slow traffic as well as marking the entrance to a new area.

chicane with cycle by-pass

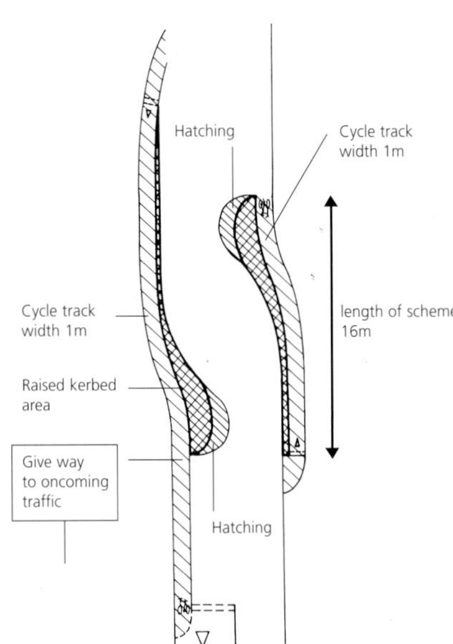

Chicanes can provide traffic calming between junctions. Wherever possible they should include a by-pass for cycles.

Reference: TRL Report 241, Cyclists at road narrowings

20mph speed limit zones

The designation of 20mph zones is an important aspect of traffic calming. The greatest advantages of such zones are that speeds and accidents are low, and that street clutter (signing of traffic calming events) is kept to a minimum.

The basic guidelines for the introduction of 20mph speed limit zones were set out in the Department of Transport's Circular Roads 4/90 published in December 1990. This was produced in response to information gathered from other countries in Europe showing that low speed limits, along with self enforcing speed restraint measures, led to a reduction in the number and severity of accidents.

20mph zones have generally been implemented in areas that are residential in character, although they have also been used in some shopping streets. Local authorities now have the power to declare 20mph zones without referral to the DETR.

20mph zone signs must be erected at all entrances to a zone. Within the zone neither 20mph repeat signs nor traffic calming signs (e.g. signs for road humps, chicanes) are required. Therefore a high quality, uncluttered environment can be more easily achieved. At all exits to a zone, a sign indicating the speed limit of the adjoining road must be displayed.

The creation of gateways is recommended at the entrances to zones, along with a change in surfacing material or texture. These inform drivers that they are entering an area of special character within which they must behave accordingly. Alternatively, a narrowing of the carriageway with a road hump at entrances can have the same effect upon drivers.

In general, the use of traffic calming features at a spacing of between 40 and 60 metres will be adequate to sustain an average speed of 20mph through a zone. Ideally these features should be designed into the overall layout of the development rather than treated as later additions.

In many areas it is desirable to have average speeds much lower than 20mph. It is better to achieve this through the careful design of the street layout, rather than by trying to introduce lower speed limits, which may be unenforceable.

See Traffic Advisory Leaflet 7/91 '20mph Speed Limit Zones', DOT Traffic Advisory Unit May 1991 and DOT Circular Roads 4/90 '20mph Speed Limit Zones.'

Parking

Where and how cars are parked is critical to the quality of housing areas, new or old. The location of parking is something which can arouse immensely strong feelings. A very careful balance has to be struck between the expectations of car owners, in particular the desire to park as near their houses as possible, and the need to maintain the character of the overall setting.

Adequate cycle parking is also a consideration in all residential developments. With houses this can generally be assumed to be within the property, but specific provision should be made for cycle parking at flats.

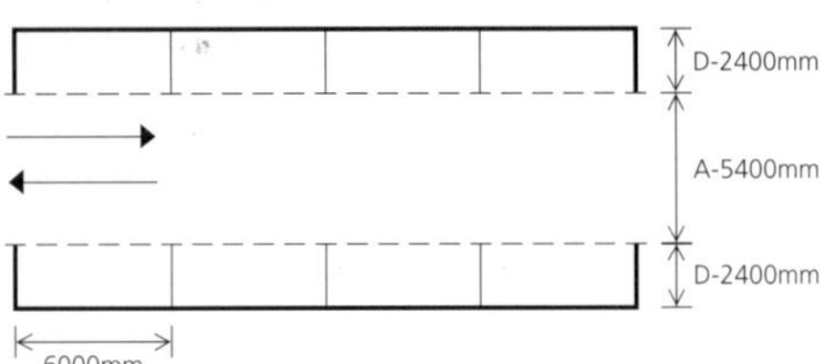

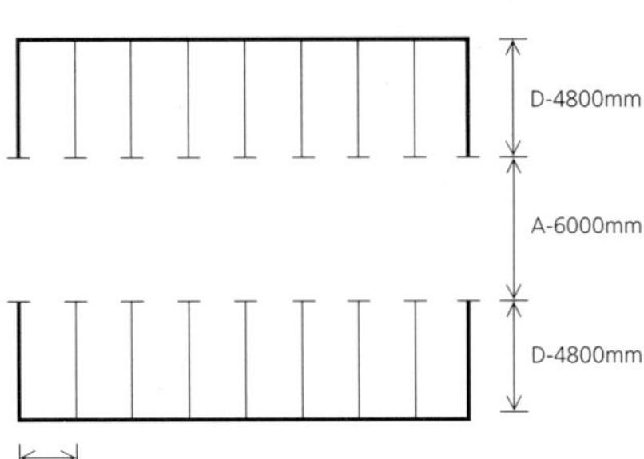

DB32 gives the dimensions for grouped parking bays, reproduced here. These dimensions can be applied to a variety of layouts.

Reference: DB32 p61

In courts & squares

The design of parking courts and squares should ensure they are overlooked, either by adjoining houses or by buildings entered from the parking areas. To avoid parked cars dominating the surroundings there should generally be no more than 10 spaces in a courtyard.

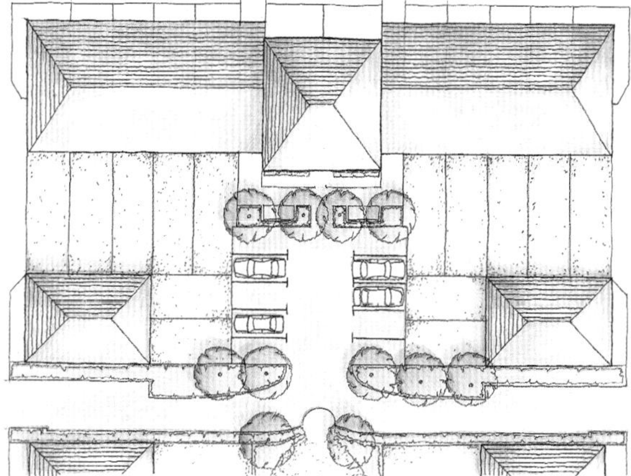

Courtyard parking well overlooked

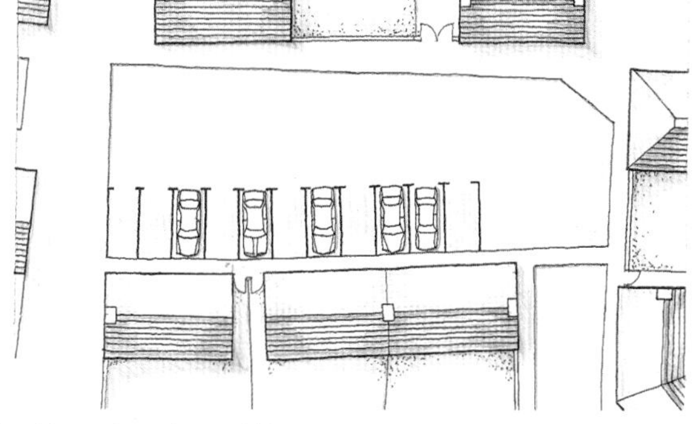

Parking takes place within a square, but does not dominate it.

In curtilage
Parking within the curtilage need not break up the street frontage. Cars can be parked at the side of the house, or can be enclosed by short lengths of wall which continue the building edge. Parking spaces at the rear can be used flexibly: when the household doesn't have a car, the garden can be enlarged.

In curtilage parking spaces can be grassed over if not needed.

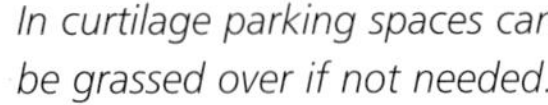

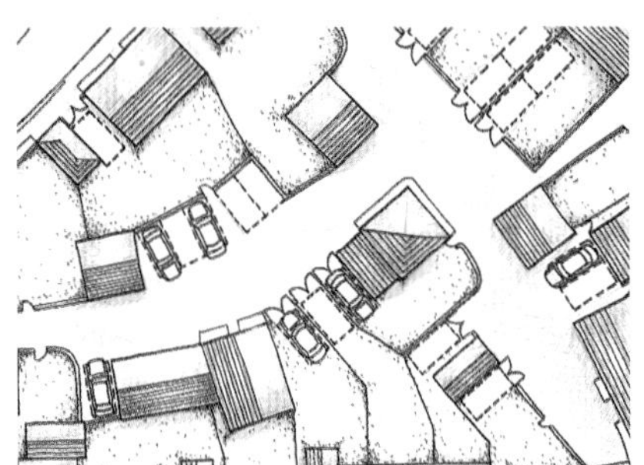

Walls dividing parked cars reduce their overall impact.

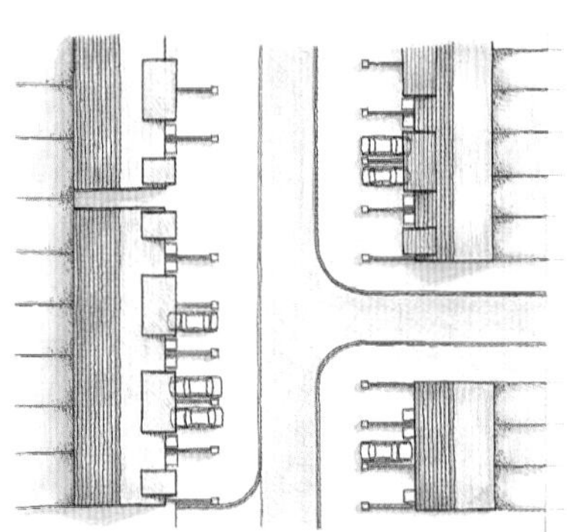

Cars are partly hidden by garden walls.

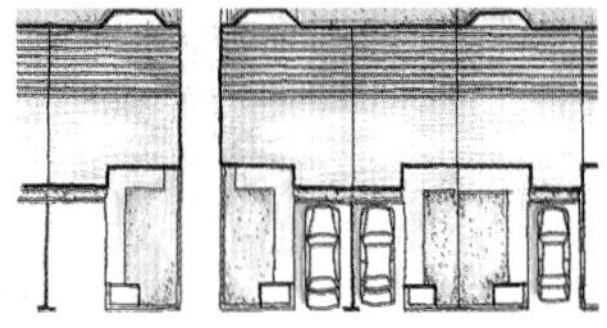

On-street

A certain amount of on-street parking brings activity to the street. Where casual parking is likely to take place, streets should be designed to accommodate it. The priority is that vehicles should not be allowed to dominate the space, or to inconvenience pedestrians and cyclists.

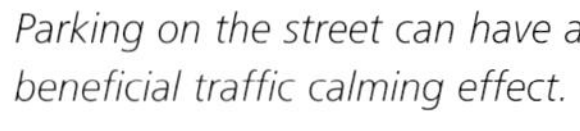

Parking on the street can have a beneficial traffic calming effect.

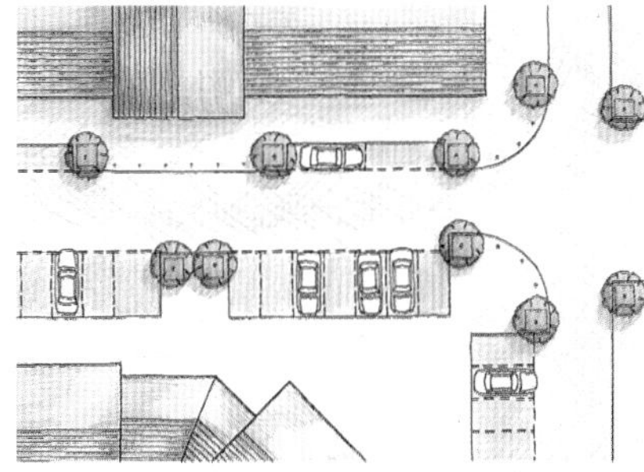

At Chingford Hall, Waltham Forest, on-street parking is part of the adopted roadspace.

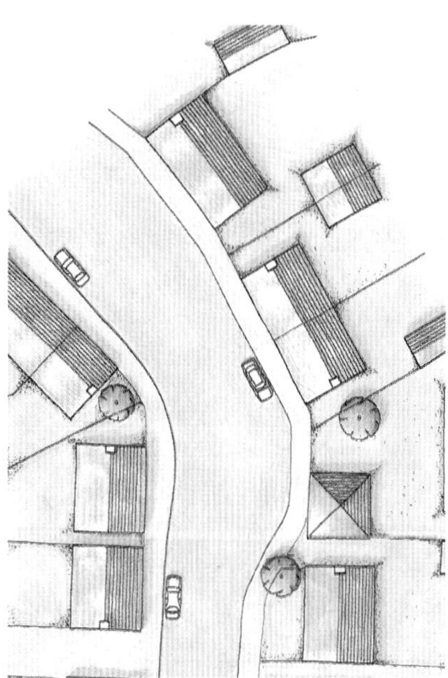

At Broadwindsor in Dorset the whole street between building frontages has been adopted. Some car parking takes place on the adopted street.

Forms of movement
Walking

A movement strategy for walking, cycling and public transport should be the starting point for designing accessible neighbourhoods.

Recommended minimum widths of footway as shown in DB32. The dimensions in brackets allow for greater ease of movement: the aim should be to achieve this better standard of provision

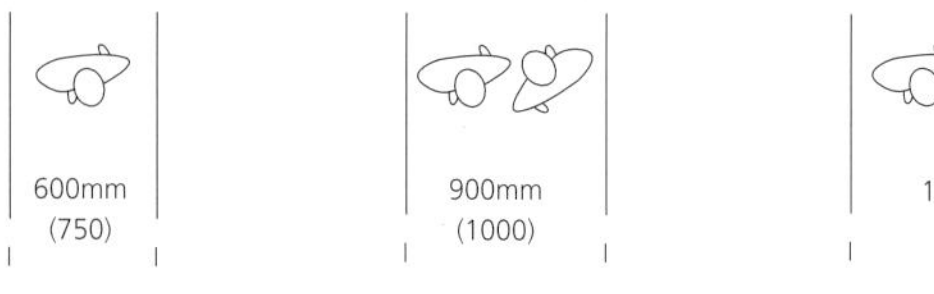

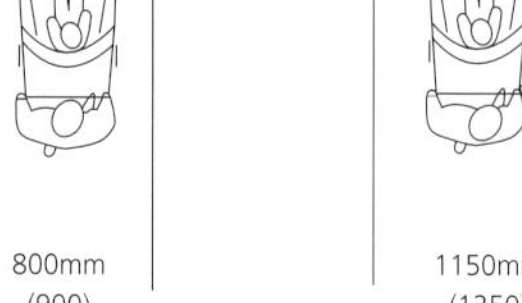
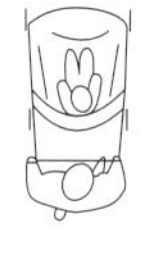

Walking has been too often overlooked, though it is the principal form of travel for trips of under one mile.

A public realm which is safe and well cared for is a good reason to walk. In providing for people on foot the key considerations are:

- *The provision of good quality footways.*
- *People prefer to walk along streets where they can be seen by drivers, residents and other pedestrians.*
- *If segregated footpaths are provided, they need to be well-connected and overlooked by houses and other buildings.*
- *All measures that slow down traffic help pedestrians feel safer. At junctions the use of raised surfaces and tight radii make it easier for pedestrians to cross.*

In residential areas the way that people get around on foot should never be left to chance. All areas should have footways, footpaths or shared surfaces.

Buildings, spaces and materials all help orientate people on foot.

Raised crossings are an advantage for pedestrians and wheelchair users.

Dropped kerbs at crossing places, together with tactile surfaces, should be an integral part of all road and footpath layouts.

Well-designed shared surfaces avoid conflicts of movement yet encourage other activities to take place. Subtle variations of material or bold changes of detail are appropriate in different situations.

Reference: DB32 p56

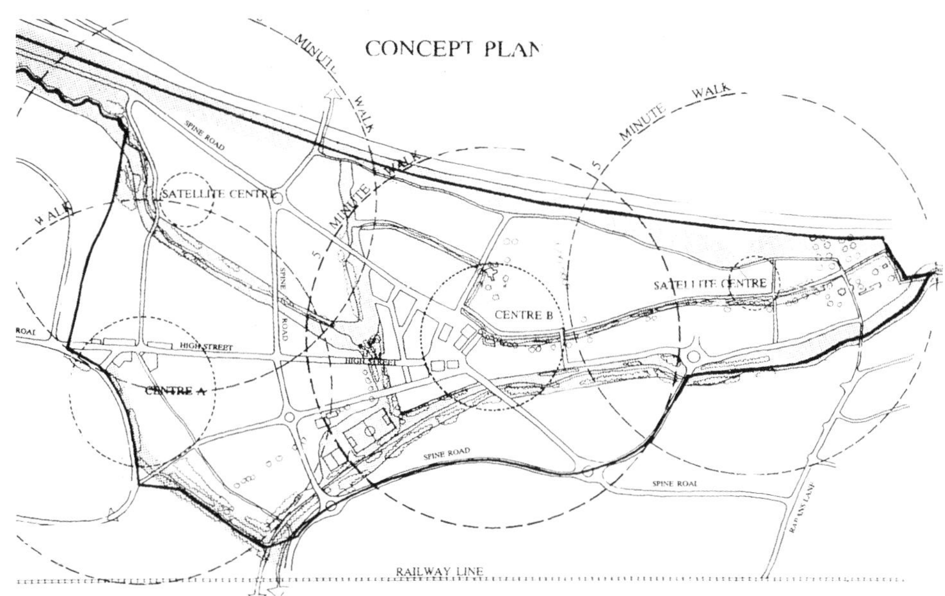

Walkable neighbourhoods at Coldharbour Farm, Aylesbury. The larger circles indicate five minute walking distances from village centres.

Where space permits, footways can be separated from the road. They should always be over-looked and well-connected.

Footpaths should lead where people want to go, rather than follow a preconceived geometry.

Footpaths in new development should be positive, direct and barrier-free.

Cycling

Layouts should be designed to encourage cycling, including cycling by unaccompanied children of 12 years and upwards. The key points to bear in mind are:

- *Wherever possible roads should be designed so as to be safe for cyclists.*
- *Traffic calming can reduce the need for segregated cycle tracks.*
- *Traffic calming measures should be designed with cyclists in mind, e.g. chicanes should not force cyclists into the path of vehicles.*
- *Like everyone else, cyclists prefer clear, coherent routes. Disjointed sections of cycle route are ineffective.*
- *Pedestrians and cyclists can share the same space, but an arrangement with a raised kerb, as shown here, is helpful in segregating cyclists from pedestrians. This arrangement also has distinct advantages for blind and partially-sighted people.*

In existing areas, the introduction of shared cyclist-pedestrian routes can bring major benefits to the local environment.

Dimensions for shared cyclist/ pedestrian routes, segregated by a change in level. These are the minimum dimensions allowing one-way cycle traffic to safely pass pedestrians and wheelchair users. Wherever possible the width of the cycle track should be increased to 2m. If change of level is not feasible, an alternative is the use of a raised line between the cycle track and footpath.

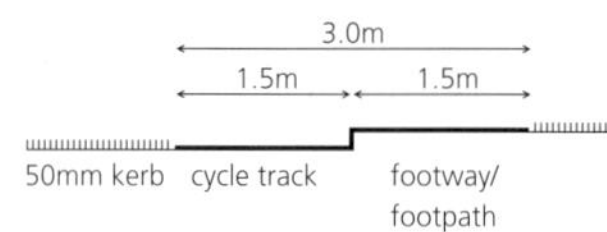

Kerb segregated facility open on both sides

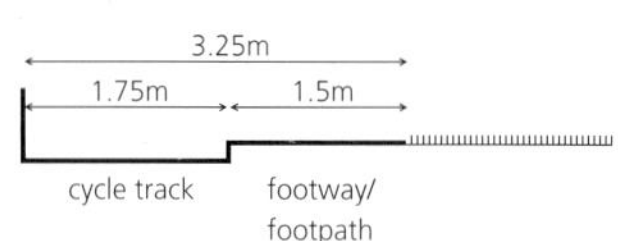

Kerbs segregated facility bounded on cycle track side

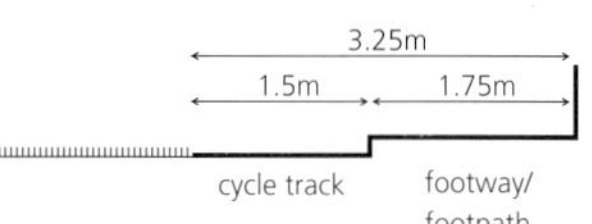

Kerbs segregated facility bounded on footway/footpath side

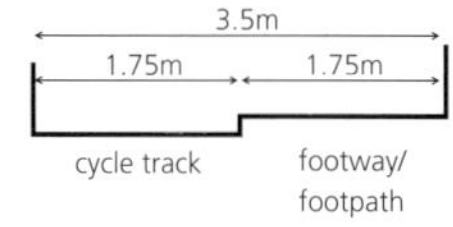

Kerbs segregated facility bounded on both sides

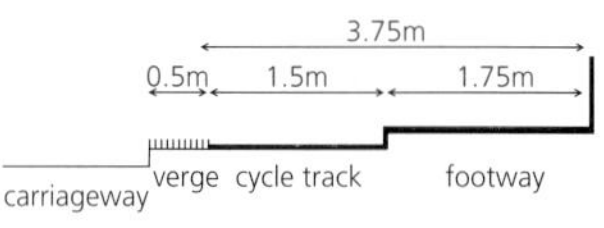

Kerbs segregated facility bounded on footway side with verge between cycle track and adjacent carriageway

Illegally parked cars are a particular hazard to pedestrians and cyclists.

Separate cycle tracks are a major incentive for people to cycle who otherwise are intimidated by traffic.

References: DOT Local Transport Note 2/86: shared use by cyclists and pedestrians. Institution of Highways and Transportation, Cycle-friendly Infrastructure - Guidelines for Planning and Design (1996)

Buses

Efforts to persuade people to leave their cars at home must be balanced by the promotion of attractive alternatives. For journeys beyond the local neighbourhood this generally means the provision of a good bus service.

Bus provision should feature high on the agenda of all discussions concerning new development. Developers should discuss with potential operators the kind of service that can be provided and the type of bus that will be used. Local authorities can ensure that consideration is given to bus provision from the development brief onwards, though they cannot dictate the type of bus on a particular route.

Generally buses require a 6m road width, which is slightly wider than the ideal for a traffic calmed domestic road. That is all the more reason for considering carefully how bus routes can be integrated with other routes through an area. In exceptional circumstances special bus links through an area may be considered.

Bus stops should be located where they are available to as many people as possible.

A continuous street network is more attractive to public transport than one which is closed and restrictive. Loop roads can help operators to provide efficient services.

Places that work well and are cared for

Maintenance
Regular maintenance is essential to ensure that well designed and constructed places look their best and are not allowed to deteriorate in the long term. It is not solely the care and maintenance of the fabric that is important: dirt and litter must also be regularly cleared away.

Local residents should have a feeling that the street belongs to them: if they see the street as an extension to their dwelling then well cared for spaces can be created. For instance planting strips next to dwellings can encourage residents to take a more active role in the care of their street.

Maintenance of the footway is as important as maintenance of the carriageway, including the cleaning of ice in winter.

Materials
Choice of materials (including trees and landscaping) is important. Materials uscd should fit into and respect the local context. Good quality materials should be used so that they will last. Sustainable resources that do not harm or promote damage to the environment should be chosen.

Street furniture must be of a durable nature and resistant to vandalism. It should fit into and complement the local context of an area. Use of signs should be minimised.

Carefully-chosen materials help create a well looked after environment.

Utilities in the streets

Because utilities have a statutory right to install apparatus in the highway, service corridors usually follow the routes taken by roads and footpaths. However, alternative routes may sometimes be more economic, and may also be better for those living in an area should the services have to be dug up at a later date. Subject to an agreement with the service utilities regarding future maintenance, services can be routed away from the adopted carriageway. The need for utility vehicles to gain access for maintenance should always be borne in mind.

The paths that pedestrians want to take do not always coincide with the routes followed by services. When footpaths and services are planned to follow different routes designers should remember the need for service routes to be provided to each house. In many places this can be achieved by bringing mains services to houses from the back or through communal areas.

Essential equipment boxes such as telephone and cable company and traffic signal control boxes are usually positioned on pavements, where they can appear unsightly and cause obstruction to pedestrians. Early discussion with utilities may allow them to be sited elsewhere, for instance set into boundary walls or masked by shrubbery, provided that easy access can be maintained.

Manhole covers and telecommunication covers in the footway should be carefully phased so as not to distract from the street design. Covers should be aligned to use parallel kerbs or paving material, or be placed in grass verges where they will be less obtrusive.

If there is sufficient space, landscape features and utilities can be coordinated. Where existing trees occur, footpaths can be narrowed and the services below can be bunched to avoid the tree pits.

Services are frequently laid beneath a 2000mm wide footway, but such a width is often inappropriate. Where a narrower footway is preferable, the services beneath it can be bunched.

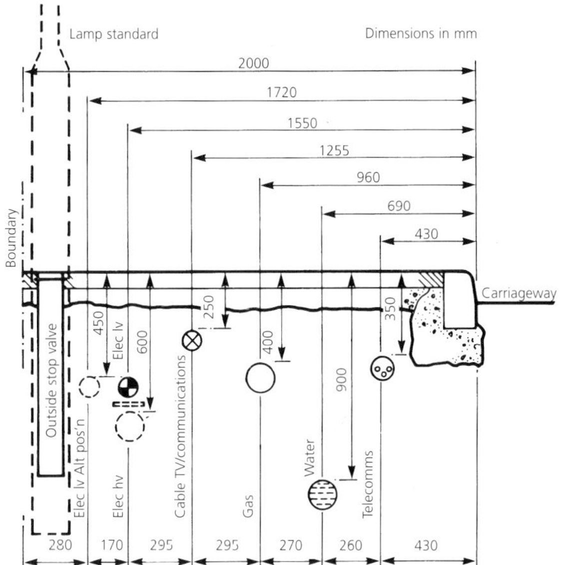

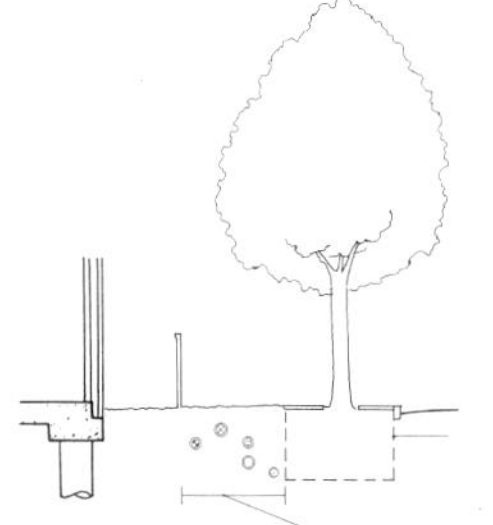

With the agreement of the statutory authorities, services can be locally grouped to avoid features such as trees.

A back street or footpath can form a route for mains services.

Reference: National Joint Utilities group, Publications 7 and 10.

Layout design should take account of access for refuse collection, and of the location of dustbins.

Dustbin shelters should be treated as part of the overall design, not as an afterthought.

Refuse Collection
Refuse collection is an important consideration in designing a development, but like service utilities it should not be allowed to dominate the shaping of an area. For example, turning heads on traditional culs de sac provide for the refuse vehicle yet they do not help to create good spaces. A through road would often be a better solution.

Refuse collection points should be easy to reach for collectors and within maximum walking distances as identified by the local council. Adequate access and egress for refuse vehicles should be allowed (including, where necessary, space to turn around and reverse, and room for other vehicles to pass when a refuse lorry is stationary).

Emergency Vehicles
Adequate access must be provided for emergency vehicles. Consultation with the emergency services is essential. Traffic calming measures must not hinder the movement of emergency vehicles. Emergency routes do not necessarily have to follow vehicular routes. A pedestrian street can be designed to allow for emergency vehicles to have access along their full length, taking care that the design does not allow other vehicles to enter.

A pedestrian street can provide a route for emergency vehicles.

Removable posts allow access for emergency vehicles.

Lighting

Lighting is not always welcome. Light spillage can be detrimental to certain areas, particularly in the countryside, so lighting levels should be gauged to suit the local context. The local authority should be consulted about lighting levels.

By mounting street lights on buildings the amount of clutter in the street can be reduced. Consideration is needed to ensure that wall mounted lights are away from bedroom windows. Lights on a building can enhance the visual appearance of the building and give it greater prominence within the overall street hierarchy.

Lighting levels within a development should create a secure environment. Dark corners or alleyways should be avoided and lamps must also be regularly maintained to ensure that they are clean and in good working order.

Lamp posts in prominent positions can be used to define an area and create spaces. For instance two lamp posts at the entrance to a road can help create a gateway effect which will help to mark an area as special, in which drivers should behave differently.

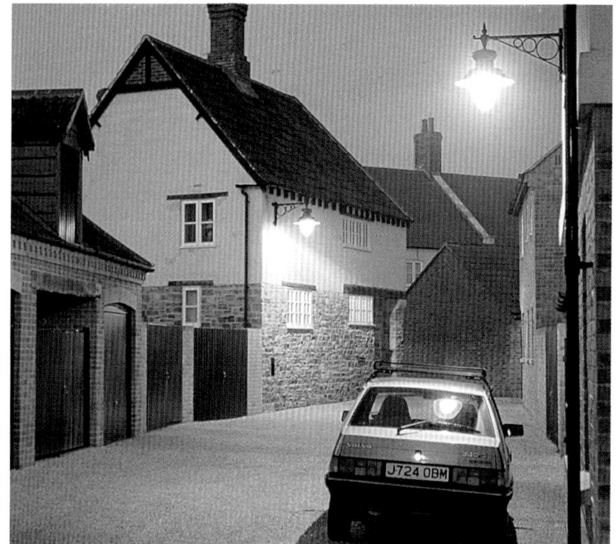

Reference: DOE and Countryside Commission, Lighting in the countryside: Towards good practice (1997)

Conclusion

The aim of this guide has been to show how the information provided in Design Bulletin 32 can be applied in creating sustainable and well-designed residential areas. Almost all of the illustrations are of projects which have been completed in the last few years, and thus are proof of what can be achieved within the current guidelines. They include examples from many kinds of location - inner city, suburban and rural - and many different parts of the country. On the evidence shown here, the ideas in DB32 are being taken up, though not as universally as was intended. Where the few have shown the way, it is now hoped countless more will follow.

In order to encourage the maximum flexibility this guide, like Design Bulletin 32 on which it is based, is as non-prescriptive as possible. Engineering requirements of function and safety are vital, and are taken fully into account, but the main emphasis is on the broad precepts of good development.

These precepts can best be summarised in the form of seven questions which should be asked about all new housing projects and about the improvement of existing housing areas. All those involved should keep these questions in mind, even when they do not relate directly to their responsibilities. Good developments are the product of a comprehensive approach, in which all parties seek to avoid taking up entrenched positions.

The pressure to provide for new households over the coming decades means that the issues of house design and housing layout will not go away. On the contrary, the demand for new homes means that it is more important than ever that these issues should be properly addressed. The alarmed response that has greeted the predictions of the number of new homes that we shall need is partly because of the quality of what has been provided in the past. If the demand is met through the building of places which are appreciated and cared for, plus the sensitive revival of existing areas, what seems to many to be an insuperable problem will have been turned to the best effect.

The seven key questions:

- *Have the main characteristics of the locality been fully understood and taken into account? These include the local topography, existing building types and layouts, trees and planting, and existing movement routes and linkages.*

- *Has a framework for development been drawn up and agreed? A framework (or development brief) is an essential prerequisite for projects of any size, whether it be a small group of houses on an infill site or a major edge-of-town development.*

- *Does the framework design aim to create a distinctive place through the density and layout of buildings and spaces?*

- *Has every effort been made to introduce or retain mixed use, as a way of enhancing the vitality of the development and reducing the need to travel?*

- *Do the streets and spaces contribute to making a high quality public realm, for the enjoyment of people of all ages, or are they designed primarily for the movement of vehicles?*

- *Does the framework provide for all forms of travel, including walking, cycling and public transport?*

- *Has full account been taken of the need to create places which will be safe and well cared for, and where the statutory services are integrated but do not dominate the layout?*

Further reading

1 The Historical Development of Towns

Edmund N. Bacon, *Design of Cities* (1967)
Arthur M. Edwards, *The Design of Suburbia* (1981)
Mark Girouard, *The English Town* (1990)
Peter Hall, *Cities of Tomorrow* (1988)
Spiro Kostof, *The City Shaped* (1991)
Spiro Kostof, *The City Assembled* (1992)
Lewis Mumford, *The City in History: Its Origins, Its Transformations, and Its Prospects* (1961)
Camillo Sitte, *The Art of Building Cities* (New York 1945: first published in German, 1889)
Raymond Unwin, *Town Planning in Practice* (1909)

2 Housing Layout and Urban Design

Tony Aldous, *Urban Villages* (Urban Villages Group, 1992)
Peter Calthorpe, *The Next American Metropolis* (1993)
Ian Colquhoun and Peter G. Fauset, *Housing Design in Practice* (1991)
Countryside Commission, *Village Design. Making local character count; new development* (1996)
Department of the Environment, *Quality in Town and Country – A Discussion Document* (1994)
DOE, *Planning Policy Guidance 1: General Policy and Principles* (rev. edn. 1997)
DOE, *Planning Policy Guidance 3: Housing* (1992)
Greater London Council, *An Introduction to Housing Layout* (1978)
Allan B. Jacobs, *Great Streets* (1993)
Mike Jenks, et al, *The Compact City: A Sustainable Urban Form?* (1996)
Kevin Lynch, *Good City Form* (1984)
Francis Tibbalds, *Making People – Friendly Towns* (1992)
University of the West of England and Local Government Management Board, *Guide to Sustainable Settlements* (1995)

3 Transport and Road Design

County Surveyors' Society, *Traffic Calming in Practice* (1994)
DOE/ DOT, *Planning Policy Guidance 13: Transport* (1994)
DOE/ DOT, *PPG13: A Guide to Better Practice* (1996)
DOE/ DOT, *Design Bulletin 32, Residential Roads and Footpaths – Layout Considerations* (2nd edn. 1992)
DOT, *Developing a Strategy for Walking* (1996)
DOT, *The National Cycling Strategy* (1996)
DOT, Traffic Advisory Leaflets, especially:
1/87: *Measures to Control Traffic for the Benefit of Residents*
2/93: *20mph Speed Limit Zones*
3/93: *Traffic Calming Special Authorisations*
7/93: *Traffic Calming Regulations*
2/94: *Entry Treatments*
9/94: *Horizontal Deflections*
3/95: *Cycle Routes*
1/96: *Traffic Management in Historic Areas*
9/96: *Cycling Bibliography*
10/96: *Traffic Calming Bibliography*
DETR, *A New Deal for Transport: Better for Everyone* (1998)
Carmen Hass-Klau, et al, *Civilised Streets: A Guide to Traffic Calming* (1992)
Mayer Hillman, *Children, Transport and the Quality of Life* (Policy Studies Institute, 1993).
Institution of Highways and Transportation, *Cycle-friendly Infrastructure – Guidelines for Planning and Design* (1996)
Institution of Highways and Transportation, *Transport in the Urban Environment* (1997)
National Joint Utilities Group Publication 7: *Recommended positioning of utilities apparatus for new works on new developments and in existing streets* (1997)
Publication 10: *Guidelines for the planning, installation and maintenance of utility services in proximity to trees* (1995)
Royal Commission on Environmental Pollution, Eighteenth report: *Transport and the Environment* (1994); Twentieth report: *Transport and Environment, developments since 1994* (1997)
Sustrans, *The National Cycle Network: Guidelines and Practical Details, Issue 2* (1997)

4 Landscape Design

Brian Clouston, *Landscape Design with Plants* (1990)
Joanna Gibbons and Bernard Oberholzer, *Urban Streetscapes: a Workbook for Designers* (1991)
Clifford Tandy, *Handbook of Urban Landscape* (1970)

5 Crime and Security

Association of Chief Police Officers Project and Design Group, *Secured by Design* (1994)
DOE Circular 5/94, *Planning Out Crime*
Oscar Newman, *Defensible Space: People and Design in the Violent City* (1972)
Barry Poyner and Barry Webb, *Crime Free Housing* (1991)

6 Disabled Access

Centre on the Environment for the Handicapped *Access for Disabled People: Design Guidance Notes for Developers* (1985)
Tessa Palfreyman, *Designing for Accessibility – An Introductory Guide* (1994)

Principal places illustrated

The numbers refer to the page on which the scheme is illustrated.

Abbotsbury, Dorset 1992–4
Architect: Ken Morgan Architects
Client: Raglan Housing Association and C.F. Fry & Son Ltd p.43

Beverley, Friary Court Eastgate, 1986–91
Architects: Ins Partnership with Richard Swaine
Client: Beverley Borough Council p.27

Beverley, St. Andrew Street
Architects: David Crease and Partners
Client: St. Andrew Street Development Co-operative Ltd. p.69 (middle)

Britannia Village, West Silvertown, London E16, 1996–
Architects: Tibbalds Monro
Client: Wimpey Homes
p.45, p.66 (lower middle), p.74 (upper left)

Broadwindsor, Dorset, 1992–4
Development by C.G. Fry & Son Ltd
p.37, p.67 (top and bottom right)

Bury St Edmunds – Moreton Hall, 1994–
Planning framework by St Edmundsbury Borough Council p.36

Chingford Hall, Waltham Forest, London E4
Phase 1 1994–5
Architect: Hunt Thompson Associates
Client: Waltham Forest Housing Action Trust
p.67 (lower middle right)

Coldharbour Farm, Aylesbury, 1996–
Masterplan by John Simpson & Partners
p.29, pp.33–35, p.69

Corfe Castle, Dorset – Abbots Cottages, 1996
Architect: Ken Morgan Architects
Client: Corfe Castle Charities
p.40 (upper), p.72 (bottom right)

Dickens Heath, Solihull, 1997
Masterplan proposal by the Barton Willmore Partnership
pp.51–53

Gateshead, Lumley Walk Dunston, 1991–3
Architects: Jane Darbyshire and David Kendall Ltd
Client: Two Castles Housing Association
p.20, p.44, p.66 (bottom), p.74 (upper middle right)

Great Notley, Garden village, near Braintree, Essex, 1986–
Development by Countryside Properties plc.
p.39 (upper right), p.40 (lower), p.56, p.68 (upper and lower left), p.69 (middle left and right), p.71 (bottom left)

Greenland Passage, Surrey Docks, London, SE16, 1986–9
Architects: Kjaer and Richter, with Macintosh, Haines and Kennedy
Client: Islef U.K. Ltd, p.50

Holly Street, Hackney, London E8, 1992–
Architect: Levitt Bernstein Associates
Client: Hackney Council Comprehensive Estates Initiative, with Laing Partnership Housing and the Consortium of Housing Associations. p.42

Hovingham, North Yorkshire, C. 1990
Architect: Francis Johnson & Partners
Client: The Hovingham Estate and the Joseph Rowntree Memorial Trust p.48

Mothers Square, Hackney, London E5, 1987–90
Architect: Hunt Thompson Associates
Client: Newlon Housing Trust, Access Homes, and City & Hackney Health Authority
p.38 (bottom right)

Noak Bridge, Essex, 1978–81
Development by Basildon Development Corporation
p.60, p.65 (upper middle, left and right), p.67 (upper left, upper middle left and right), p.69 (bottom right)

Old Royal Free Square, Islington, London N1
1990
Architects: Pollard Thomas Edwards and Levitt Bernstein
Clients: Islington & Hackney Housing Association and Circle 33 Housing Association p.6

Poundbury, Dorset
1994–
Masterplan: Leon Krier
Lead Consultants: Alan Baxter & Associates
Client: Duchy of Cornwall
p.13, p.25 pp.30–31, p.55, p.64, p.65 (lower middle left and right; bottom left and right), p.66 (upper and upper middle), p.68 (middle left, bottom right), p.73 (bottom right), p.74 (lower middle right), p.75 (upper right, bottom left).

South Woodham Ferrers, Essex
1973–
Masterplan: Essex County Council
p.10 (upper left), p.38 (upper right), p.39 (bottom), p.41, p.60

Wick Village, Hackney, London E9
1993–5
Architects: Levitt Bernstein Associates
Client: Wick Village Tenants Management Co–operative and London Borough of Hackney
p.28, p.38 (bottom left), p.39 (middle), p.65 (upper), p.68 (upper right), p.72 (upper right, middle left), p.74 (bottom left)

Illustration credits
Aerofilms, p.15, p.30; John Adams, p.17 (based on *Transport Statistics Great Britain 1995 and Air Traffic Forecasts for the United Kingdom 1994)*; Barton Willmore Partnership, p.51, p.52(x2), p.53 (x2); Building, p.27 (x3); Cheshire County Council, Archives and Local Studies Dept, p.19 (middle right); Ian Colquhoun, p.6; Country Life, p.48; Countryside Properties plc, p.56 (upper); Jane Darbyshire and David Kendall, p.20, p.44 (x4); Department of the Environment, Transport and the Regions, p.61 (x3), p.62 (upper and lower right); Ian Dobbie, p.38 (bottom right); Essex County Council, p41; Mark Fiennes, p.65 (bottom left and right); Leon Krier, p.22 (upper two), p.24 (x2), p.25 (lower); Levitt Bernstein and Associates, p.28 (upper left), p.39 (middle), p.42 (upper); London Metropolitan Archives, p.19 (upper left); Ken Morgan Architects, p.40 (upper), p.43 (upper), p.72 (middle right); Royal Commission on Historical Monuments, p.18 (x2); St. Edmundsbury Borough Council, p.36 (x3); John Simpson and Partners, p.29 (x3), pp.33–35, p.69 (upper); Sustrans/Julia Bayne, p.9 (lower middle), p.10 (lower left), p.39 (upper left), p.77; Tibbalds Monro, p.45 (upper), p.74 (upper left) (x3); Urban Villages Forum, p.16 (upper left, lower right), p.9 (upper right and middle two), p.75 (upper right); John Warburton-Lee, p.10 (upper left), p.13 (x3), p.31 (all except bottom left), p.33 (x3), p.38 (upper right), p.39 (upper right and bottom), p.40 (lower), p.43 (x6), p.55 (2), p.56 (bottom 3), p.64, p.55 (middle 4), p.66 (upper 2), p.67 (all except lower middle right), p.68 (all except upper right), p.69 (middle left, middle and lower right), p.71 (bottom left), p.73 (bottom right), p.74 (bottom right), p.75 (bottom left, upper right); all other illustrations have been supplied by Alan Baxter & Associates.

AIRLIFE'S CLASSIC AIRLINERS

LOCKHE

CONSTELLATION

LOCKHEED C

AIRLIFE'S CLASSIC AIRLINERS

ONSTELLATION

Jim Winchester

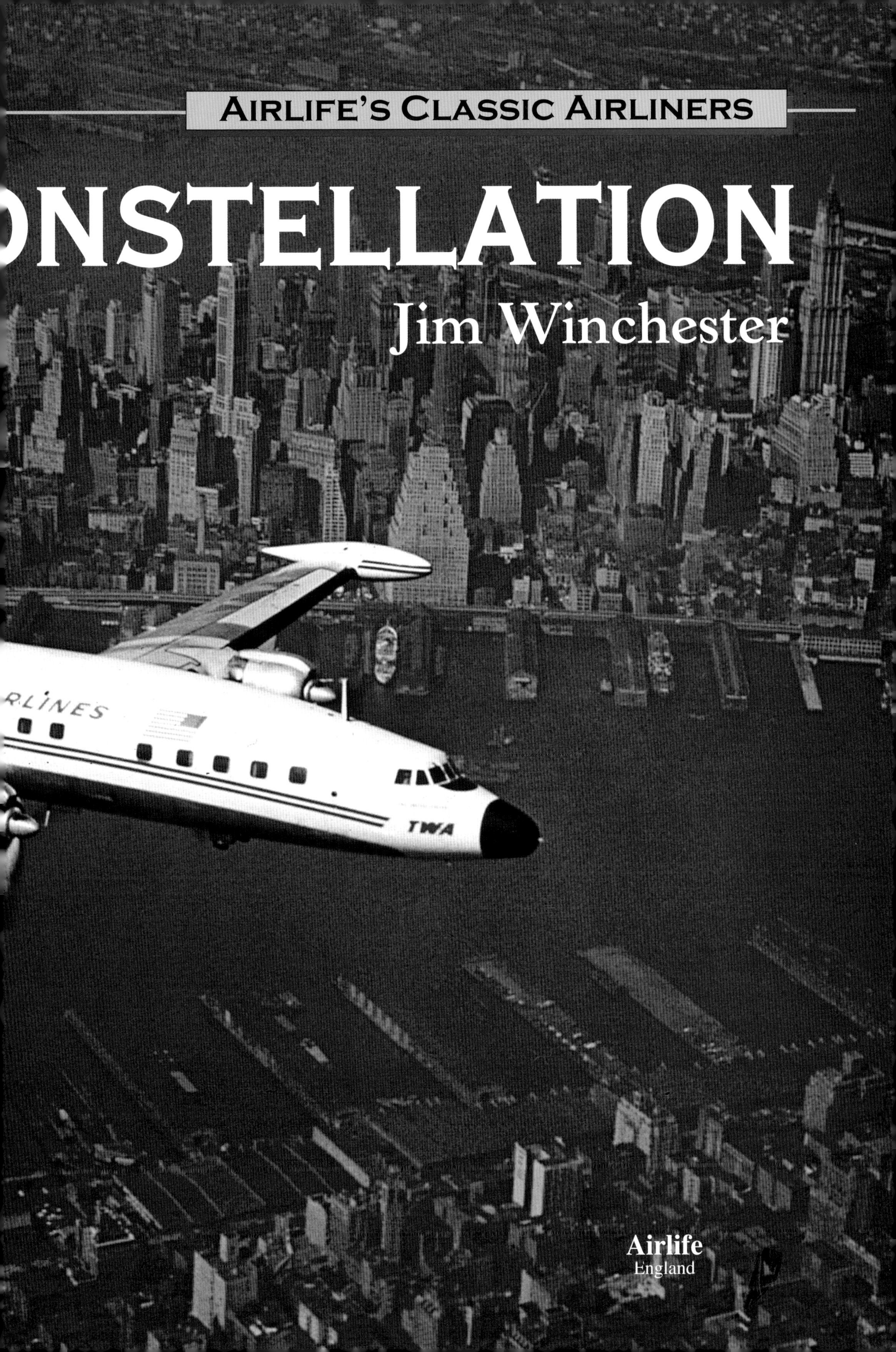

Airlife
England

First published in the UK in 2001
by Airlife Publishing Ltd

British Library Cataloguing-in-Publication Data
A catalogue record for this book
is available from the British Library

ISBN 1 84037 228 1

Printed in China

Airlife Publishing Ltd
101 Longden Road, Shrewsbury, SY3 9EB, England
E-mail: airlife@airlifebooks.com
Website: www.airlifebooks.com

PREVIOUS SPREAD: TWA Super Constellation over New York city
(Author's Collection)

BELOW: Some of Cubana's Constellation flights from May to Havana in the mid-1950s featured a Calypso band in association with the Tropicana resort.
(Lockheed via author)

CONTENTS

1 Design and Development

A STAR IS BORN

When Lockheed's four-engined airliner proposal, known as the Model L-44, was made public in April 1939, it could be seen that this was a great leap forward in airliner design and for transportation in the USA. At that time, the Douglas DC-3 had been in service for less than three years, and while it had revolutionised air travel in terms of speed and comfort, a trip from New York to Los Angeles by DC-3 still took 17 hours and involved three intermediate stops.

The Model L-44 was an elegant design, with a tapering fuselage and a wide twin-finned tail, and provision for 32 passengers. All the design elements had been proven in the successful Lockheed L-10 Electra, and this new project, named Excalibur to maintain the theme of myth and legend then in use by the company for its products, closely resembled a scaled-up tricycle-undercarriage Model 10. Powered by a quartet of R-1830 engines, the Excalibur would be a match for the DC-4E that Douglas had proposed in conjunction with Transcontinental and Western Airlines (TWA), United, American and Pan Am in 1935. Cruising at 269mph (433km/h) at 12,000ft (3,658m), it would cut hours and at least one stop from the journey between the American east and west coasts. Later sketches of the Excalibur show a central third fin on a tail

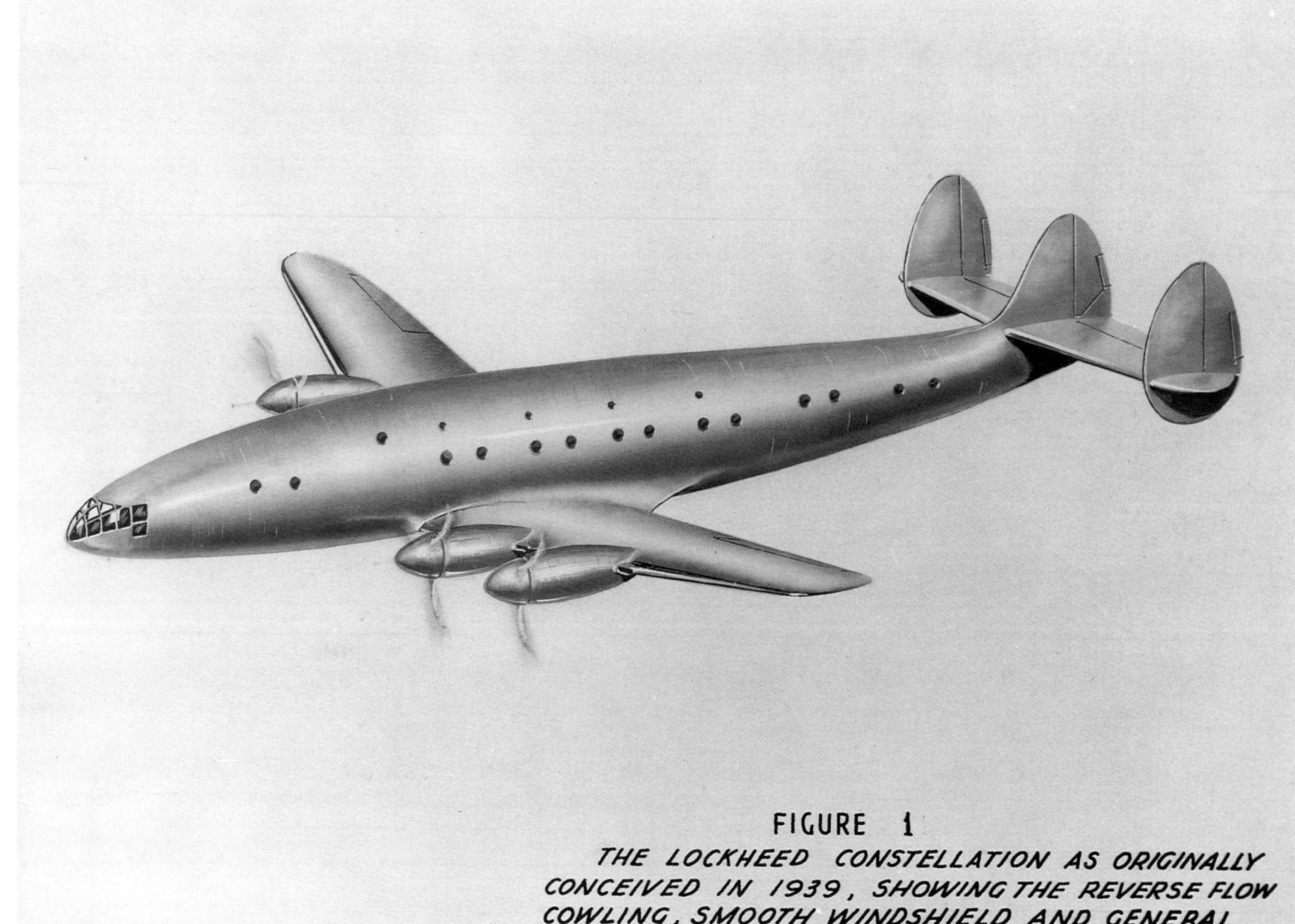

unit that stood only a little over 3ft (0.9m) higher than the crown of the fuselage, and a tricycle undercarriage. The Excalibur was given the Temporary Designation Number (TDN) L-105 before it received the Model Number L-44, and a mock-up was constructed, consisting of at least a fuselage, tail and port wing.

The last configuration studied, which was a 36-seater with many features that would later be found on the Constellation, was designated L-144 or Excalibur V. Lockheed's Vega subsidiary assigned the TDN V-115 to the same design, for which they presumably hoped to share production.

By this stage, however, Douglas had a virtual stranglehold on the market. The vast majority of airliners in service in the USA were DC-3s, and there seemed no reason why the DC-4E would not also be an equal success, taken up in vast quantities by happy airline customers. In order to push technology and trans-national business forward, a greater leap was really needed, but this would require massive investment and a firm commitment from the airlines.

On 21 June 1939, only two months after the L-44 was announced, tycoon and aviation pioneer Howard Hughes called a secret meeting at his bungalow at the Beverly Hills Hotel. With Hughes was the head of TWA, Jack L. Frye, and joining them were three of the most important men at Lockheed: President Robert E. Gross, Vice-President and Chief Engineer Hall L. Hibbard, and Chief Research Engineer Clarence 'Kelly' Johnson. Hughes owned the majority of TWA stock, and wanted an airliner that would eclipse the competition and give 'his' airline the first non-stop trans-continental services. In exchange for financing a new design, the two airline men would get an agreement that would prevent Lockheed selling it to any direct competitors for two years after it entered service. Together the men sat down and pencilled out what TWA wanted and what Lockheed thought they could achieve.

This was no incremental step in aircraft design: the new model would be 100mph (161km/h) faster, fly 10,000ft (3,048m) higher (because it was pressurised), and have true trans-continental range — New York–Los Angeles non-stop. Because this would be a premium service, affordable only by top executives, Hollywood stars and the like, a maximum of 20 passengers was specified, all in sleeper compartments. The profits would come from the express mail and freight that could be carried — some 1,800lbs (816kg) worth. A document in the hands of someone in LA — by tomorrow! Imagine that!

Filling the remaining space would be a crew of six (four flight crew and two stewardesses) and 800lbs (363kg) of passenger baggage — equivalent to 40lb (18kg) per person. Johnson argued that 20 passengers were too few for an aircraft that could potentially carry 100 and Hughes agreed to consider this and other suggestions. Contrary to legend, Hughes did not design the Constellation, although his influence was to be felt in many aspects of its design.

LEFT: This 1939 drawing shows the layout of the Constellation (or 'Excalibur V') as proposed at that time. The reverse-flow cowlings, which gave the impression of in-line engines, and the streamlined nose were dropped soon after, but otherwise all the elements of the production Constellation are here. *John Stroud Collection/The Aviation Picture Library*

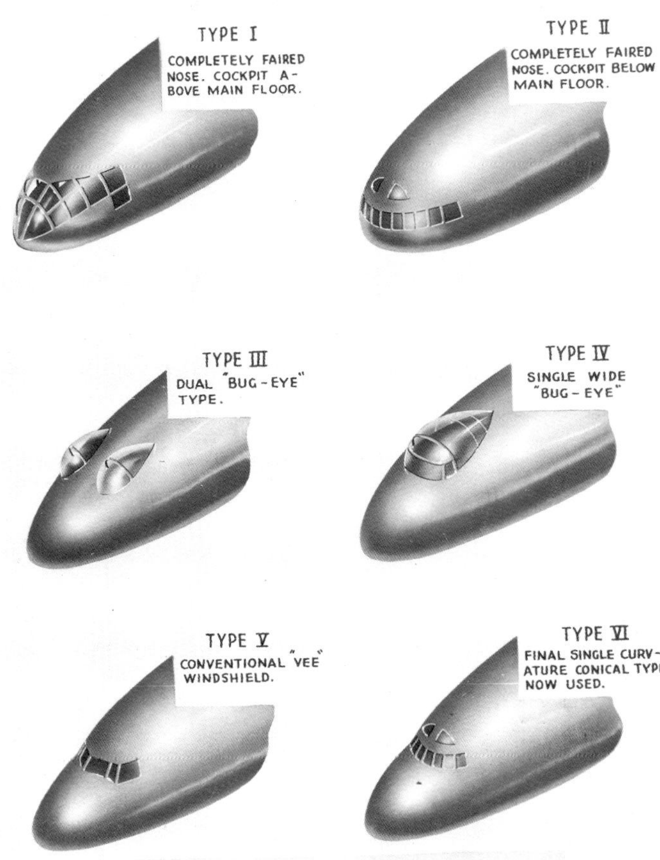

ABOVE: A post-war document shows the different nose and windscreen designs considered for the Constellation. Hints of the Boeing 307, B-29 and the Douglas 'Mixmaster' can be seen. The 'Type VI' design that was eventually chosen was the most practical, but not the best for visibility. *John Stroud Collection/The Aviation Picture Library*

The Lockheed engineers left the meeting buzzing with ideas. But how could they meet this exacting requirement? After all, the performance specified was greater than any bomber or transport aircraft then in service. They all agreed on four engines, but would that be four small, lightweight engines, or four powerful but heavy ones? After careful analysis of projected figures, four large 1,900hp Wright-Cyclone R-2600s were chosen, the largest engines then available.

Most vestiges of the Excalibur were discarded, except for the general layout and the triple tail. The whole design was scaled up, from a length of 74ft (22.5m) to 95ft (29m) and a span of 95ft to 123ft (37.5m). At least six different nose and cockpit configurations, including completely faired wind-screens, were studied (see illustration) before a conventional stepped windscreen was chosen to fit within a tapered nose section. The conventional design chosen gave the same drag co-efficient as the completely faired-in variant and by using flat, rather than curved panels, it conferred comparable visibility to the DC-3. One innovation tested in the laboratory but never fitted was a defrosting mechanism 'utilising infra-red rays', although details of this remain obscure. Somewhat oddly, the new design was given an earlier TDN of L-104, but the later Model Number L-49.

ABOVE AND LEFT: Lockheed made more use of wind tunnels for the Constellation than had ever been used before and five different installations were used. Seen above is a beautifully crafted metal model being tested in a small tunnel. While on the left a twin-finned tailplane mock-up is mounted in an inverted position for local airflow trials. *Aeroplane*

Three weeks after the initial meeting, the group met again, this time at Hughes' mansion at Hancock Park. The sketches and figures they brought with them had little in common with the Excalibur, and Hughes was very impressed, scattering the blueprints on the floor and crawling from one to another. The drawings showed an elegant four-engined airliner with a slender dolphin-like fuselage, upswept at the rear to a huge triple-finned tail. Faired completely into the narrow nose, the cockpit featured a deep wrap-around windscreen. The engines appeared to be inline units with large spinners, but in fact were radials with so-called reverse-flow cowlings.

The rationale behind the unusual fuselage shape was three-fold. Because the fuselage was already high off the ground to give clearance for the propellers, the droop of the nose helped reduce the length of the nosegear. The rear fuselage was swept up to keep the tail surfaces clear of the airflow over the wing, especially with flaps down. Drag was also reduced because the curve of the fuselage followed that of the wing section. Later attempts by some at TWA to have a conventional fuselage substituted, on the grounds of ease of production and better use of space, were blocked by Kelly Johnson and Hughes in the interests of speed. The curvaceous hull gave an extra two to three knots speed over a constant section unit, and speed was the *raison d'être* of the L-49.

Triple fins gave the required keel area without excessive height that could not be accommodated by the hangars of the day. They also gave the L-49, a relatively small aircraft with large engines, the requisite directional stability. The great width of the tailplane served to keep the outer fins away from the 'unfavourable slipstream effects' of the propellers.

The wing design was essentially a scaled-up version of that used on the Model 22, better known as the P-38 Lightning, which had first flown in January 1939. The wing was a NACA

ABOVE: A varied group of Lockheed officials, engineers and USAAF officers watch as the No.4 engine of the Connie prototype turns over before its first flight, on 9 January 1943. Despite extensive photographic coverage at the time, few images of this historic event have survived. *Michael Stroud Collection*

RIGHT:The control surfaces of the Connie were put through many thousands of cycles in a hydraulic test rig. *Aeroplane*

section with no aerodynamic twist. This was chosen rather than a 'speedier' laminar-flow section because of better lift and stall characteristics. Massive Fowler flaps in two sections would help the wing, optimised for cruising, stay in the air at a relatively slow landing speed. A very powerful elevator would be needed to counteract the resultant ground effect, and this was one of the reasons for the choice of hydraulically boosted controls from the beginning.

Hughes asked for a price. Robert Gross gave him one: $450,000 — an unheard of figure for a landplane airliner then. Hughes thought for a few minutes. TWA was not in that kind of financial position. Finally he said: 'Hell, I guess I'll have to pay for them myself. Build 'em Bob, and send the bill to the Hughes Tool Company.' The initial order was for nine aircraft, but was soon followed by another for 31 more. In total the Hughes/TWA order was worth $18 million, the largest commercial order for aircraft that had been made up to that time.

In exchange for this vote of confidence, Lockheed was bound by an agreement not to sell L-49s to any other airlines offering trans-continental services for two years after delivery to TWA, or after the thirty-fifth aircraft had been delivered. The paperwork for the initial order was completed on 10 July 1940 with the Hughes Tool Company being the nominal purchaser. This ostensibly kept the actual operator secret, but it didn't take a genius to see that the aircraft were destined for TWA. When the Model 49 design was unveiled to the wider market, Pan American Airways (Pan Am) quickly ordered 40 Constellations to be delivered concurrently with the TWA order. It was stipulated that these be used for Pan Am's trans-oceanic services only, so as not to compete with TWA.

ABOVE: Olive drab warpaint hardly suited the elegant lines of the Constellation, and only the first aircraft was so camouflaged. Aware that the Model 49's future lay in the civil market, Lockheed made sure their logo was prominently displayed. This was unique for an aircraft that was Army property and of dubious legality. *Aeroplane*

BELOW: The first Constellation underwent more hours of testing than any previous transport aircraft. The interior was filled with test equipment and the crew wore parachutes (as seen here) in case they had to bail out. *Aeroplane*

At about this time the name 'Constellation' was bestowed on the L-49 (or L-049 as it was usually written on company documents). With the exception of the Electra and the stillborn Excalibur, previous Lockheed aircraft bore astronomical names, mainly of specific constellations (Sirius, Vega, Orion). The L-49 was given the all-encompassing name Constellation to follow this theme, which continued into the 1970s with the StarLifter, Galaxy and TriStar, although mythological names such as Hercules and Neptune were also used.

Before the design was finalised, over 500 wind-tunnel tests were conducted in tunnels operated by the University of Washington, NACA, the California Institute of Technology and Lockheed's own Aerodynamic Laboratory. Three NACA tunnels, the high-speed, 19ft (5.8m) and spinning tunnels were used, and an unprecedented body of data was accumulated for an airliner design.

The definitive basic configuration was set out on Lockheed Drawing No. 250,000 and then a drafting department of 350 workers set to work drawing all of the thousands of components that would make up the Constellation.

In the initial stages of detail design, the engine was changed from the proven Wright R-2600 of 1,900hp to the new and as yet unflown 2,200hp Wright R-3350. Despite the risks and expense of this new powerplant, Kelly Johnson and 'Tommy' Tomlinson of TWA argued that its reserves of power would allow for safety, durability (through use at lower power settings) and the airframe development which was sure to come. The wisdom of this decision can be seen in the fact that versions of the R-3350 were to power all production models of Constellation and Super Constellation. Another factor was a specific fuel consumption 26 percent lower, despite 22 percent greater power. The reverse-flow cowlings, which worked by feeding air from an intake on the wing leading edge and

ABOVE: A line up of some of the first C-69s is seen awaiting modifications at Burbank. Many adjustments and improvements were needed before the Army, let alone the airlines, would accept the Constellation. Note the 'eyebrow' windows which were a feature of the C-69. *Aeroplane*

twisting it through pipes back to the front of the engine, were abandoned in favour of conventional close cowlings with hinged 'petal' sections for access.

From the detail drawings a full-scale functional mock-up was constructed. This was connected up to a Ford-built test rig and subjected to 200 hours of extreme control cycling. 'Extreme' meant that the control wheels were moved fore and aft and left and right to their stops 1,000 times an hour. The landing gear was put through 2,000 cycles and all sub-systems were run simultaneously for 25 'flight' hours. Additional stresses were put on the ailerons and landing gear by making them work in opposition to railway car springs and lead slabs on an incline. The hydraulic flight controls were tested for function in a $30,000 pressure chamber (converted from an oil storage tank) at extremes of altitude and temperature — as low as -70°F (21°C) at 55,000ft (16,760m). A mock-up nose undercarriage unit was towed at high speed around the Burbank airfield by a vehicle to evaluate the effect of punctures and to test the design generally.

The new engines and various cowl combinations were tested on a company-owned PV-1 Ventura. The oversize R-3350s gave the patrol bomber a very pugnacious appearance, like a

ABOVE: L-049 noses are seen under construction in the Burbank factory. The astrodomes on the upper fuselage were seen on C-69s and civil L-049s as well as C-121 military Constellations. With factory space at a premium and the clement Californian weather, nearly completed aircraft were wheeled outside for final fitting out. *The Aviation Picture Library*

BELOW: American Overseas Airlines, predecessor of today's American Airlines, ordered four (later seven) L-049s and were the third US airline to fly the Connie. One of the latter batch, NC90925, ***Flagship Philadelphia*** is seen undergoing final completion at Burbank in early 1946. *The Aviation Picture Library*

LEFT: The complex Constellation programme required new testing methods. Among Lockheed's innovations was a special camera that photographed take-offs against a grid to measure performance at various weights. This aircraft may be the prototype, which was stripped of its camouflage after the initial series of tests. *Aeroplane*

boxer holding up his guard, and the curious-looking aircraft was named 'Ven-tellation' — being a hybrid of the Ventura and the Constellation. After Lockheed's tests, Wright bought the aircraft for its own development work.

Despite a launch order of eighty-four L-49s (including four from KLM of the Netherlands), construction could not begin right away. By 1940 Lockheed production was at full stretch, building aircraft to meet urgent British requirements as the war in Europe grew ever more serious. These orders included 1,500 A-28/A-29 Hudsons and 667 P-38 Lightnings which took precedence over development of commercial models, even before the USA entered the war. Despite America's isolationist policies, the government was preparing for involvement in the war by building up its own armed forces as well as those of friendly nations.

A Commercial Aircraft Priority Committee was established which served to restrict to a minimum the number of non-military types being built. By early 1941 it was clear that there would be no production capacity for the Constellation airliner. For one thing, after the fall of Holland to Nazi Germany, KLM had understandably dropped out, and the potential for further orders from European airlines for the time being was nil. Pan Am was also seeing its potential transatlantic destinations fall one after another to the Nazi invaders. The army was interested in the Connie for its own purposes, however, and ordered 180 as freighters and troop transports under the designation C-69B. A further bomber version, the XB-30, never got off the drawing board.

The TWA and Pan Am aircraft were 'drafted' on 20 September 1942, before their construction had even begun. As with a conscripted soldier, the Connies would 'belong' to the army for the duration of hostilities but would be returned after the war. However, the airlines would still gain experience with the L-49 as they would maintain and operate them on contract to the government.

Finally, in November 1942 the first Constellation rolled from the doors of the Burbank factory, having been constructed in great secrecy in the Engineering Experimental Shop. The sleek aircraft was not in the polished metal and red trim of Transcontinental and Western Air as had been envisaged by

BELOW: Only a few of the C-69s served with the US forces after the war, and 42-94533 was the only one known to wear the 'Buzz code' letters 'CM'. Note also the Post-1947 national insignia with the central red stripe. This aircraft, the fourth of five C-69-5s, was sold to TWA in 1951 and became N54212 ***Star of Piccadilly***. *Michael Stroud Collection*

Howard Hughes and Lockheed's executives nearly three years before, but in the dull olive drab and neutral grey colours of the US Army Air Forces (USAAF). Perhaps uniquely for a wartime military aircraft, the aircraft, designated C-69 with the construction number 1961 and the civil registration NX25600, wore company logos on the nose and tail.

Not only was the general appearance of the new aircraft striking, but a number of other features were true innovations for an airliner. Among these were reversible-pitch propellers, hydraulically-boosted control surfaces, a flight engineer's station, electric de-icing and cabin pressurisation — although this latter system was not fitted to the first prototype and in fact had appeared before on the Boeing 307, which had been built in very small numbers.

On 9 January 1943, the aircraft and the weather conditions were perfect for the first flight. Climbing aboard on that sunny morning were five men: legendary Boeing test pilot Edward T. 'Eddie' Allen, Lockheed chief engineering test pilot Milo Burcham, engineers Rudy Thoren and Dick Stanton, and Kelly Johnson. Allen had been 'borrowed' from Boeing because he was one of the few men with flight experience of the new R-3350 engine, having test-flown the B-29 bomber with these powerplants following its first flight on 21 September the previous year. Kelly Johnson's presence was a sign of confidence in his design, but it would be unthinkable today for a chief designer to make the inaugural flight in his creation.

The engines were given a good long run-up, and then a high-speed taxy was made down the runway virtually to take-off speed. As the power was retarded a flare of flame was seen to issue from an engine, making many observers think that a fire had broken out. Problems with engine fires on the B-29 had led to some disquiet about this choice of engine for the Connie, and Lockheed had proceeded with studies into an R-2600 powered version. The big Wrights were fine, however, and without further ado the prototype returned to the end of

BELOW: Before the Constellation entered service, the airlines undertook an extensive programme of pilot and crew training. This view shows a Pan Am crew on a training flight over New York and about to give the workers and tourists in the Empire State Building a thrill. *Aeroplane*

ABOVE: The final C-69 was bailed back to the manufacturer for a variety of tests, including of the 'Speedpak' freight pannier seen here in this photo issued in April 1946. The '79' marking refers to the last two digits of the construction number (1979). After the war, TWA operated 1979 (as N86536) *Star of Rome* until 1958. *John Stroud Collection/The Aviation Picture Library*

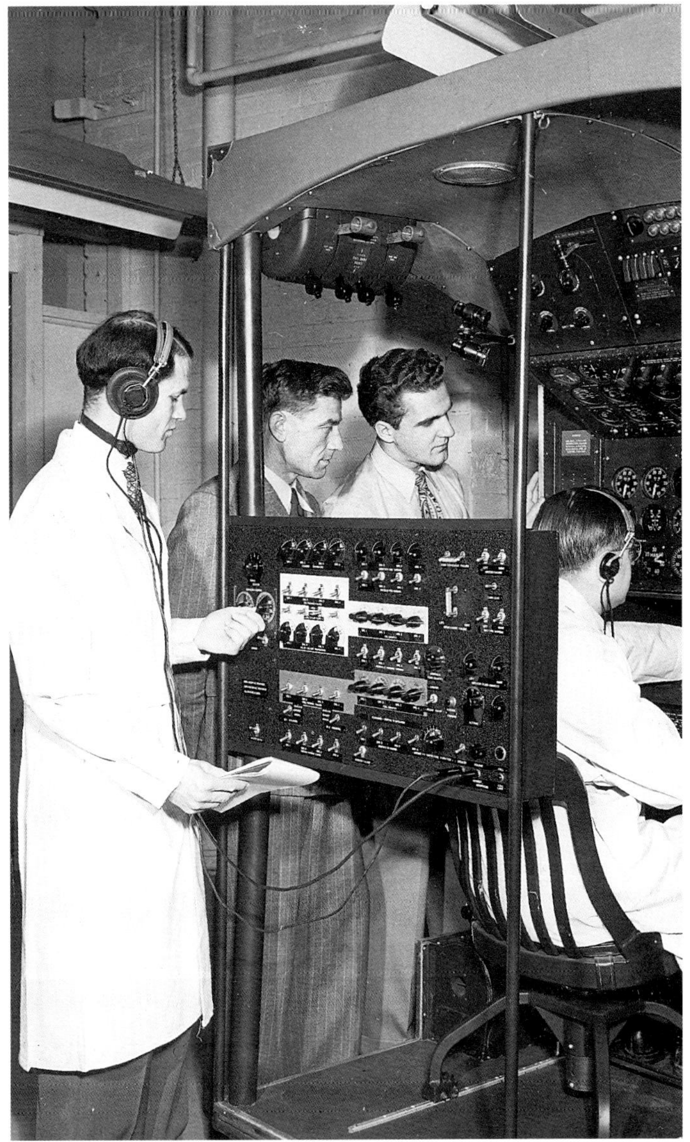

RIGHT: The Constellation was not the first airliner with a flight engineer, but was the first to be produced in great numbers. Lockheed trained many hundreds of flight engineers to handle the complex systems of the Connie, including this group from Air France, using a ground-based simulator. *Aeroplane*

Burbank's runway, revved some more, set off down the runway and soared into the blue California sky.

While the workers who had built her watched from every vantage point including the hangar roofs, 'Connie' circled the field twice with gear down and then turned north towards Muroc dry lake in the High Desert. Two camera ships, a B-17 and a Lodestar, took photographs before the prototype retracted its gear, climbed to 10,000ft (3,050m) and began a series of stall tests, stability tests and steep turns.

The last task was a speed test during which the contracted specification was exceeded by a considerable margin. Touchdown at Muroc 58 minutes after take-off was not, however, the signal for the end of a successful day. NX25600 was flown again five times more before the day was out, establishing a record that has rarely, if ever, been exceeded. There was little to report in the test log, because everything proceeded as expected. Eddie Allen said that he was no longer needed and went back to Boeing. Sadly he was to lose his life less than two months later in the crash of the second XB-29. Milo Burcham was also destined to die before the year was out, testing the second XP-80 Shooting Star.

A few modifications were made to 1961's aileron power boost which conspired to delay its next flight until 18 January. On this day a broken hydraulic line caused trouble and further

ABOVE: Howard Hughes used his influence with the government to the full in obtaining use of C-69s for route proving and publicity flights that benefited TWA (then called Transcontinental and Western Air). The second C-69 in TWA colours but still wearing its USAAF serial, was used in the record-breaking if controversial April 1944 Los Angeles–Washington flight. *Michael Stroud Collection*

delays so the opportunity was taken to fit the undercarriage doors and new stainless-steel flame shields. Although six flights had taken place on the first day, it was not until 5 February that the tenth flight was completed, and only one more had been accomplished by the 20th when tragic events elsewhere were to further delay the programme.

On 23 February, yet another fire in one of the R-3350s fitted to the second XB-29 forced Eddie Allen to turn back to Boeing Field in Seattle. Although the fire appeared to be out, it had in fact spread to the wing spar, which caused the structure to fail, and the big bomber crashed into a meat packing plant. All on board and many on the ground perished. The army's Air Material Command grounded the Constellation pending the outcome of the crash investigation. On 25 March this was extended until modified engines less prone to the induction system fires that had plagued the B-29 programme became available. These new engines with single-speed superchargers were not fitted until mid-May.

When flight testing of the prototype resumed in earnest on 18 June, it was as exhaustive as the ground testing, and was more comprehensive than that for any previous large aircraft. The highly-instrumented aircraft was loaded with up to 20,000lb (9,070kg) of water that could be pumped between 17 tanks to represent different passenger loads and centre of gravity (c of g) conditions. Filled by a four-inch fire hose, the water ballast could be shifted fully in ten minutes or dumped in 20 as required, a technique that replaced the manual transfer of lead bars between boxes bolted to the floor. This saved a lot of flight test time at the going rate of $6,200 per hour.

Stall tests were conducted with both forward and aft c of g; climbs were made on two, three and four engines. The fuel was heated to simulate summer take-off conditions where pumping efficiency is reduced. Temperatures were recorded at 144 points, including all cylinders on No.2 engine and on the hottest cylinder on the other three. Recordings of temperatures, vibration and other stresses were taken by two engineers, an oscillograph operator and a flight observer, as well as four Automatic Observers (or AOs). The AOs were small groups of instruments connected to a particular system such as cabin pressurisation and photographed by synchronised 35mm cameras, 'snapping' frames at a rate ranging from one to 120 frames per minute. At the end of a typical test flight, which might be a six-hour circuit taking in San Francisco and San Diego, followed by a minimum-stop landing, perhaps 1,600ft (488m) of film and 200ft (61m) of oscillograph record would be handed over to the ground engineers for study.

The first aircraft was quickly followed by others, which had many refinements over the 'minimum equipment' prototype such as cabin pressurisation and representative seating layouts.

On 28 July, NX25600 became 43-10309 when it was handed over to the USAAF at Las Vegas, but in fact never left Lockheed's hands for it was immediately loaned back to the company for further testing. Fuel tank leaks became a persistent problem, and 1961 spent three months in San Diego having this problem rectified by the Rohr Company. In June 1944, the

Army stripped off the camouflage paint and began its own series of tests the following month. Maximum weight trials at up to 90,000lb (40,800kg) showed the need for increased control boost to provide lighter control forces.

During the Army tests, the Connie carried a special celebrity. He was none other than Orville Wright, the first man to fly a powered aircraft. Only 41 years separated Orville's first flight at Kittyhawk, North Carolina, and this one — his last. The reason was a press flight to mark the arrival of the first C-69 at Wright Field, Ohio. The surviving Wright brother avoided public events, and it was a surprise that he turned up on this day at all (26 April 1944), and climbed aboard.

There was little in common between Orville's 1903 Flyer and the Constellation. The Wright name connected the power-plants of the two aircraft, but the Flyer's Wright engine would not have kept even the pressurisation system (powered by an accessory drive from one Wright R-3350) of the Connie running.

A short while into the flight, and after some reluctance, Orville took the controls and was alone in the cockpit for a moment while the pilot allowed another officer to take the left seat. 'I guess I ran the whole plane for a minute . . . ' he said back on the ground, 'but I let the machine take care of itself. I always said that airplanes could fly themselves if you let them alone.'

Photographs show a grinning Orville Wright in the co-pilot's seat. It is clear that he thought the Constellation was a pretty good flying machine.

RIGHT: Appropriately, a galaxy of film stars lined up to help Howard Hughes publicise the entry into service of the glamourous Constellation. *Michael Stroud Collection*

BELOW: Pan Am were the first airline to operate transatlantic services. Their first aircraft, the *UNO* (United Nations Organisation) *Clipper* is seen making its first landing at Hurn on 12 Jan 1946, which stood in as the UK's main international airport until Heathrow was completed. *Aeroplane*

2 In Detail

CHANGING WITH THE TIMES

Although all models of the Constellation family appear superficially similar, there is a world of difference between the original L-049 flown in January 1943 and the ultimate L-1649 Starliner delivered to Air France in February 1958. Between these two models there were many changes because the basic design was altered to accommodate more passengers, more freight, larger engines and new technologies such as radar.

During the course of production, the maximum take-off weight rose from 86,500lb (39,27kg) for the L-049 to 130,000lb (59,020kg) for the L-1049C and 156,000lb (70,824kg) for the L-1649.

This 'nose-to-tail' technical description of the Constellation begins with the basic variants, noting slight differences where applicable followed by the specific features of the successive models.

All Constellations, Super Constellations and Starliners had the same basic external configuration, with the main change being the new wing on the L-1649 Starliner. The Constellation family were four-engined land planes with a tricycle landing gear and a low-set wing which, on the L-049 through L-1049, was swept at the leading edge by 7.5 degrees and also had 7.5 degrees of dihedral. High-lift devices consisted of trailing edge flaps of the Fowler type. The four engines were of the radial piston type driving three-bladed metal propellers. The fuselage was of non-parallel section, tapering at each end with a downward curve at the nose and an upward curve at the tail.

NOSE

One reason for the characteristic curved fuselage was to reduce the length of the nose-wheel leg, but nonetheless it remained one of the longest units ever fitted to a piston-engined aircraft. On the first L-049s it was a non-steerable unit and ground manoeuvering was accomplished by applying bursts of power and rudder inputs. This made handling much more difficult than necessary (not to say hazardous to ground staff and equipment) and a steerable unit was introduced during L-049 production. This resulted in steering pistons and a fulcrum being mounted on the nose gear leg just above the upper torque link.

Dual nose wheels were an innovation not seen before on a transport aircraft and were necessary due to the high stresses placed on the nose gear. It was proved in testing that one tyre could go flat at speed without affecting the directional control of the aircraft. The toe-out of the 33in (84cm) diameter tyres was an unusual and characteristic feature of the Connie. The rearward-retracting nose gear was attached by struts to the gear doors and these were pulled shut as the gear was raised.

NOSE AND COCKPIT

The blunt nose of the C-69 featured a very large hemispherical landing light cover in the lower half. This was vulnerable to breakage and the lights were later relocated to the fulcrum on the nose gear leg.

An astrodome for taking star sightings was fitted to the second and subsequent C-69s. The original C-69s had 'eyebrow' skylight windows above the pilots' seats, but these disappeared when production switched to the civilian L-049.

In the cockpit the pilots sat behind a shallow nine-panel windscreen. After evaluating several configurations, the Lockheed design team chose this layout as the best compromise between aerodynamics and visibility. The latter was said to be 'no worse than the DC-3', which meant that it was not all that good. Before the advent of weather radar, a useful piece of cockpit equipment was a pair of binoculars so that a route through clouds and their expected turbulence could be spotted in good time and planned for.

The pilots' instrument panel was narrow but not overloaded with dials and indicators. This was partly because most engine instruments were on the flight engineer's panel and repeaters for left and right engine pairs (with dual needles) were seen as sufficient for the pilots. These were mounted in the central part of the main panel above the autopilot panel. Each pilot had essentially the same instruments, although the command pilot in the left seat had a couple more that included the radio altimeter.

Between the pilots' seats was a large central pedestal atop which were mounted the throttles, autopilot controls, propeller governor controls and control surface booster engaging levers. These controls were all mounted offset to the left for easier use by the pilot. Rudder and aileron trim tab controls were mounted on the rear vertical face of the console in equal reach of each pilot, while the flaps and landing gear were the co-pilot's responsibility, their control levers being on the upper right of the console. Elevator trim was adjusted by large control wheels on either side of the forward console. On Super Constellations and Starliners, the hand-wound trim levers were replaced by twist knobs and the back of the console was reshaped.

The flight engineer sat facing to the right (when seen from the rear) at the starboard side of the cockpit. Adjacent to the engineer's station, which duplicated the engine instruments and controls on the main instrument panel, was the crew entry door. A small window in the door with a wide-angle curvature on it allowed the engineer a view of the No.3 engine which was the first to be started in the pre-take-off sequence. A mirror and another wide-angle window allowed some view of the left-hand engines.

On the other side of the cockpit to the flight engineer and facing aft sat the radio operator, at least on most Connies in service up to the 1960s and on military versions. Miniaturisation of radio equipment saw the phasing out of radio operators and the transferral of their duties to the pilots, in much the same way that flight engineers have been replaced by computerisation since the late 1980s.

Most Connies of all types carried a navigator's position although navigators themselves tended to be found more often in the early years and on military versions. The navigator's station on an L-049 was a model of simplicity in comparison to

LEFT: The Constellation Historical Association's C-121C shows off its elegant radar nose and nosegear unit with its characteristic toed-out twin wheels. *Author*

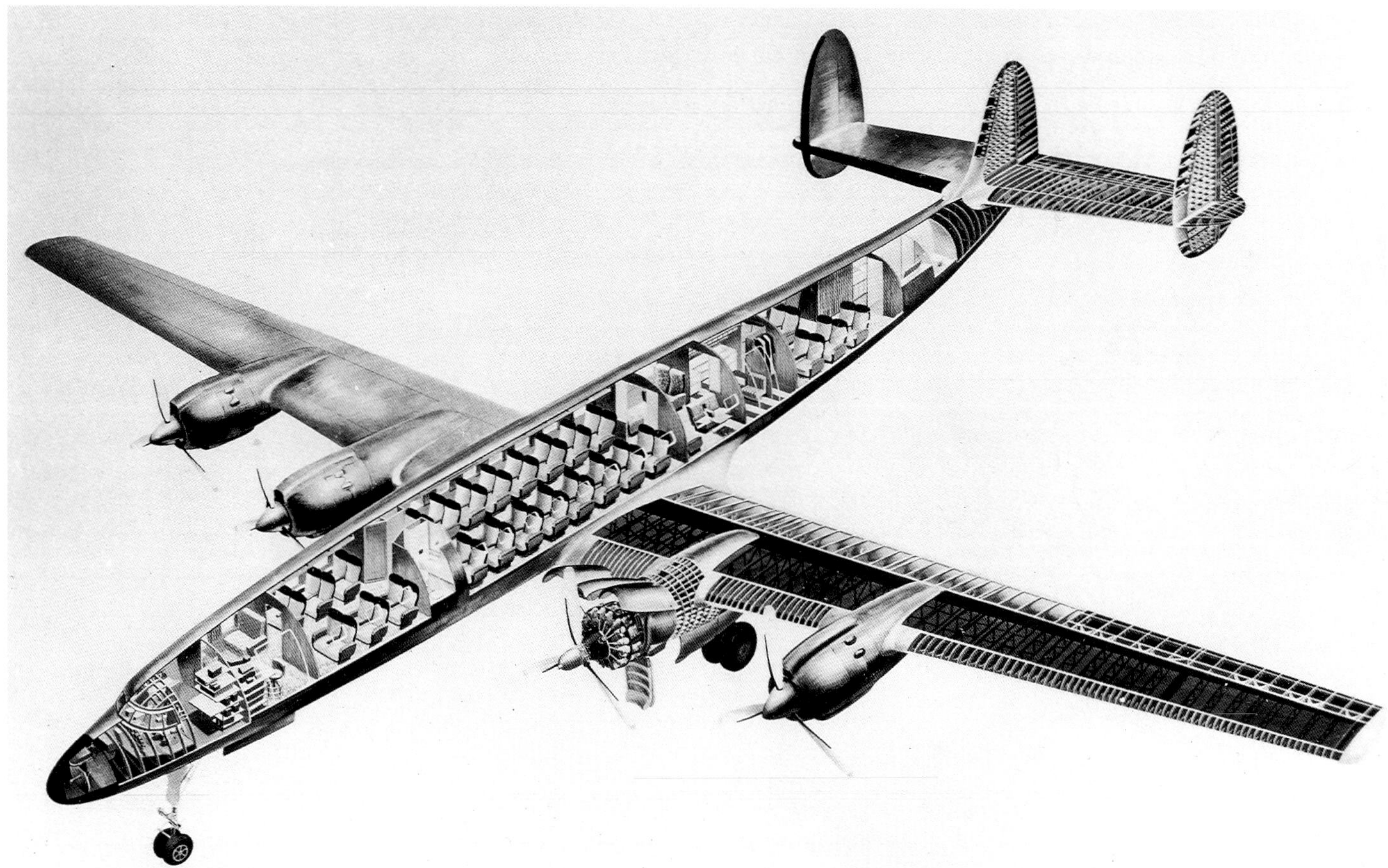

ABOVE: Cutaway showing key structures, components and seating arrangements. *John Stroud Collection/The Aviation Picture Library*

the other crew positions, consisting of a stool, a table with a drawer for maps, sextants and so on, a compass and a panel with four instruments — clock, airspeed indicator, chronometer and altimeter. This station was situated in a compartment behind the cockpit on the left side of the fuselage.

THE FUSELAGE

The external shape of the fuselage was so designed in order to raise the tail and lower the nose. As stated earlier, a lower nose meant a shorter nose gear (and better visibility). The tail needed to be high to keep it clear from the airflow over the wings, especially with flaps extended. An added benefit claimed by the designers was that a fuselage shape which approximated the wing section reduced drag and increased range. In fact, this contributed little to performance and made the Connie both harder to manufacture and to load efficiently.

The cabin pressurisation system was driven off the No. 1 and No. 4 engines and was able to maintain sea-level air pressure up to an altitude of 9,000ft (2,743m), and a pressure altitude of 5,000ft (1,524m) up to 15,500ft (4,724m). Pressurisation was controlled by the flight engineer.

A duct ran the length of the cabin ceiling with cabin heating and cooling air and riser ducts circled the fuselage at the centre of the fuselage, abeam of the position of the wing trailing edge fillet. A pipe exhausted surplus cabin heat through the port fillet. The refrigeration system was able to cool the aircraft interior to 75°F (23.9°C) from an outside temperature of 110°F (43.3°C). Cabin conditioning was also powered by the outer engines. Failure of both outboard engines would necessitate an immediate descent to a safe altitude.

Lockheed denoted configurations by number, such as L-749-79-31 with the first two digits after the model number signifying the engine and the last two digits, the interior layout. Thus an L-749-79-31 was fitted with the 749C18-BD1 (military designation R-3350-75) engines and was built for 42 day passengers or 22 night passengers in sleepers, and seven crew. The same configuration was usually available across a range of models to allow fleet commonality.

Other examples of interior layout, of which there were over 50 offered for the original Connie series alone, included the — 12 (60-seat 'club' layout aircraft operated by Eastern) and the — 22 (48 day/20 sleeper, plus four sitting) 'over-ocean' aircraft operated by TWA. Club seating consisted of pairs of seats facing each other. Many of the sleeper/convertible models offered by Lockheed and ordered as such were converted to all-seaters before delivery.

Seat pitch in a standard day layout was typically 41in (104cm), about 10in (25cm) more than is usually found in the economy class of today's airliners.

The short-bodied Connies had three emergency exits in addition to the passenger doors on the port side of the fuselage. Two of these were also on the port side, at windows two and four in the main cabin, with the third at window four on the

ABOVE: The front end of a BOAC L-049 shows many of the details of the earliest Constellations including the landing light housing in the nose. Compare the nosegear leg with the C-121 unit on the previous page with its cross-piston steering unit and strut-mounted landing lights.
John Stroud Collection/The Aviation Picture Library

RIGHT: Driving force for the Constellation, Super Constellation and Starliner was the Wright Double Cyclone. On the C-121 this was the 18-cylinder R-3350-91 turbo-compound version. This was known as the DA2 engine for civil applications and was rated at 3,250hp (2,535kW) at 2,900rpm. *Author*

starboard side. The exits were a horizontal oval shape and rather small.

The two cargo compartments, one forward and one aft of the main spar, were pressurised and could be accessed in flight through hatches in the floor. Hatches in the lower fuselage allowed access from the ground.

Because the Connie had a greater lifting capacity than its cabin volume allowed for, Lockheed developed the 'Speedpak'. This was a bulbous cargo pod that fitted to the underside of the fuselage outside of the pressure hull. It had its own wheels so that it could be loaded and unloaded away from the aircraft and rolled into position before being hauled up by its own internal

Above: The skylight windows mark this cockpit as belonging to a C-69 or an early L-049. Note also the central control pedestal with throttles and large elevator trim wheels. The main panel was relatively simple as most of the engine instruments were on the engineer's panel. *Aeroplane*

Right: The flight engineer's panel of an L-049 had duplicate engine and propeller controls. The vertical panel at the left was the master electrical panel. *The Aviation Picture Library*

Above Right: The instrument layout of the L-649/749 showed a more logical arrangement than that of the -049. Note the more extensive overhead panel and the nosewheel steering tiller wheel which is at the extreme left. *Author's Collection*

hoist system. A rubber gasket ensured a seal against the fuselage and the unit had its own fire detection and fighting system, linked to the cockpit through electrical connections. Eastern Air Lines was the biggest user of the Speedpak which could be fitted to the L-049 through L-749A models. Capacity was 8,300lb (3,768kg). The speed penalty was only 12mph (19.3km/h) and the range penalty was about four per cent. Although most 'short' Connies were equipped with mounting points, and several airlines took them up (including Eastern, KLM, Air France, Qantas and El Al), only 75 of the Speedpak units were produced.

One problem with freight use of the Connie was that neither the fuselage doors nor the Speedpaks could accommodate very bulky items. Freight doors were later to be fitted to many L-749s by Lockheed Aircraft Services (LAS) and others, a solution that did not overcome the inherent problem of the fuselage's great height from the ground and the resultant need for hoists and forklifts.

The fuselage was built from eight sections, which made 'stretching' the Connie design by adding extra sections a relatively easy process. On the Connie and Super Connie, the stub wing was built as part of the fuselage.

MAIN GEAR

Each main gear leg had a single oleo-pneumatic strut with an axle fastened directly to the strut piston. Dual main wheels with 49in (124cm) diameter tyres had independent double-brake connections so that a failure was unlikely to affect both wheels on a unit at the same time. The unit extended and retracted forward with hydraulic power and was secured by mechanical safety locks in both positions. Flush doors fully enclosed the gear unit when retracted.

WINGS

The full cantilever wing was constructed of all-metal stressed-skin panels in inboard, outboard and wingtip sections. The ailerons and trim tabs were fabric covered. The internal structure was based around two box beams and an auxilliary leading-edge beam. Each inner wing panel contained two fuel tanks. A third tank was fitted into the outer panels of L-749s and refitted to many earlier models.

The two-section flaps were fitted to the inner wing section and extended outwards and downwards (Fowler flaps). The extension angle at the trailing edge was 42° on the L-049 and more on the L-649 and subsequent models. Manual backup was available to extend the flaps in the case of hydraulic failure.

ENGINES

The massive 18-cylinder twin-row R-3350 engines on the L-049 were of course heavier than the R-2600-14s that were originally suggested. Dry weight was 2,760lb for each of the R-3350 'Duplex Cyclones'. Figures calculated by Kelly

ABOVE: Four-abreast seating was more common on aircraft configured for international routes and domestic first-class only services. Five-abreast layouts had narrower seats with the extra row added to the starboard side. *Aeroplane*

RIGHT: 'Club' seating was an available factory option, but not taken up by many airlines. Sleeping berths were more commonly found, but only accommodated eight passengers at best. *Aeroplane*

Johnson showed that, for a given airframe weight, the weight of the larger engines was absorbed in lower fuel consumption after 775 miles (1,247km) of flight (this basic calculation holds true today). From this point on, the R-3350s were more economical. The civil designation of the original L-049 R-3350 engine was the 745C18BA-1 which had conventional carburettors. After the Reading, Pennsylvania, crash, one of the modifications made was the replacement of carburettors with fuel injection, leading to a designation change to 745C18BA-3. Engine variants were usually referred to by the last part of their designation, ie, BA-3.

At take-off, the early R-3350s were rated at 2,200bhp at 2,800rpm with 100 Octane fuel. The flight engineer kept track of the 18 ignition coils and 36 spark plugs on each of the four engines using a device called an ignition analyser which incorporated an oscilloscope-type screen.

To absorb the massive power of these engines, 15ft (4.57m) diameter propellers were needed, and this dimension affected both the length of the undercarriage legs and the fuselage shape. The propellers were either 15ft (4.57m) Curtiss-Electric or 15ft 2in (4.63m) Hamilton Standards. The Connie was the first transport aircraft to be licensed with reversible propellers, which helped give it good landing performance for its size. A built-in mechanism made it impossible to reverse the propeller pitch in flight.

The R3350-CA1 delivered with late-model L-749As (and offered as a retrofit option on 749s and 749As) featured 'jet stacks' which provided a bit of extra thrust by reducing exhaust back pressure. Up to 15mph extra was obtained by their use in cruising flight, but they caused a big increase in cabin noise levels and their actual effect on performance was debatable. Later, the jet stacks, which consisted of ten small exhausts mounted in a circle rather than one single exhaust coming from a collector ring, were fitted to some TWA L-049s.

ABOVE: Well-dressed passengers settle in before take-off in an early Connie. Air travel remained out of the reach of all but the well-off until the 1960s. *Author's Collection*

LEFT: The Super Constellation introduced a designer interior and a lounge with a side-facing sofa. Wood panelled bulkheads helped reduce the 'tube' effect of earlier Connies. *Aeroplane*

The empennage unit was all metal except for the rudders and rudder trim tabs. Each outboard fin was a complex item made up of about a dozen sub-assemblies and extended below the horizontal stabiliser, whereas the centre fin and rudder did not. The metal-clad elevators were interchangeable left and right.

At the very end of the fuselage underside there was a retractable tail bumper skid on the L-049, lowered with the undercarriage to provide protection against tail scraping at take-off or landing. This was deleted from later versions.

A feature of the C-69 and L-049 was in-flight access to the engines through a crawlway in the leading edge of the wing, entered through the forward baggage compartment, which had a hatch in the forward cabin floor. This type of access was found on several transport aircraft of the era, but appears to have been little if ever used in service by Constellation flight engineers.

TAIL GROUP

The characteristic triple-tail design of the Constellation came about as a way of keeping the height of the aircraft down while still providing the maximum fin and rudder area for stability.

SUPER CONNIE

As introduced in 1951, the L-1049 had the same nose profile as the L-049—L-749 series. Weather radar arrived to change the profile of the Constellation in the mid-1950s and the APS-42 set as fitted to military Connies was soon adopted for commercial use, beginning with its installation in three TWA L-1049Gs in April and May 1955.

Commercial weather radars included the AVQ-10 made by RCA and the Bendix RDR-7. The 36in (94cm) dish was not circular, having a 'slice' taken off the top to allow for the maximum horizontal diameter (and thus horizontal definition). Although Lockheed would have preferred individual panel-

mounted scopes for each pilot there was simply no room, so a telescoping display unit was fitted in the floor between their seats. The preferred location for the transmitter-receiver unit (in the main radio rack) gave too long a run for the wave guide cables, so a position in the nose was found, with an 'elevator' rack to ease maintenance from below.

The new radome had a beneficial side effect in that there was space behind the antenna for a flush VOR antenna, allowing the removal of the drag-inducing 'goat horn' type antenna from the cockpit roof.

ABOVE: One of Pan Am's later L-049s (note the nosewheel steering unit) runs up its engines at Burbank. A slow shutter speed has made the propeller blades all but invisible. *John Stroud Collection/The Aviation Picture Library*

FAR RIGHT: The first 60 or so L-049s were steered with its partially castoring nosewheels by differential mainwheel braking and application of engine power. Later examples had hydraulic nosewheel steering.
John Stroud Collection/The Aviation Picture Library

RIGHT: A passenger's-eye view of the No.2 powerplant of a Constellation. The aperture foward of the open cooling flap is the crankcase oil breather outlet and the four louvres at rear are cooling vents for the engine accessory compartment.
John Stroud Collection/The Aviation Picture Library

Above: Although high off the ground, access to the Constellation's engines was aided by the 'butterfly' cowlings as shown here on a C-69. C-69s used the R-3350-35 and -35A (BA2 and BA4) engines, although the XC-69 flew with Pratt & Whitney R-2800s for a period. *Author's Collection*

Above: Engineers work on the top cylinders and Curtiss Electric propeller of an Air France L-749. The engine version here was the 2,500-hp BD-1. The same version was used on the military C-121A as the R-3350-75. Note the prominent cuffs on the propeller roots. *Aeroplane*

MODEL	LENGTH	WINGSPAN	WING AREA	HEIGHT	EMPTY WEIGHT	MAX T/O WEIGHT	R-3350	T/O POWER
L-049	95ft 2in (29.01m)	123ft (37.49m)	1,650sq ft (153.29m²)	23ft 8in (7.21m)	48,630lb (22,058kg)	93,000lb (42,185kg)	BA-3	2,200hp (1,641kW)
L-649	95ft 2in (29.01m)	123ft (37.49m)	1,650sq ft (153.29m²)	23ft 8in (7.21m)	55,000lb (24,947kg)	94,000lb (42,637kg)	BD-1	2,500hp (1,864kW)
L-749A	97 ft 4in* (29.01m)	123ft (37.49m)	1,650sq ft (153.29m²)	22ft 5in (6.82m)	56,590lb (25,669kg)	107,000lb (48,534kg)	BD-1	2,500hp (1,864kW)
L-1049	113ft 7in (34.63m)	123ft (37.49m)	1,650sq ft (153.29m²)	24ft 9in (7.56m)	69,000lb (31,298kg)	120,000lb (54,430kg)	CB-1	2,800hp (2,088kW)
L-1049G	116ft 2in* (35.39m)	123 ft 5 in+ (37.62m)	1,650sq ft (153.29m²)	24ft 9in (7.56m)	73,016lb (33,119kg)	137,500lb (62,368kg)	DA-3	3,250hp (2,423kW)
WV-2	116ft 2in (35.39m)	123ft 5in+ (37.62m)	1,650sq ft (153.29m²)	27ft (8.23m)	80,611lb (36,589kg)	127,600lb (57,918kg)	-34	3,250hp (2,423kW)
C-121C	116ft 2in* (35.39m)	123ft (37.62m)	1,650sq ft (153.29m²)	24ft 9in (7.56m)	72,815lb (33,051kg)	137,500lb (62,411kg)	-93	3,250hp (2,423kW)
L-1649A	116ft 2in (35.39m)	150ft (45.72m)	1,850sq ft (171.87m²)	23ft 5in (7.13m)	85,262lb (38,700kg)	156,000lb (70,808kg)	EA-2	3,400hp (2,523kW)

+ span with tip tanks   ** length with radar nose*

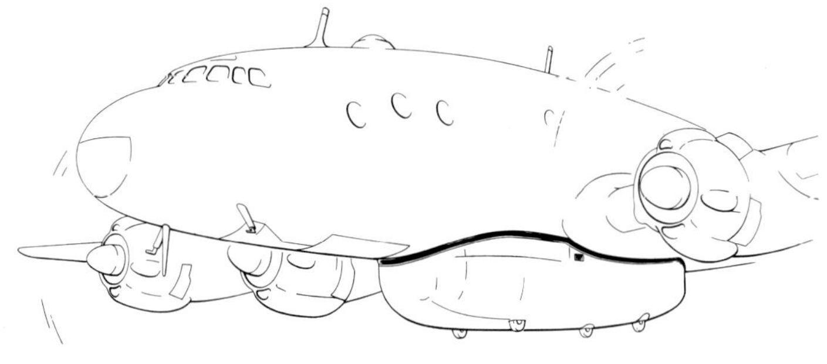

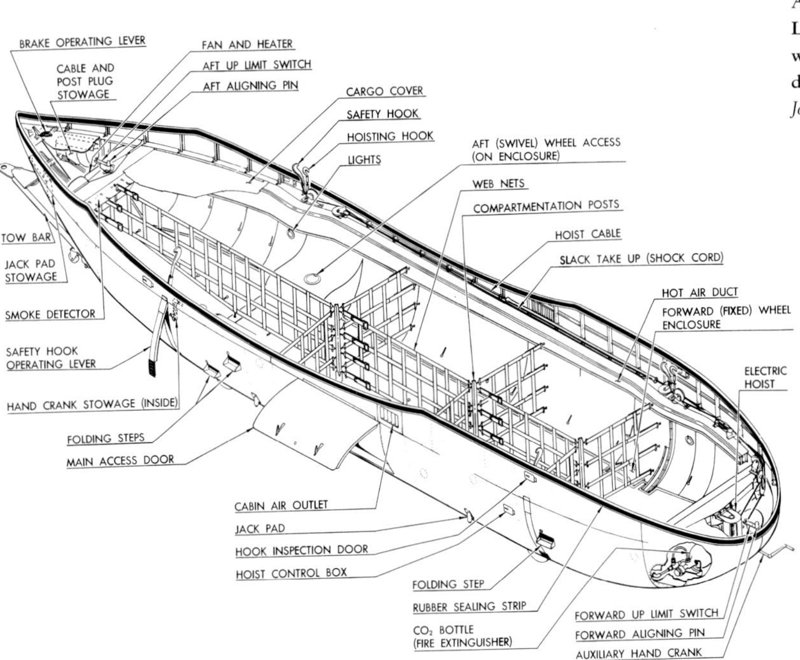

A Lockheed drawing shows the features of Lockheed's Speedpak freight pannier. The unit was quite sophisticated with heating, smoke detectors and fire extiguishers.
John Stroud Collection/The Aviation Picture Library

Above: The Speedpak would be lowered to the ground and moved on its own wheels to the terminal or, as seen here, to a collection point beside the aircraft This latter method had several obvious disadvantages. The couple here appear to have a particular liking for plum puddings.
John Stroud Collection/The Aviation Picture Library

The 1049 and subsequent models featured a new windscreen with seven rather than nine windows. The depth was also increased by 3.5in (89mm) at the top, an increase made possible by flattening the fuselage mould line (profile) above the cockpit which also gave the pilots about 7in (17cm) more headroom.

The hydraulic nosewheel steering was controlled by the pilot with a small wheel on the left-hand side of the cockpit. This was effective up to about 70kts (130km/h) on take-off, when the rudders became effective.

Fuselage length was increased by 18ft 4.75in (5.64m) by adding sections forward and aft of the wing. The forward section was 128.8in (325cm) long by 139.3in (354cm) in diameter and the aft section was 92in (233cm) long by 136.6in (347cm) in diameter. Cabin noise levels progressively increased until the L-1049C arrived with its turbo-compound engines. Improved soundproofing design reduced the interior noise levels of the L-1049G even more, slightly lower than those of the L-049,

Model	Max speed	Cruise speed	Ceiling	Max range
L-049	295kts (547km/h)	272kts (504km/h)	25,300ft (7,711m)	3,470nm (6,427km)
L-649	306kts (567km/h)	284kts (526km/h)	25,700ft (7,833m)	5,000nm (9,529km)
L-749A	300kts (556km/h)	n/k	24,100ft (7,346m)	4,210nm (7,796km)
L-1049	n/k	294kts (545km/h)	25,700ft (7,833m)	n/k
L-1049G	318kts (589km/h)	294kts (545km/h)	23,200ft (7,071m)	4,134nm (7,655km)
WV-2	279kts (517km/h)	262kts (486km/h)	19,000ft (5,791m)	4,013nm (7,431km)
C-121C	320kts (593km/h)	309kts (573km/h)	27,300ft (8,321m)	1,810nm (3,342km)
L-1649A	327kts (606km/h)	294kts (545km/h)	23,700ft (7,224m)	5,460nm (10,111km)

ABOVE: This view of the interior of the Global Aeronautical Foundation's EC-121T gives a good overview of the cockpit of a Super Constellation. Note the seven-panel windscreen as opposed to the nine-panel unit of earlier Connies. *All photos in this section are taken by the Author*

RIGHT: Between the pilots was a control pedestal with throttles, propeller pitch controls and wheels and knobs for three-axis trim control. Instruments on the centre panel included manifold pressure and tachometer gauges, and flap indicators.

BELOW: The pilot's control wheel of the C-121C, and to the left, the nosegear steering wheel. On earlier aircraft, this was a half-circle tiller, but it needed two hands to operate at slow speeds so was enlarged.

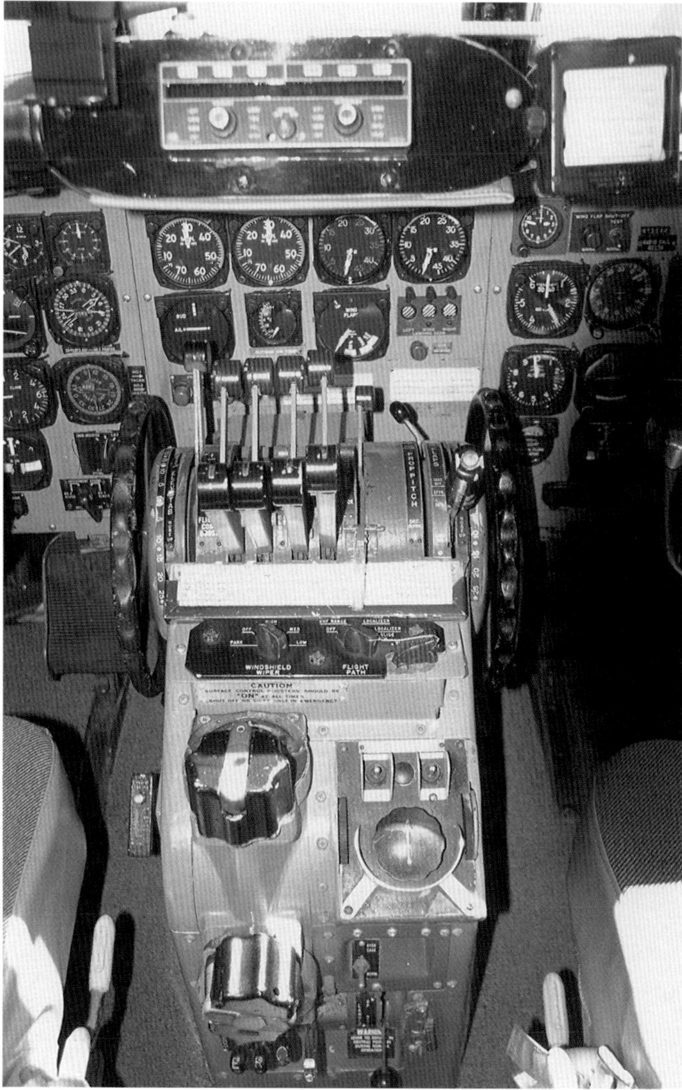

Above Left: The overhead control panel on the Super Constellation was a noted hazard to pilots' heads, although it was raised and cut back compared to earlier models. At the rear were the fuel dump controls.

Above Right: The Flight Engineer's panel was considerably more complicated for the Super Constellation than for the O-49 - 749 series. The sloping upper panel had quantity gauges for all seven fuel tanks on its top row.

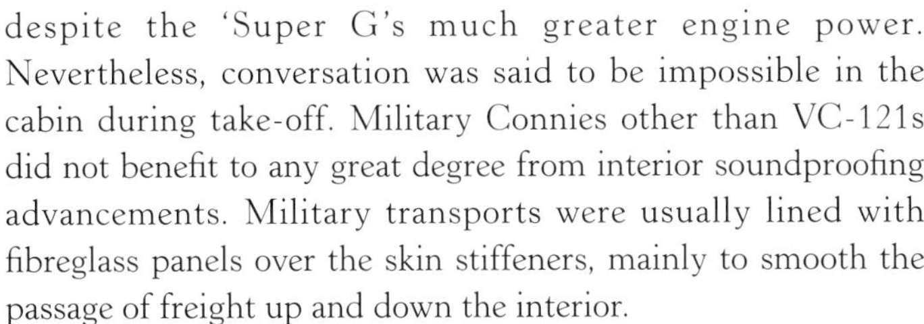

despite the 'Super G's much greater engine power. Nevertheless, conversation was said to be impossible in the cabin during take-off. Military Connies other than VC-121s did not benefit to any great degree from interior soundproofing advancements. Military transports were usually lined with fibreglass panels over the skin stiffeners, mainly to smooth the passage of freight up and down the interior.

One change that came about through bitter experience was the provision of more emergency exits. There were now four on each side, at windows 4, 5, 9 and 19, as counted from the forward starboard window. It should be noted that there were usually fewer windows on the port side due to the presence of the passenger doors. Windows of the Super Constellation were basically square, rather than circular as on the Connie.

First Class compartments and lounges were located at the rear when fitted, and sleeping berths forward of these, but as with the 'short' Connie, cabin specifications varied greatly on the 1049 series. KLM's first aircraft had (from tail to nose), a first class cabin with 11 seats, the lounge (eight seats), a 'Tourist' cabin for 40 and another first class cabin seating 12 for a total of 63. Toilets were at the extreme tail and ahead of the main section, and bulkheads helped reduce the 'tunnel' effect common to the narrow-bodied airliners of the time. This was partly due to the influence of top designer Henry Dreyfuss, who followed in the steps of Raymond Loewy for TWA by designing the interiors for KLM and Air France, at a cost of $1.5 million. Airliners were nothing but a 'big pickle' said Loewy, so by using natural wood finishes, fine-art murals, small tables and lamps, and soft indirect lighting, Dreyfuss made the Super Connie more homely and welcoming to the new generation of post-war air travellers. Even in those days there were complaints that legroom was tight for the taller-than- average passenger.

The profusion of interior configurations continued. TWA had at least 60 variations, from 32 sleepers to 74 tourist seats on its L-1049Gs and Starliners alone.

Improvements in the pressurisation system allowed a

sea-level pressure to be maintained up to 12,500ft (3,810m) and a cabin altitude of 5,000ft (1,524m) to 20,000ft (6,096m). A new electrical system with a fault finder ensured that only the faulty generator was cut off in the event of a failure, and not all of them as was previously possible.

On the R7V-1 (C-121A), a useful increase in payload was achieved without a significant increase in weight by using a higher grade of aluminium (75ST) and integral stiffening in the wing skins. This payload increase, and the installation of freight doors made civilian freight and 'combi' versions viable.

The most significant change was probably the Wright DA-1 turbo-compound engine. Sandwiched between the front and rear supercharger housings as found on standard R-3350s was a series of three power recovery turbines. These were driven by exhaust gases from six of the 18 cylinders through three separate 'siamesed' exhaust pipes. In turn, this exhaust power was transmitted through a shaft, bevel gears and a fluid coupling back to the main crankshaft. The result was that a lot of 'wasted' exhaust energy was returned to become useful power without the need for larger engines and a major structural redesign. With development these turbo-compound engines were to give 1,000hp more take-off power compared to the most powerful 'stock' R-3350 for little increase in weight.

One problem with the turbo compound engines was excessive exhaust flaming. In the climb, flames would come out of the turbine exhaust hoods and carry back as far as the trailing edge of the wing. This was not only alarming to crew and passengers, but also a hazard in the event of leaking or venting fuel. It took hundreds of hours of flight-testing and $2 million to prevent 'flaming'.

Tip tanks

The tip tanks, originally developed for the early-warning version for the Navy, were tested on the prototype Super

ABOVE: The completed wing of a Starliner is moved between buildings at Burbank on a foggy morning. The wings of the L-1049Gs, Hs, RC-121s and WVs in the background were made in left and right halves and attached to stubs on the centre-section. Production of Super Constellations continued in parallel with the Starliner, and in fact the last aircraft constructed was a WV-2. The last deliveries were L-1049Hs from a cancelled order. *Aeroplane*

LEFT: This view of the prototype L-1649 together with an L-1049H for Qantas shows the main external differences — the new wing and the different spacing of the engines of the Starliner. This perspective makes the Starliner seem much larger, but in fact all dimensions except those of the wing were the same for the Starliner and a radar-equipped L-1049. *Author's Collection*

RIGHT AND BELOW: The wing-tip tanks on an L-1049G (right) and an EC-121T. These tanks added 609US gal (2,305 litres) to the fuel capacity, but not much drag due to their refined streamlining. The probes on the EC-121 tank were not found on many military Super Constellations. *Lufthansa/The Aviation Picture Library, Below: Author*

ABOVE: Many civil Constellations were converted with freight doors by LAS (Lockheed Air Service) before Lockheed began to offer new-build freighters and convertible aircraft on the market. One problem with the freighter is seen above on L-1049G VT-DJX (delivered 1958, converted 1960) — a forklift or similar equipment was needed for loading and unloading, a process that could take several hours. *John Stroud Collection/The Aviation Picture Library*

Connie ('Old 1961'). With a capacity of 609US gals (2,305l), the tanks added an extra weight of 3,900lb (1,771kg) when full and considerable bending moment to each wing tip. This was partly balanced by the extra lift and smoothed airflow that the tanks themselves brought. The wingspan was only increased by 5in (12.7cm) by the addition of the tanks. Each extra gallon in the tip tanks gave a little over half-a-mile extra range. A bladder-type five-cell fuel tank was provided for the centreline. These features were incorporated in the 'Super G' and L-1049H.

The Constellation proved particularly suitable for carrying a large dorsal radome in the early warning role because of its triple-finned tail configuration which allowed full control without rudder 'blanking' even in heavy crosswind conditions. On the PO-1W prototypes the outer fins were extended in height by 18in (46cm) for greater authority. This was incorporated onto all the civilian and military Super Constellations as was an extension of the centre fin that brought all units to the same height. Super Constellation rudders were metal, rather than fabric covered.

STARLINER

The L-1649 came along as a high-speed, long-range version able to compete with jets. The year the Starliner appeared was the same that saw the first flight of the Boeing 707, and the result was that only 44 of this ultimate Constellation was built. The P-38-derived wing of the Constellation and Super Constellation was abandoned, and a completely new wing without the symmetrical taper or curved tips was designed. The leading edge now had no sweepback, but the pronounced taper of the trailing edge gave the Starliner planform a slight swept-forward appearance. The wing was now produced as two halves, joined at the centre, with a single large fuel tank in each wing and a new large centre-section tank.

The version of the Duplex Cyclone use on the Starliner was the 3,400hp EA-2. The inboard engines were positioned further outboard and further forward, with the outboard engines spaced further from their neighbours than on the Connie and Super Connies. This was partly to provide clearance between the new 16ft 10in (5.13m) propellers, or more correctly, to keep the outer pair, which were mounted 1ft 5in (43cm) further aft, out of the wash of the inner pair. Again, a choice of Curtiss-Electric and Hamilton Standard propellers was offered.

Another reason for the movement of the engines outboard was to give a reduction in cabin noise, which was also achieved by reducing the propeller gearing ratio to 0.35, resulting in lower tip speeds. A contemporary 'Flight' correspondent said that the decibel level was 'pleasantly unobtrusive', but that comparing noise by ear was like comparing drinks. 'The only easy method is to sample several, one after the other, though the only result is likely to be a worse confusion than existed at the beginning.'

To the relief of the passengers, there were now four toilets - two ahead of the main passenger cabin and two at the rear.

Despite having the same nominal capacity of the L-1049G (99 passengers), the number of emergency window exits was reduced and the four provided were bunched together at windows 10 and 11.

BELOW: The Constellation's distinctive — and beautiful — tail kept the height of the aircraft down while providing the maximum fin and rudder area for stability. *Lockheed*

ABOVE: TWA'S NC88514 showing well the width of the tail assembly and the stairs for passenger embarkation.*John Stroud Collection/The Aviation Picture Library*

LEFT: Luggage loading the hard way: fork lifts were essential before the days of standardised pallets and containers. *The Aviation Picture Library*

BELOW: A comprehensive lineup of Lockheed transports is headed by the first Super Constellation (c/n 4001) and the last 'regular' Connie (L-749A 2677) and tailed by the massive, but unsuccessful Constitution military transport. In between are examples of the Lockheed Models 10, 12 and 14 airliners of the 1930s. *The Aviation Picture Library*

OPPOSITE PAGE, ABOVE: A Lockheed worker disengages the safety hook before lowering a Speedpak. Although a few airlines were enthusiastic users of the Speedpak, not a great number of the expensive units were sold. The arrival of the Super Constellation made more freight space available without need for the drag-inducing external pannier. *John Stroud Collection/The Aviation Picture Library*

OPPOSITE PAGE, BELOW: G-AHEJ ***Bristol*** was the first Constellation delivered to BOAC, in April 1946. This chilly scene probably shows the aircraft's arrival at Dorval, Quebec, where BOAC took delivery of this, the 15th Connie built, together with G-AHEK, -'EL, -'EM and –'EN, named ***Berwick, Bangor, Balmoral*** and ***Baltimore*** respectively. *John Stroud Collection/The Aviation Picture Library*

3 PRODUCTION

NC90922 *Flagship Copenhagen* was the 52nd Connie built and was handed over to American Overseas Airlines in March 1946. For many years the Burbank ramp throbbed with the sound of Wright Double Cyclone engines on test. *John Stroud Collection/The Aviation Picture Library*

ABBREVIATIONS USED IN THE PRODUCTION TABLES:

AEW	Airborne Early Warning
AEW&C Wg	AEW and Control Wing
AEWMATRON	AEW Maintenance Squadron
AFSC	Air Force Systems Command
CAUSA	Compania Aeronautica Uruguaya SA
COMNAVAIRPAC	Commander, Naval Air Force, Pacific
DMAFB	Davis Monthan Air Force Base, Arizona
Dest.	Destroyed
FAETULANT	Fleet AEW Training Unit
LANSA	Linéas Aéreas Patagonias Argentinas SRL
LAPSA	Lloyd Aereo Paraguayo SA
L/n	Last noted
MATS	Military Air Transport Service
NADU	Naval Air Development Unit
NATC	Naval Air Test Center
Pres.	Preserved
Scr.	Scrapped
W/o	Written off

Note: Last user is (where it can be established) the last to fly the aircraft in their colours

Note: Where registration prefixes X and C dropped not noted

ABOVE: L-1049s for Trans-Canada Air Lines roll through the paint shop in the spring of 1954. The airline took delivery of five L-1049Cs and three L-1049Es during that year. L-1049Gs and Hs followed between 1956 and 1959. *Aeroplane*

C/N	Ordered as	Built as	1st Reg.	For	Del Date	Other Reg	Last user	Fate
1961	L-049-46-10	XC-69	NX25600	TWA/USAAF	28.7.43	43-10309	Lockheed A/c Co	Scrapped Burbank CA 1959
1962	L-049-46-10	C-69-1-LO	43-10310	TWA/USAAF	16.4.44	N38936	Flying Tiger Line	w/o 22/1/53
1963	L-049-46-10	C-69-1-LO	43-10311	TWA/USAAF	27.10.44	NC67952	Trenton Aviation	Scr. Trenton, NJ 1965
1964	L-049-46-10	C-69-1-LO	43-10312	TWA/USAAF	18.10.44	NC67953	LAPSA Paraguay	Scr. Viracopos,Brazil 1965
1965	L-049-46-10	C-69-1-LO	43-10313	TWA/USAAF	25.1.45	NC90827, RX-123, 4X-AKA, HB-IEA, G-ARXE	Britannia	Scr. Luton UK 1965
1966	L-049-46-10	C-69-1-LO	43-10314	TWA/USAAF	6.2.45	—	USAAF	wreck to French gov Ditched. Scr. 1951
1967	L-049-46-10	C-69-1-LO	43-10315	TWA/USAAF	19.2.45	NC90828, RX-124, NC67930, 4X-AKB, HB-IEB, G-AVRP	Britannia	Scr. Luton UK 1965
1968	L-049-46-10	C-69-1-LO	43-10316	TWA/USAAF	11.5.45	NC90829, RX-121, 4X-AKC	El Al	Shot down Bulgaria 1955
1969	L-049-46-10	C-69-1-LO	43-10317	TWA/USAAF	21.4.45	NC67901, NC90830, OE-IFA	Falcon Airways	Scr. Vienna 1966
1970	L-049-46-10	C-69-5-LO	42-94549	TWA/USAAF	28.7.45	NC90831, N9409H	TWA	Preserved, Pima Air & Space Museum
1971	L-049-46-10	C-69C-1-LO	42-94550	TWA/USAAF	4.8.45	NX54212, G-AKCE, N2741A	Modern Air Transport	Scr. 1964
1972	L-049-46-10	C-69-5-LO	42-94551	TWA/USAAF	23.7.45	—	TWA op. for USAAF	w/o 18/9/45
1973	L-049-46-10	C-69-5-LO	42-94552	TWA/USAAF	2.5.45	—	USAAF	Dest. static tests Wright Field 1946
1974	L-049-46-10	C-69-5-LO	42-94553	TWA/USAAF	10.5.46	NX54214, 'NC70000', N54212	McCulloch Propeties	Scr. Long Beach CA 1965
1975	L-049-46-10	L-049-51-26	G-AHEJ	BOAC	26.4.46	N2740A	Falcon Airways	Scr. Biggin Hill, UK 1962
1976	L-049-46-10	L-049-51-26	G-AHEK	BOAC	6.4.46	N2737A	Imperial	w/o 8.11.61
1977	L-049-46-10	L-049-51-26	G-AHEL	BOAC	6.4.46	N2736A, 5Y-ABF	Britair East Africa	Scr. Shannon, Ire. 1968
1978	L-049-46-10	L-049-51-26	G-AHEM	BOAC	6.4.46	N2735A	Capital Airlines	w/o 12.5.59
1979	L-049-46-10	C-69-5-LO	42-94558	TWA/USAAF	31.8.45	NC86536	TWA	Scr. Las Vegas NV 1965
1980	L-049-46-10	L-049-51-26	G-AHEN	BOAC	6.4.46	N74192, 4X-AKD,HB-IED	Britannia	Scr. Luton UK 1965

ABOVE: Eastern Air Lines had a fleet of nearly 50 Super Constellations in addition to L-049s, - 649s and -749s. Here some of the first Eastern Super Connies can be seen during fitting out in mid-late 1951. Note that the tail unit has been fitted only to the near aircraft. *The John Stroud Collection/The Aviation Picture Library*

C/N	Ordered as	Built as	1st Reg.	For	Del Date	Other Reg	Last user	Fate
2021	L-049-46-19	L-049-51-25	NC86500	TWA	15.11.45	—	TWA	Scr. Kansas City 1964
2022	L-049-46-19	L-049-51-25	NC86501	TWA	7.12.45	—	TWA	Scr. Las Vegas NV 1964
2023	L-049-51-25	L-049-46-25	NC86502	TWA	20.12.45	—	TWA	Scr. Las Vegas NV 1964
2024	L-049-51-25	L-049-46-25	NC86503	TWA	1.1.46	—	ASA International	Scr. Burbank CA 1970
2025	L-049-51-25		NC86504	TWA	16.1.45	—	Paradise Airlines	w/o 1.3.64
2026	L-049-51-26		NC86505	TWA	28.11.45	—	TWA	w/o 28.12.46
2027	L-049-51-26		NC86506	TWA	6.12.45	—	Aerospace Traveller	Scr. Burbank CA 1973
2028	L-049-51-26		NC86507	TWA	13.12.45	—	TWA	w/o 18.11.47
2029	L-049-51-26		NC86508	TWA	30.12.45	—	TWA	w/o 11.5.4
2030	L-049-51-25		NC86509	TWA	29.1.46	—	TWA	Scr. Las Vegas NV 1966
2031	L-049-51-26		NC88831	Pan Am	5.2.46	—	Pan Am	w/o 24.9.46
2032	L-049-51-26		NC88832	Pan Am	19.2.46	PP-PDJ	Panair do Brasil	w/o 16.6.55
2033	L-049-51-26		NC88833	Pan Am	24.2.46	PP-PDD	Panair do Brasil	Scr. Rio de Janeiro 1969
2034	L-049-51-26		NC86510	TWA	30.11.45	—	TWA	w/o 29.3.46
2035	L-049-51-26		NC86511	TWA	19.12.45	—	TWA	w/o 1.9.61
2036	L-049-51-26		NC88836	Pan Am	5.1.46	CU-T547, G-ARHK, 4X-AOK	Israel Aircraft Ind.	Scr. Israel 1969
2037	L-049-51-26		NC88837	Pan Am	12.1.46	PP-PDG	Amazonese	w/o 29.5.72
2038	L-049-51-26		N88838	Pan Am	21.1.46	PP-PDF	Panair do Brasil	Scr. Brazil 1974
2039	L-049-51-26		NC86512	TWA	10.1.46	—	TWA	w/o 12.10.46
2040	L-049-51-26		NC86513	TWA	8.2.46	—	TWA	w/o 11.7.46
2041	L-049-51-25		NC86514	TWA	9.2.46	—	TWA	Scr. Las Vegas NM 1964

C/N	Ordered as	Built as	1st Reg.	For	Del Date	Other Reg	Last user	Fate
2042	L-049-51-25		NC86515	TWA	15.2.46	—	TWA	Scr. Las Vegas NV 1964
2043	L-049-51-25		NC86516	TWA	19.2.46	—	TWA	Scr. Las Vegas NV 1964
2044	L-049-51-25		NC86517	TWA	19.2.46	—	San Francisco Schools	Scr. San Francisco CA 1973
2045	L-049-51-26		NC88845	Pan Am	25.2.46	—	Pan Am	w/o 19.6.47
2046	L-049-51-26		NC88846	Pan Am	1.3.46	—	Pan Am	w/o 22.6.51
2047	L-049-51-26		NC88847	Pan Am	8.3.46	PP-PDE	Panair do Brasil	w/o 14.12.62
2048	L-049-51-26		NC88848	Pan Am	18.4.46	PP-PCB	Panair do Brasil	Scr. Brazil 1969
2049	L-049-51-26		NC88849	Pan Am	22.3.46	PP-PCF	Panair do Brasil	Scr. Brazil 1969
2050	L-049-51-26		NC88850	Pan Am	20.3.46	PP-PDH	Panair do Brasil	Scr. Brazil 1974
2051	L-049-51-27		NC90921	American Overseas	9.4.46	G-AMUP, N2738A,	Britannia	Scr. Luton UK 1965
2052	L-049-51-27		NC90922	American Overseas	25.4.46	XA-MAG, PP-PDP	Panair do Brasil	Scr. Brazil 1970
2053	L-049-51-27		NC90923	American Overseas	29.3.46	—	American Flyers	Scr. California CA 1967
2054	L-049-51-27		NC90924	American Overseas	4.4.46	—	TWA	Scr. Las Vegas NV 1964
2055	L-049-51-26		NC88855	Pan Am	23.4.46	—	American Flyers	Scr. Lancaster CA 1971
2056	L-049-51-26		NC88856	Pan Am	15.4.46	PP-PDC	Panair do Brasil	w/o 26.1.46
2057	L-049-51-26		NC88857	Pan Am	29.4.46	PP-PDI	Panair do Brasil	Scr. Brazil 1970
2058	L-049-51-26		NC88858	Pan Am	24.4.46	—	Pan Am	w/o 15.4.48
2059	L-049-51-26		NC88859	Pan Am	30.4.46	PP-PDX, XA-MAH, PP-PDQ	Panair do Brasil	Scr. Brazil 1969
2060	L-049-51-26		NC88860	Pan Am	1.5.46	PP-PCR	Panair do Brasil	Scr. Brazil 1969
2061	L-049-51-26		NC88861	Pan Am	14.5.46	CU-T532, CU-T547, 4X-AKE, HB-IEC	Israel Aircaft Industries	Scr. Israel late 1965
2062	L-049-51-26		NC88862	Pan Am	14.5.46	PP-PCG	Panair do Brasil	w/o 28.7.50
2063	L-049-51-27		NC90925	American Overseas	15.5.46	—	Delta Air Lines	Scr. Ardmore OK 1967
2064	L-049-51-27		NC90926	American Overseas	15.5.46	—	ASA International	Scr. Oakland CA 1976
2065	L-049-51-27		NC90927	American Overseas	20.5.46	G-AMUR, N2739A	Capital Airlines	Scr. Trenton NJ 1966
2066	L-049-51-25		NC90616	Pan Am	23.5.46	NC88865, PP-PDA	Panair do Brasil	w/o 17.6.53
2067	L-049-51-25		NC90617	Pan Am	27.5.46	N88868	American Flyers	Scr. Galveston TX 1974
2068	L-049-51-26	L-049-46-26	PH-TAU	KLM	3.10.46	N86531, N864H	Gulf & Western	Disco, New Orleans (Scr.1983)
2069	L-049-51-26	L-049-46-26	PH-TAV	KLM	29.8.46	N86532, LV-PWK, CC-CAA	T.A. Squella SA	Restaurant Santiago (Scr. 1979)
2070	L-049-51-26	L-049-46-26	PH-TAW	KLM	11.9.46	N6000C, HI-260	Quisqueyana	Scr. Santo Domingo 1980
2071	L-049-51-26	L-049-46-26	PH-TAX	KLM	10.9.46	PH-TDA, N86533	Rymar	Stored Asuncion, Paraguay
2072	L-049-51-26	L-049-46-26	F-BAZA	Air France	18.9.46	N9412H	Air Nevada	Kiwi Airlines restaurant, Greenwood Lake NJ
2073	L-049-51-26	L-049-46-26	F-BAZB	Air France	4.12.46	N9410H	TWA	Scr. Kansas City MO 1964
2074	L-049-51-26	L-049-46-26	F-BAZC	Air France	10.12.46	N9409H	TWA	Scr. Long Beach CA 1966
2075	L-049-51-26	L-049-46-26	F-BAZD	Air France	13.12.46	N9414H	Quisqueyana	Scr. Miami FL 1970
2076	L-049-51-26	L-049-46-26	NC90814	TWA	7.10.46	—	Nevada Airmotive	Scr. Long Beach CA 1964
2077	L-049-51-26	L-049-46-26	NC90815	TWA	22.9.46	N90815	Belmont Aviation	Scr. Long Beach CA 1965
2078	L-049-51-26	L-049-46-26	NC90816	TWA	25.9.46	—	Aero Sacasa	Scr. Ft Lauderdale FL after 1982
2079	L-049-51-25	L-049-46-25	NC90817	TWA	28.9.46	—	TWA	Scr. Las Vegas NV 1964
2080	L-049-51-25	L-049-46-25	NC90818	TWA	5.10.46	—	Eastern Air Lines	Scr. Las Vegas NV 1964
2081	L-049-51-25	L-049-46-25	NC90819	TWA (del to LAV)	31.10.46	YV-C-AME, N2520B	Lloyd Airlines?	In park, Santa Cruz, Bolivia
2082	L-049-51-25	L-049-46-25	NC90820	TWA (del to LAV)	31.10.46	YV-C-AMI, N2521B	Magic City Airways	Scr. Miami FL 1968
2083	L-049-51-25	L-049-46-25	NC90821	TWA (del to KLM)	21.2.47	PH-TEN	KLM	w/o 21.10.48
2084	L-049-51-25	L-049-46-25	NC90822	TWA (del to KLM)	21.2.47	PH-TEO	TWA	Scr. Kansas City 1964
2085	L-049-51-25	L-049-46-25	NC90823	TWA	28.3.47	HI-270	TRADO	Scr. Santo Domingo 1980
2086	L-049-51-25	L-049-46-25	NC90824	TWA	6.5.47	—	TWA	w/o 25.11.48

C/N	Ordered as	Built as	1st Reg.	For	Del Date	Other Reg	Last user	Fate
2087	L-049-51-25	L-049-46-25	NC90825	TWA	15.5.47	—	TWA	Scr. Long Beach CA 1964
2088	L-049-51-25	L-049-46-25	NC90826	TWA	19.5.47	—	TWA	Scr. Las Vegas NV 1966
2503	L-649-79-21	L-749-79-22	NC86520	Pan Am	6.6.47	XA-GOQ, F-BAZR, F-ZVMV	French AF CEV	Pres. Musee de L'Air, Paris
2504	L-649-79-21	L-749-79-35	NC86521	Air-India	16.3.48	VT-CQS, VH-EAF, G-ANTF, N9861F	ACE Freighters	Burnt out Coventry 1970
2505	L-649-79-21	L-749-79-35	NC86522	Air-India	26.3.48	VT-CQR, VH-EAE, G-ANTG, N1552V	Western Airlines	Scr. Kenai AK after 1973
2506	L-649-79-21	L-749-79-35	NC86532	Air-India	26.4.48	VT-CQP	Air-India	w/o 3.11.50
2512	L-649-79-21	L-749-79-46	F-BAZQ	Air France	18.4.47	CN-CCR	Royal Air Maroc	Scr. Casablanca 1975 Morocco
2513	L-649-79-21	L-749-79-46	F-BAZI	Air France	26.5.47	N2717A	Air France	w/o 25.8.54
2514	L-649-79-21	L-749-79-46	F-BAZJ	Air France	26.6.47	F-SSFJ (callsign)	SGAC	Scr. Toulouse 1975
2515	L-649-79-21	L-749-79-46	F-BAZK	Air France	22.3.48	CC-CCM	Royal Air Maroc 1964	Scr. Casablanca, Morocco
2518	L-649-84-24	L-649-79-12	NX101A	Eastern Air Lines	19.3.47	OB-WAB-733, OB-R-733	LANSA	Scr. Lima, Peru after 1968
2519	L-649-84-24	L-649-79-12	NC102A	Eastern Air Lines	13.5.47	OB-R-785	LANSA	Scr. Lima, Peru 1974
2520	L-649-84-24	L-649-79-12	NC103A	Eastern Air Lines	23.5.47	HI-140	Quisqueyana	Scr. Santo Dominigo 1976
2521	L-649-84-24	L-649-79-12	NC104A	Eastern Air Lines	28.5.47	OB-R-771	LANSA	w/o 27.4.76
2522	L-649-84-24	L-649-79-12	NC105A	Eastern Air Lines	30.5.47	HI-207, HI-332	TRADO	l/n derelict Agua Jira Colombia
2523	L-649-84-24	L-649-79-12	NC106A	Eastern Air Lines	5.6.47	HI-129	Quisqueyana	Scr. Santo Dominigo 1977
2524	L-649-84-24	L-649-79-12	NC107A	Eastern Air Lines	8.6.47	—	Eastern	Scr. Burbank CA 1969
2525	L-649-79-22	L-749-79-22	NC86527	Pan Am	24.8.47	F-BAZU	Air France	Fire trainer Vilgenis France, Scr. 1976
2526	L-649-79-22	L-749-79-22	NC86528	Pan Am	24.8.47	F-BAZV	Air France	Scr. Paris-Orly 1968
2527	L-649-79-22	L-749-79-22	NC86529	Pan Am	24.8.47	F-BAZX	Air France	w/o 24.12.58
2528	L-649-79-22	L-749-79-22	NC86530	Pan Am	24.8.47	F-BAZY, F-SSFY (callsign)	SGAC	Scr. France after 1971
2529	L-649-84-24	L-649-79-12	NC108A	Eastern Air Lines	17.7.47	—	Eastern	Scr. Fox Field CA 1972
2530	L-649-84-24	L-649-79-12	NC109A	Eastern Air Lines	20.7.47	—	Great Lakes Airlines	Scr. Burbank CA 1964
2531	L-649-84-24	L-649-79-12	NC110A	Eastern Air Lines	23.7.47	—	Eastern	Scr. damaged, Philadelphia PA 1961
2532	L-649-84-24	L-649-79-12	NC111A	Eastern Air Lines	19.7.47	—	Eastern	w/o 21.1.48
2533	L-649-84-24	L-649-79-12	NC112A	Eastern Air Lines	30.7.47	—	Eastern	w/o 21.12.55
2534	L-649-84-24	L-649-79-12	NC113A	Eastern Air Lines	28.7.47	XA-MOA, OB-WAC-740, OB-R-740	LANSA	Scr. Lima, Peru 1981
2535	L-649-84-24	L-649-79-12	NC114A	Eastern Air Lines	2.8.47	OB-R-743	LANSA	Scr. Lima, Peru 1980
2538	L-649-79-22	L-749-79-22	F-BAZL	Air France	19.8.47	6V-AAR	Senegal Govt.	Scr. Toussus-le-Noble, France 1979
2540	L-649-79-22	L-749-79-22	PH-TEP	KLM	12.8.47	TI-1044P, LV-PZX	AER	Scr. Montevideo, Uruguay 1982
2541	L-649-79-22	L-749-79-22	PH-TER	KLM	12.8.47	—	KLM	w/o 23.6.49
2544	L-649-79-22	L-749-79-22	PH-TBD	KLM	15.10.47	N90622, G-ANVD, N6689N, HK-650, OB-R-914	Trans Peruana	Scr. Lima, Peru 1975
2545	L-649-79-22	L-749-79-22	F-BAZM	TWA (del Air France)	25.8.47	'F-SSFM' (callsign)	SGAC	w/o 7.2.61
2546	L-649-79-22	L-749-79-22	F-BAZN	TWA (del Air France)	25.8.47	—	Air France	w/o 28.10.49
2547	L-649-79-22	L-749-79-22	F-BAZO	TWA (del Air France)	17.9.47	'F-SSSO' (callsign)	SGAC	Scr. St Yan, France 1971
2548	L-649-79-22	L-749-79-22	NC86534	TWA (del Aerlinte)	16.9.47	EI-ACR, G-ALAK, CX-BHD,CP-797, OB-R-899	COPISA	Scr. Miami FL 1971
2549	L-649-79-22	L-749-79-22	NC86535	TWA (del Aerlinte)	28.8.47	EI-ACS, G-ALAL	COPISA	Scr. Miami FL 1974
2550	L-649-79-22	L-749-79-22	F-BAZP	Air France	21.9.47	'F-SSFP' (callsign)	SGAC	Motel attraction, Couchy, France. Scr. 1973

C/N	ORDERED AS	BUILT AS	1ST REG.	FOR	DEL DATE	OTHER REG	LAST USER	FATE
2551	L-749-79-33		PH-TDC	KLM	22.10.47	N90607, G-ANUV, N983OF, HL-102, OE-IFE	Aero Transport	Scr. Amsterdam, NL 1966
2552	L-649-84-12	L-649-79-22	PH-TES	Eastern Air Lines	9.9.47	PH-LDS	KLM	Scr. Amsterdam NL 1963
2553	L-649-84-12	L-649-79-22	PH-TET	Eastern Air Lines	25.9.47	PH-LDT, TI-1045P, N7777G, G-CONI	Lanzair	Pres. Sci Museum, Wroughton
2554	L-649-84-12	L-749-79-32	EI-ADA	Eastern (del Aerlinte)	16.9.47	G-ALAM	BOAC	w/o 13.3.54
2555	L-649-84-12	L-749-79-22	EI-ADD	Eastern (del Aerlinte)	16.9.47	G-ALAN, N1554V	Pacific Northern	w/o 14.6.60
2556	L-649-84-12	L-749-79-33	PH-TDD	Eastern (del KLM)	24.10.47	N90623, G-ANUX, N22CS, N1593V	C.R. Soto	Last noted derelict in Lima, Peru
2557	L-649-84-12	L-749-79-33	PH-TDE	Eastern (del KLM)	24.10.47	N90625, G-ANUY, N6688N, HK-651, OB-R-915	Trans Peruana	Scr. Lima 1975
2558	L-749-79-33		PH-TDF	KLM	29.10.47	—	KLM	w/o 12.7.49
2559	L-749-79-33		PH-TDG	KLM	7.11.47	N90621, G-ANUZ, N9812F	World Wide	Scr. Fox Field CA 1971
2560	L-749-79-34		YV-C-AMA	LAV	29.9.47	—	LAV	w/o 28.7.56
2561	L-749-79-34		YV-C-AMU	LAV	30.9.47	N9744Z	LAV	Scr. Hartford CT, Sept 1962
2562	L-749-79-31		VH-EAA	Qantas	4.10.47	G-ANUP, OE-IFO, LX-IOK	Interocean	w/o 13.9.64
2564	L-749-79-33		PH-TDH	KLM	13.11.47	N90608, G-ANVA, N6687N, HK-652, OB-R-916	Trans Peruana	Scr. Peru c.1970
2565	L-749-79-33	L-749-79-31	VH-EAB	Qantas	8.10.47	G-ANUR, N1949, CX-BHC	Aerolineas Uruguayas	Scr. Montevideo, Urugury c.1970
2566	L-649-79-22	L-749-79-32	EI-ADE	Air France (del Aerlinte)	9.10.47	G-ALAO, N4902C, OB-R-802	COPISA	Scr. Lima, Peru c.1980
2572	L-749-79-31		VH-EAC	Qantas	10.10.47	XA-LIO	Aerovias Guest	Scr. Burbank CA 1963
2573	L-749-79-31		VH-EAD	Qantas	18.10.47	XA-LIP, N9733Z	Aerovias Guest	Scr. Fox Field CA 1971
2577	L-749-79-22		NC91201	TWA	25.3.48	—	TWA	Scr. Kansas City MO 1968
2578	L-749-79-22		NC91202	TWA	2.4.48	—	TWA	Scr. Kansas City MO 1968
2579	L-749-79-22		NC91203	TWA	21.3.48	—	TWA	Scr. Kansas City MO 1968
2580	L-749-79-22		NC91204	TWA	7.5.48	—	TWA	Scr. Kansas City MO 1968
2581	L-749-79-22		NC91205	TWA	19.5.48	—	TWA	Scr. Kansas City MO 1968
2582	L-749-79-22		NC91206		TWA	28.5.48	TWA	Scr. Kansas City MO 1968
2583	L-749-79-22		NC91207		TWA	10.6.48	TWA	Scr. Kansas City MO 1968
2584	L-749-79-22		NC91208		TWA	24.6.48	TWA	Scr. Kansas City MO 1968
2585	L-749-79-22		NC91209		TWA	25.7.48	TWA	Scr. Kansas City MO 1968
2586	L-749-79-22		NC91210	TWA	22.7.48	—	TWA	Scr. Oklahoma City after 1963
2587	L-749-79-22		NC91211	TWA	29.7.48	—	TWA	Scr. Kansas City MO 1968
2588	L-749-79-22		NC91212	TWA	21.6.48	—	TWA	Scr. Kansas City MO 1968
2589	L-749-79-33	L-749A-79-33	PH-TDI	KLM	22.10.48	N90624, G-ANVB, N9813F	Miami Airlines	Scr. Miami FL 1963
2590	L-749-79-33	L-749A-79-33	PH-TDK	KLM	9.11.48	—	KLM	Scr. Amsterdam NL 1963
2600	L-749	VC-121B	48-608	USAF 1254 ATS (SM)	12.11.48	N608AS	Silver Skies Inc.	Stored at Tuscon Ryan Apt. AZ Henry Oliver III
2601	L-749A-79-36	C-121A	48-609	USAF 1254 ATS (SM)	31.12.48	N9464, C-GXKO, N494TW	Conifair	Vern Raburn, Airworthy Avra Valley AZ
2602	L-749A-79-36	C-121A	48-610	USAF, bailed to LAS	22.11.48	N9907E, N9463	Christler Flying Service	Columbine II Inc. Santa Fe NM
2603	L-749A-79-36	C-121A	48-611	USAF MATS Atlantic	31.12.48	N611AS, HI-393	Argo SA	L/n stored Santo Domingo 1994
2604	L-749-79-38	C-121A	48-612	USAF MATS Atlantic	18.1.49	N9465, C-GXKR, N749VR	Conifair	Dutch Const. Ass. Stored Avra Valley
2605	L-749-79-38	C-121A	48-613	USAF MATS Atlantic	26.1.49	N422NA	NASA	Pres. Planes of Fame, Valle AZ
2606	L-749-79-38	C-121A	48-614	USAF MATS Atlantic	6.2.49	7101 ABW	—	Pres. Pima AZ *Columbine*
2607	L-749-79-38	C-121A	48-615	USAF MATS Atlantic	16.2.49	N9466, HI-328	Argo SA	w/o 26.10.81

C/N	Ordered as	Built as	1st Reg.	For	Del Date	Other Reg	Last user	Fate
2608	L-749A-79-36	C-121A	48-616	MATS Atlantic	8.3.49	ET-T-35	Ethiopian Govt	w/o 10.7.57
2609	L-749A-79-36	C-121A	48-617	MATS Atlantic	24.3.49	N9467, C-GXKS	Beaver Air Spray	w/o 21.6.79
2610	L-749A-79-12		N115A	Eastern Air Lines	6.2.49	OB-R-833	RIPSA	Scr. Lima Peru 1982
2611	L-749A-79-12		N116A	Eastern Air Lines	16.2.49	N116	FAA	w/o 26.4.62
2612	L-749A-79-43	PO-1W	124437	USN WV-1	5.3.50	N7623C, N119, N1192	FAA	Scr. 1969
2613	L-749A-79-43	PO-1W	124438	USN WV-1	12.8.49	N7624C, N120, N1206	Air International	Pres. Salina KS
2614	L-749A-79-12		N117A	Eastern Air Lines	7.9.49	OB-WAA-732, OB-R-732	LANSA	Scr. Lima, Peru after 1968
2615	L-749A-79-12		N118A	Eastern Air Lines	27.10.49	HH-ABA	Air Haiti	Disappeared 11.11.61
2616	L-749A-79-12		N119A	Eastern Air Lines	11.11.49	—	Eastern	w/o 19.10.53
2617	L-749A-79-12		N120A	Eastern Air Lines	22.11.49	—	Trans Southern Co.	w/o 4.8.69
2618	L-749A-79-12		N121A	Eastern Air Lines	7.12.49	—	Eastern	Scr. Fox Field 1965
2619	L-749A-79-44		VT-DAR	Air-India	10.10.49	XA-MEW, N5596A, LV-PBH, LV-IIC	Aerolineas Carreras	S cr. Montevideo, Uruguay 1982
2620	L-749A-79-44		VT-DAS	Air-India	10.1.50	XA-MEU, N5595A	Miami Airlines	w/o 20.6.61
2621	L-749A-79-33		PH-TDN	KLM	19.8.50	—	KLM	Scr. Amsterdam NL 1963
2622	L-749A-79-33		PH-TDO	KLM	16.9.49	N10403, PH-LDO	KLM	Scr. Amsterdam NL 1963
2623	L-749A-79-50		ZS-DBR	Sth African Govt (SAA)	24.4.50	4X-AOL, G-ASYS	ACE Freighters	Scr. Coventry UK 1967
2624	L-749A-79-46		F-BAZE	Air France	11.1.50	—	Air Algérie	w/o 26.4.62
2625	L-749A-79-46		F-BAZF	Air France	20.1.50	F-SSFF (callsign)	French Govt	Abandoned Corfu 1973
2626	L-749A-79-46		F-BAZG	Air France	31.1.50	—	Air France	w/o 17.12.55
2627	L-749A-79-46		F-BAZH	Air France	8.2.50	CN-CPP, OB-R-898	COPISA	Scr. Lima, Peru 1973
2628	L-749A-79-46		F-BAZS	Air France	17.2.50	—	Air France	w/o 3.8.53
2629	L-749A-79-46		F-BAZT	Air France	24.2.50	F-SSFT (callsign)	EARS 99	Scr. St. Yan 1971
2630	L-749A-79-50		ZS-DBS	Sth African Govt (SAA)	7.6.50	G-ASYF	ACE Freighters	Scr. Miami FL 1969
2631	L-749A-79-50		ZS-DBT	Sth African Govt	20.6.50 (SAA)	4X-AOM, G-ASYT	ACE Freighters	Scr. Coventry UK 1967
2632	L-749A-79-50		ZS-DBU	Sth African Govt (SAA)	31.7.50	N148, G-ASYU	ACE Freighters	Scr. Woensdrecht, NL 1967
2633	L-749A-79-52		N6001C	Sth African Govt (SAA)	24.3.50	—	TWA	Scr. Kansas City MO 1966
2634	L-749A-79-52		N6002C	TWA	11.4.50	—	All-American Eng.	Scr. Miami FL 1970
2635	L-749A-79-52		N6003C	TWA	24.4.50	—	TWA	Scr. Kansas City MO 1973
2636	L-749A-79-52		N6004C	TWA	2.5.50	—	TWA	w/o 31.8.50
2637	L-749A-79-52		N6005C	TWA	19.5.50	—	TWA	Scr. Kansas City MO 1968
2638	L-749A-79-33		PH-TDP	KLM	19.5.50	—	KLM	Scr. Amsterdam NL 1962
2639	L-749A-79-52		N6006C	TWA	29.6.50	—	TWA	Scr. Kansas City MO 1968
2640	L-749A-79-33		PH-TFD	KLM	29.6.50	CX-BCS	CAUSA (Uruguay)	Scr. Montevideo, Uruguay 1972
2641	L-749A-79-33		PH-TFE	KLM	1.8.50	CX-BBN	CAUSA (Uruguay)	Scr. Montevideo Uruguay 1972
2642	L-649A-79-60		N86531	Chicago & Southern	1.8.50	—	TWA	Scr. Kansas City MO 1968
2643	L-749A-79-52		N6007C	TWA	18.8.50	—	TWA	Scr. Kansas City MO 1968
2644	L-749A-79-52		N6008C	TWA	7.9.50	—	TWA	Scr. Kansas City MO 1968
2645	L-749A-79-52		N6009C	TWA	11.9.50	HK-653	Trans-Peruana	Scr. Lima, Peru 1970
2646	L-749A-79-52		N6010C	TWA	20.9.50	—	TWA	Scr. Tuscon AZ 1973
2647	L-749A-79-52		N6011C	TWA	10.10.50	—	unknown	Prob. Scr. Arica Chile 1970
2648	L-749A-79-52		N6012C	TWA	16.10.50	N65	FAA	w/o 15.8.6
2649	L-749A-79-52		N6013C	TWA	26.10.50	—	TWA	Scr. Kansas City MO 1968
2650	L-749A-79-52		N6014C	TWA	6.11.50	N273R	Lanzair	Burnt out Lomé, Togo 1977
2651	L-749A-79-52		N6015C	TWA	17.11.50	—	TWA	Scr. Kansas City MO 1968

C/N	Ordered as	Built as	1st Reg.	For	Del Date	Other Reg	Last user	Fate
2652	L-749A-79-52		PH-TFF	KLM	12.7.50	—	KLM	w/o 22.3.52
2653	L-649A-79-60		N86522	Chicago & Southern	27.9.50	—	TWA	Scr. Kansas City MO 1968
2654	L-749A-79-52		N6016C	TWA	12.12.50	N121	FAA	Fire dump Tachikawa, Japan
2655	L-749A-79-52		N6017C	TWA	21.12.50	—	Western	Scr. Panama 1978
2656	L-749A-79-52		N6018C	TWA	29.12.50	—	TWA	Scr. Tuscon AZ 1973
2657	L-749A-79-52		N6019C	TWA	17.1.51	—	TWA	Scr. Kansas City MO 1968
2658	L-749A-79-52		N6020C	TWA	25.1.51	—	TWA	Scr. Tuscon AZ 1973
2659	L-649A-79-60		N86523	Chicago & Southern	21.11.50	—	Pacific Northern	Scr. Seattle WA 1966
2660	L-649A-79-60		N86524	Chicago & Southern	7.2.51	5N-86H	Concare	Derelict Faro, burnt 1990s
2661	L-749A-79-33		PH-TFG	KLM	11.1.51	PH-LDG, CX-BBM	CAUSA (Uruguay)	Scr. Montevideo Uruguay 1977
2662	L-649A-79-60		N86525	Chicago & Southern	1.2.51	5N-85H	Phoenix Air Trans	w/o 28.11.69
2663	L-749A-79-74		HK-162	Avianca	18.5.51	N4900C	LANSA	Scr. Lima Peru 1968
2664	L-749A-79-74		HK-163	Avianca	31.5.51	—	Avianca	w/o 9.8.54
2665	L-749A-79-33		VT-DEO	Air-India	3.4.51	XA-MEV	Aeronaves de Mex.	w/o 2.6.58
2666	L-749A-79-33		VT-DEP	Air-India	8.4.51	—	Air-India	w/o 11.4.55
2667	L-649-79-60		N6012C	TWA	16.4.51	HI-422	AeroChago	Scr. dmgd Santo Domingo 1988
2668	L-749A-79-52		N6022C	TWA	30.4.51	'CX-BGP' (false reg)	Leasing Consultants	Burnt out, Colombia after 1969?
2669	L-749A-79-52		N6023C	TWA	8.5.51	—	TWA	Scr. Kansas City MO 1968
2670	L-749A-79-52		N6024C	TWA	29.5.51	—	TWA	Scr. Tuscon AZ 1973
2671	L-749A-79-52		N6025C	Howard Hughes	25.6.51	G-ANNT, N4901C, N6695C	Bradley Air Museum	Destroyed by tornado 1979
2672	L-749A-79-52		N6026C	TWA	29.6.51	—	TWA	Scr. Kansas City MO 1968
2673	L-649A-79-60		N86535	Chicago & Southern	17.5.51	—	TWA	Scr. Kansas City MO 1968
2674	L-749-79-46		F-BAZZ	Air France	18.7.51	—	Air France	w/o 1.9.53
2675	L-749-79-46		F-BBDT	Air France	9.8.51	CC-CCN	Royal Air Maroc	Pres. Casablanca Morocco
2676	L-749-79-46		F-BBDU	Air France	31.8.51	CN-CCO	Royal Air Maroc	Scr. Toulouse France 1962
2677	L-749-79-46		F-BBDV	Air France	17.9.51	—	Air Algerie	Scr. Algiers after 1964

SUPER CONSTELLATIONS

C/N	Ordered as	Built as	1st Reg.	For	Del Date	Other Reg	Last user	Fate
4001	L-1049-53-67		N6201C	Lockheed (del East'n)	18.3.52	—	Baker Aviation School	Scr. Miami FL 1973
4002	L-1049-53-67		N6202C	Lockheed (del East'n)	4.4.52	—	Happy Hours Travel Club	w/o 5.8.73
4003	L-1049-53-67		N6203C	Eastern Air Lines	26.11.51	—	Av. Corp of America	Scr. W. Palm Beach FL 1975
4004	L-1049-53-67		N6204C	Eastern Air Lines	11.12.51	—	Eastern	Scr. Miami FL 1967
4005	L-1049-53-67		N6205C	Eastern Air Lines	21.12.51	—	Av. Corp of America	Scr. Miami FL 1977
4006	L-1049-53-67		N6206C	Eastern Air Lines	31.12.51	—	Hub Aviation	Scr. Ft Lauderdale FL 1980
4007	L-1049-53-67		N6207C	Eastern Air Lines	8.1.52	—	Hub Aviation	Scr. Ft Lauderdale FL 1980
4008	L-1049-53-67		N6208C	Eastern Air Lines	21.1.52	—	Av. Corp of America	Scr. Opa Locka 1973
4009	L-1049-53-67		N6209C	Eastern Air Lines	31.1.52	HI-228	AeroChago	L/n stored Santo Domingo 1986
4010	L-1049-53-67		N6210C	Eastern Air Lines	6.2.52	—	Av. Corp of America	Scr. Miami FL 1974
4011	L-1049-53-67		N6211C	Eastern Air Lines	14.2.52	—	Av. Corp of America	Scr. Opa Locka 1972
4012	L-1049-53-67		N6212C	Eastern Air Lines	2[illegible].2.52	—	Eastern	w/o 28.[illegible].5[illegible]
4013	L-1049-53-67		N6213C	Eastern Air Lines	27.2.52	—	Av. Corp of America	Scr. Opa Locka 1972
4014	L-1049-53-67		N6214C	Eastern Air Lines	8.3.52	—	Eastern	w/o 6.9.53
4015	L-1049-54-80		N6901C	Lockheed (del to TWA)	8.10.52	—	LAPA	w/o 6.3.66

C/N	Ordered as	Built as	1st Reg.	For	Del Date	Other Reg	Last User	Fate
4016	L-1049-54-80		N6902C	TWA	21.5.52	—	TWA	w/o 30.6.53
4017	L-1049-54-80		N6903C	TWA	29.5.52	—	South Pacific	Scr. Oakland CA 1965
4018	L-1049-54-80		N6904C	TWA	27.8.52	—	South Pacific	Scr. Miami FL 1968
4019	L-1049-54-80		N6905C	TWA	1.10.52	—	California Hawaiian	Scr. Kansas City MO 1964
4020	L-1049-54-80		N6906C	TWA	13.9.52	—	Vortex Inc	Scr. (damaged) Miami FL 1974
4021	L-1049-54-80		N6907C	TWA	16.10.52		TWA	w/o 16.12.52
4022	L-1049-54-80		N6908C	TWA	24.9.52		TWA	Scr. Kansas City MO 1964
4023	L-1049-54-80		N6909C	TWA	22.10.52		TWA	Scr. Kansas City MO 1964
4024	L-1049-54-80		N6910C	TWA	31.10.52		TWA	Scr. Kansas City MO 1964
4101	R7V-1		128434	USN VR-7	7.3.55	54-4048	Wyoming ANG	Scr. DM AFB AZ 1979
4102	R7V-1		128435	USN VR-7	23.6.53	54-4049	Penn ANG	Scr. DM AFB AZ 1977
4103	R7V-1		128436	USN VR-1	4.12.52	54-4050	552 AEW&C Wing	Scr. DM AFB, AZ 1977
4104	R7V-1		128437	USN VR-1	6.3.55	—	VW-11	w/o 14.1.58
4105	R7V-1		128438	USN VR-8	23.12.52	54-4051	552 AEW&C Wing	Scr. DM AFB
4106	R7V-1		128439	USN VR-8	24.12.52	54-4052	79 AEW&C Squadron	Scr. DM AFB
4107	R7V-1		128440	USN VR-1	13.5.53	—	VR-1	w/o 7.7.53
4108	R7V-1		128441	USN VR-1	23.5.53	—	VR-1	w/o 30.10.54
4109	R7V-1		128442	USN VR-8	14.6.53	54-4061	Penn. ANG	Scr. DM AFB
4110	R7V-1		128443	USN VR-1	28.6.53	—	COMNAVAIRPAC	Scr. DM AFB
4111	R7V-1		128444	USN VR-1	25.6.53	—	VXN-8	Scr. DM AFB
4112	R7V-1	RC-121C	51-3836	USAF 8th Air Div	31.12.53	—	552 AEW&C Wg	Scr. DM AFB
4113	R7V-1	RC-121C	51-3837	USAF 8th Air Div	26.1.53	—	AFSC Wright-Patterson	Scr. DM AFB
4114	R7V-1	RC-121C	51-3838	USAF 8th Air Div	27.2.53	—	8th Air Div.	w/o 21.11.53
4115	R7V-1	RC-121C	51-3839	USAF 8th Air Div	27.3.53	—	552 AEW&C Wg	Scr. DM AFB
4116	R7V-1	RC-121C	51-3840	USAF 8th Air Div	24.4.53	—	551 AEW&C Wg	Scr. DM AFB
4117	R7V-1	RC-121C	51-3841	USAF 8th Air Div	12.5.53	—	AFSC Wright-Patterson	Scr. DM AFB
4118	R7V-1	RC-121C	51-3842	USAF 8th Air Div	15.5.53	—	551 AEW&C Wing	w/o 22.3.61
4119	R7V-1	RC-121C	51-3842	USAF 8th Air Div	25.5.53	—	551 AEW&C Wing	Scr. DM AFB
4120	R7V-1	RC-121C	51-3843	USAF 8th Air Div	3.6.53	—	552 AEW&C Wing	Scr. DM AFB
4121	R7V-1	RC-121C	51-3844	USAF 8th Air Div	14.7.53	—	551 AEW&C Wing	Scr. DM AFB
4122	R7V-1		131621	USN VR-8	23.6.53	54-4053	Wyoming ANG	Scr. DM AFB
4123	R7V-1		131622	USN VR-8	23.6.53	54-4054	Wyoming ANG	Scr. DM AFB
4124	R7V-1		131623	USN VR-1	8.5.53	—	'Blue Angels'	Scr. DM AFB
4125	R7V-1		131624	USN VR-8	8.5.53	54-4056	VXE-6	Scr. DM AFB
4126	R7V-1		131625	USN VR-1	8.5.53	—	AEWTULANT	w/o 14.11.64
4127	R7V-1		131626	USN VR-8	8.5.53	—	Wyoming ANG	Scr. DM AFB
4128	R7V-1		131627	USN VR-1	8.5.53	—	VXN-8	Scr. DM AFB
4129	R7V-1		131628	USN VR-8	13.5.53	54-4058	552 AEW&C Wing	Scr. DM AFB
4130	R7V-1		131629	USN VR-1	18.5.53	54-4059	552 AEW&C Wing	Scr. DM AFB
4131	R7V-1	R7V-2	131630	USN	10.9.54	—	USN	Scr. Burbank early 1960s
4132	R7V-1	R7V-2	131631	USN	3.12.54	N7938C	USN	Scr. Litchfield Park
4133	R7V-1		131632	USN VR-8	3.8.53	54-4060	W Virginia ANG	Scr. DM AFB
4134	R7V-1		131633	USN VR-1	16.9.53	54-4072	552 AEW&C Wing	Scr. DM AFB
4135	R7V-1		131634	USN VR-8	21.9.53	54-4055	Wyoming ANG	Ground trainer, scr.Brooks AFB TX
4136	R7V-1		131635	USN VR-1	29.8.53	—	VXN-8	Scr. DM AFB
4137	R7V-1		131636	USN VR-8	28.9.53	54-4062, N2114Z, HI-583CT, N105CF	Aerochago	Super Constellation Flyers, Geneva
4138	R7V-1		131637	USN VR-8	15.10.53	54-4057	20 ADS, AFRES	Scr. DM AFB
4139	R7V-1		131638	USN VR-8	15.10.53	—	552 AEW&C Wg	Scr. DM AFB

C/N	Ordered As	Built As	1st Reg.	For	Del Date	Other Reg	Last User	Fate
4140	R7V-1		131639	USN VR-1	24.10.53	—	VR-1	w/o 17.1.55
4141	R7V-1		131640	USN VR-8	24.10.53	54-4064	Penn ANG	Scr. Pittsburgh PA
4142	R7V-1		131641	USN VR-1	31.10.53	—	VXN-8	Scr. DM AFB
4143	R7V-1		131642	USN VR-8	31.10.53	54-4065, N420NA	NASA	Explosives test Aberdeen MD
4144	R7V-1		131643	USN VR-1	31.10.53	N4247K	World Fish & Ag. Inc	L/n stored Manila 1987
4145	R7V-1		131644	USN VR-1	8.12.53	—	VXE-6	Remains wrecked in snow at McMurdo Antarctica
4146	R7V-1		131645	USN VR-8	19.1.54	54-4066	4066 MATS	w/o 12.4.62
4147	R7V-1		131646	USN VR-7	7.1.54	54-4067	Penn ANG	Scr. DM AFB
4148	R7V-1		131647	USN VR-7	19.1.54	54-4068	W Virginia ANG	Scr. DM AFB
4149	R7V-1		131648	USN VR-7	2.2.54	54-4069	MATS Westoff	w/o 28.2.59
4150	R7V-1		131649	USN VR-7	11.2.54	54-4070	Penn ANG	Scr. DM AFB
4151	R7V-1	VC-121E	131650	USAF 1254 ATG	31.8.54	53-7885	89 MAW (SM)	Pres. USAF Museum WPAFB OH
4152	R7V-1		131651	USN VR-7	4.3.54	54-4071	Penn ANG	Scr. DM AFB
4153	R7V-1		131652	USN VR-7	16.3.54	—	USN	w/o 14.5.58
4154	R7V-1		131653	USN VR-7	24.3.54	54-4073	Penn ANG	Scr. DM AFB
4155	R7V-1		131654	USN VR-7	6.4.54	HI-532CT	AeroChago	Scr. Santo Domingo 1990
4156	R7V-1		131655	USN VR-8	24.4.54	—	VXN-8	Scr. DM AFB
4157	R7V-1		131656	USN VR-7	13.5.54	54-4074	Wyoming ANG	Scr. DM AFB
4158	R7V-1		131657	USN VR-7	28.5.54	54-4075	Wyoming ANG	Scr. DM AFB
4159	R7V-1		131658	USN VR-7	12.7.54	54-4076, N421NA		NASA Scr. DM AFB
4160	R7V-1		131659	USN VR-1	15.6.54	—	USN	Southwest Metals 1982 probably scr.
4161	R7V-1	YC-121F	131660	USAF 1700 Test Sqn	4.3.55	53-8157, N9746Z	Flying Tiger Line	Used for parts for L-1049H
4162	R7V-1	YC-121F	131661	USAF 1700 Test Sqn	30.3.53	53-8158, N9749Z	Flying Tiger Line	Used for parts for L-1049H
4163	L-1049D-55-85	D-55-116	N6501C	Seaboard & Western	19.8.54	—	Capitol	Scr. Wilmington DE 1967
4164	L-1049D-55-85	D-55-116	N6502C	Seaboard & Western	2.9.54	—	Capitol	Scr. Wilmington DE 1967
4165	L-1049D-55-85	D-55-116	N6503C	Seaboard & Western	21.9.54	—	Seaboard & Western	w/o 10.11.58
4166	L-1049D-55-85	D-55-116	N6504C	Seaboard & Western	28.9.54	LV-ILW, 5T-TAC	Nth American Aircraft Trading	w/o 4.6.68
4167	R7V-1		140311	USN VR-7	30.11.54	54-4077	Wyoming ANG	Scr. DM AFB
4168	R7V-1		140312	USN VR-8	27.12.56	54-4078	Wyoming ANG	Scr. DM AFB
4169	R7V-1		140313	USN VR-7	2.2.55	54-4079	VX-8	Scr. DM AFB
4170	C-121C		54-151	USAF MATS Atlantic	22.6.55	—	W Virginia ANG	Scr. DM AFB
4171	C-121C		54-152	USAF MATS Atlantic	29.7.55	—	New Jersey ANG	Scr. DM AFB
4172	C-121C		54-153	USAF MATS Atlantic	16.9.55	—	New Jersey ANG	Scr. DM AFB
4173	C-121C		54-154	USAF MATS Atlantic	24.9.55	—	W Virginia ANG	Scr. DM AFB
4174	C-121C		54-155	USAF MATS Atlantic	20.10.55	—	Penn ANG	Pres. USAF History & Traditions Museum Lackland AFB TX
4175	C-121C		54-156	USAF MATS Atlantic	1.11.55	N73544	Constellation Hist Soc.	Airworthy, Camarillo CA
4176	C-121C		54-157	USAF MATS Atlantic	6.10.55	N4115Q, VH-EAG	Hist. Aircraft Rest Soc	Airworthy Bankstown Australia
4177	C-121C		54-158	USAF MATS Atlantic	10.10.55		New Jersey ANG	Scr. DM AFB
4178	C-121C		54-159	USAF MATS Atlantic	19.11.55		Save-A-Connie	Scr. for spares c.1987
4179	C-121C		54-160	USAF MATS Atlantic	24.10.55		AFSC	Scrapyard DMAFB 1981, prob scr.
4180	C-121C		54-161	USAF MATS Atlantic	2.11.55		New Jersey ANG	Scr. DM AFB
4181	C-121C		54-162	USAF MATS Atlantic	4.10.55		W Virginia ANG	Scr. DM AFB
4182	C-121C		54-163	USAF MATS Atlantic	10.11.55		W Virginia ANG	Scr. DM AFB
4183	C-121C		54-164	USAF MATS Atlantic	17.11.55		Penn ANG	Scr. DM AFB after 1982

C/N	Ordered as	Built as	1st Reg.	For	Del Date	Other Reg	Last user	Fate
4184	C-121C		54-165	USAF MATS Atlantic	23.11.55		MATS Atlantic	w/o 31.12.56
4185	C-121C		54-166	USAF MATS Atlantic	28.12.55		N Carolina ANG	Scr. DM AFB
4186	C-121C		54-167	USAF MATS Atlantic	28.12.55		N Carolina ANG	Scr. DM AFB
4187	C-121C		54-168	USAF MATS Atlantic	17.1.56		National Guard Bureau	Scr. DM AFB
4188	C-121C		54-169	USAF MATS Atlantic	13.1.56		New Jersey ANG	Scr. DM AFB
4189	C-121C		54-170	USAF MATS Atlantic	16.1.56		Penn ANG	Scr. DM AFB
4190	C-121C		54-171	USAF MATS Atlantic	18.1.56		New Jersey ANG	Scr. DM AFB
4191	C-121C		54-172	USAF MATS Atlantic	26.1.56	—	W Virginia ANG	Scr. DM AFB
4192	C-121C		54-173	USAF MATS Atlantic	10.2.56	N88879, HI-515CT	Aerolineas Mundo	w/o 5.4.90
4193	C-121C		54-174	USAF MATS Atlantic	17.2.56	—	HQ AFRES	Scr. DM AFB
4194	C-121C		54-175	USAF MATS Atlantic	24.2.56	—	New Jersey ANG	Scr. DM AFB
4195	C-121C		54-176	USAF MATS Atlantic	9.3.56	—	W Virginia ANG	Scr. DM AFB
4196	C-121C		54-177	USAF MATS Atlantic	27.3.56	N1104W	Classic Air	Pres NASM, Dulles Airport DC
4197	C-121C		54-178	USAF MATS Atlantic	23.3.56	—	AFSC	Scr. DM AFB
4198	C-121C		54-179	USAF MATS Atlantic	5.4.56	—	Penn ANG	Scr. DM AFB
4199	C-121C		54-180	USAF MATS Atlantic	14.4.56	—	Penn ANG	Pres. Charleston AFB CA
4200	C-121C		54-181	USAF MATS Atlantic	26.4.56	—	National Guard Bureau	Scr. DM AFB
4201	C-121C		54-182	USAF MATS Atlantic	11.5.56	—	New Jersey ANG	Scr. DM AFB
4202	C-121C		54-183	USAF MATS Atlantic	23.5.56	N515AC, HI-548CT	AeroChago	Prob. scr. Santo Domingo after1993
4301	PO-2W		126512	USN NATC	29.10.53	—	Penn ANG	Scr. Litchfield Park AZ
4302	PO-2W		126513	USN FAETULANT	16.4.54	—	USN 'Proj Magnet'	Remains at McMurdo, Antarctica
4303	PO-2W		128323	USN VW-1	31.12.53	—	Pacific Missile Range	Scr. Litchfield Park AZ
4304	WV-2		128324	USN NADU Patuxent	29.1.54	—	NATC Patuxent	Scr. DM AFB
4305	WV-2		128325	USN VW-2	2.2.54	—	Scr. Litchfield Park	Scr. Litchfield Park AZ
4306	WV-2		128326	USN NADU Patuxent	30.4.54	—	NATC Patuxent	Scr. Litchfield Park AZ
4307	WV-2		128327	USN NADU S. Weymouth	30.6.54	—	NADU S.Weymouth	w/o 9.12.54
4308	WV-2		128328	USN NADU Patuxent	29.6.54	—	NADU Patuxent	Scr. DM AFB
4309	WV-2		128329	USN VW-2	18.8.54	—	VW-13	Scr. Litchfield Park AZ
4310	WV-2		128330	USN VW-1	18.10.54	—	VQ-2	w/o 22.5.62
4311	WV-2		128331	USN VW-2	16.7.54	—	VQ-2	Scr. DM AFB
4312	WV-2		128332	USN VW-1	26.7.54	—	VQ-2	Scr. DM AFB
4313	WV-2		135746	USN VW-1	5.8.54	—	VW-2	Scr. Litchfield Park AZ
4314	WV-2		135747	USN VW-2	13.8.54	—	VQ-1	w/o 20.8.62
4315	WV-2		135748	USN VW-2	2.9.54	—	VW-15	Scr. Litchfield Park AZ
4316	WV-2		135749	USN VW-1	3.9.54	—	VQ-1	Shot down 15.4.69
4317	WV-2		135750	VW-2	7.9.54	—	NAS Patuxent	Scr. Litchfield Park AZ
4318	WV-2		135751	VW-1	13.9.54	—	VQ-1	w/o 3.3.66
4319	WV-2		135752	VW-1	29.11.54	—	VQ-2	Scr. DM AFB
4320	WV-2		135753	VW-2	4.1.54	—	NRL Patuxent	Scr. DM AFB
4321	WV-2		135754	VW-1	4.1.55	—	NADU South Weymouth	Scr. Litchfield Park, AZ
4322	WV-2		135755	VW-1	21.12.54	—	VW-3	Scr. DM AFB
4323	WV-2		135756	VW-1	15.1.55	—	VAQ-33	Scr. DM AFB
4324	WV-2		135757	VW-2	10.2.55	—	VQ-2	Scr. DM AFB
4325	WV-2		135758	VW-1	3.2.55	—	Pacific Missile Range	Scr. DM AFB
4326	WV-2		135759	VW-2	18.2.55	—	VW-11	Scr. Litchfield Park AZ
4327	WV-2		135760	VW-2	17.2.55	—	VW-4	Scr. Litchfield Park AZ

C/N	Ordered as	Built as	1st Reg.	For	Del Date	Other Reg	Last user	Fate
4328	WV-2		135761	VW-13	1.3.55	—	VW-13	Scr. Litchfield Park AZ
4329	RC-121D		52-3411	USAF 8th Air Div	10.9.54	—	552 AEW&C Wing	Scr. Litchfield Park AZ
4330	RC-121D		52-3412	USAF 8th Air Div	25.8.54	—	552 AEW&C Wing	Scr. DM AFB
4331	RC-121D		52-3413	USAF 8th Air Div	18.9.54		552 AEW&C Wing	Scr. DM AFB
4332	RC-121D		54-3414	USAF Air Dev Ctr	11.8.54		552 AEW&C Wing	Scr. DM AFB
4333	RC-121D		54-3415	USAF 8th Air Div	20.8.54	—	79 AEW&C Wing	Scr. DM AFB
4334	RC-121D		54-3416	USAF 8th Air Div	14.9.54	—	552 AEW&C Wing	Scr. DM AFB
4335	RC-121D		54-3417	USAF 8th Air Div	28.9.54	N4275L	79 AEW&C Wing	Pres. Helena Vocational Tech Center MT
4336	RC-121D		54-3418	USAF 8th Air Div	16.10.56	N4257U '52-3418'	79 AEW&C Wing	Pres. Combat Air Museum Topeka-Forbes KS
4337	RC-121D		54-3419	USAF 8th Air Div	2.11.54	—	552 AEW&C Wing	Scr. DM AFB
4338	RC-121D		54-3420	USAF 8th Air Div	26.11.54	—	551AEW&C Wing	Scr. DM AFB
4339	RC-121D		54-3421	USAF 8th Air Div	30.12.54	—	552 AEW&C Wing	Scr. DM AFB
4340	RC-121D		54-3422	USAF 8th Air Div	7.1.55	—	552 AEW&C Wing	Scr. DM AFB
4341	RC-121D		54-3423	USAF 8th Air Div	12.1.55	—	79 AEW&C Wing	Last noted DM AFB 1982
4342	RC-121D		54-3424	USAF 8th Air Div	12.1.55	—	79 AEW&C Wing	Last noted DM AFB 1982
4343	RC-121D		54-3425	USAF 8th Air Div	17.1.55	—	79 AEW&C Wing	Pres. Air & Space Museum Peterson CO
4344	WV-2		137887	VW-1	4.3.55	—	VW-1	Scr. Litchfield Park AZ
4345	WV-2		137888	VW-1	4.3.55	—	VW-1	Scr. Litchfield Park AZ
4346	WV-2		137889	VW-11	19.5.55	—	NADC Johnsville	Scr. DM AFB
4347	WV-2		137890	VW-2	7.3.55	55-0552?	PMTC	Pres. Tinker AFB Air Park OK
4348	RC-121D		53-533	551 AEW&C Wg	1.2.55	—	551AEW&C Wing	Scr. DM AFB
4349	RC-121D		53-534	551 AEW&C Wg	16.3.55	—	552 AEW&C Wing	Scr. DM AFB
4350	RC-121D		53-535	552 AEW&C Wg	24.3.55	N51006??	551AEW&C Wing	Stored Minden Corp Yard Tuscon AZ
4351	RC-121D		53-536	552 AEW&C Wg	24.3.55	—	551AEW&C Wing	Scr. DM AFB
4352	RC-121D		53-537	552 AEW&C Wg	4.3.55	—	79 AEW&C Wing	Scr. DM AFB
4353	RC-121D		53-538	552 AEW&C Wg	28.2.55	—	551AEW&C Wing	Scr. DM AFB
4354	RC-121D		53-539	552 AEW&C Wg	28.2.55	—	551AEW&C Wing	Scr. DM AFB
4355	RC-121D		53-540	552 AEW&C Wg	18.5.55	—	551AEW&C Wing	Scr. DM AFB
4356	RC-121D		53-541	552 AEW&C Wg	8.6.55	—	552 AEW&C Wg	Scr. DMAFB
4357	RC-121D		53-542	552 AEW&C Wg	27.4.55	—	552 AEW&C Wing	Scr. DMAFB
4358	RC-121D		53-543	552 AEW&C Wg	21.7.55	—	79 AEW&C Wing	Scr. DM AFB
4359	RC-121D		53-544	551 AEW&C Wg	1.7.55	—	551AEW&C Wing	Scr. DM AFB
4360	RC-121D		53-545	552 AEW&C Wg	15.7.55	—	552 AEW&C Wing	Scr. DM AFB
4361	RC-121D		53-546	552 AEW&C Wg	22.7.55	—	79 AEW&C Wing	Scr. DM AFB
4362	RC-121D		53-547	552 AEW&C Wg	28.9.55	—	552 AEW&C Wing	Scr. DM AFB
4363	RC-121D		53-548	551 AEW&C Wg	18.8.55	N548GF	Global Aeronautical Foundation	Airworthy, Camarillo CA
4364	RC-121D		53-549	552 AEW&C Wg	26.8.55	—	551AEW&C Wing	w/o 25.4.67
4365	RC-121D		53-550	552 AEW&C Wg	14.8.55	—	552 AEW&C Wing	Scr. DM AFB
4366	RC-121D		53-551	552 AEW&C Wg	29.9.55	—	551AEW&C Wing	Scr. DM AFB
4367	RC-121D		53-552	551 AEW&C Wg	14.10.55	—	79 AEW&C Wing	Scr. DM AFB
4368	RC-121D		53-553	552 AEW&C Wg	12.10.55	—	551AEW&C Wing	Scr. DM AFB
4369	RC-121D		53-554	552 AEW&C Wg	14.10.55	—	79 AEW&C Wing	Pres. Pima Air & Space Museum AZ
4370	RC-121D		53-555	552 AEW&C Wg	16.11.55	—	552 AEW&C Wing	USAF Museum WP AFB OH
4371	RC-121D		53-556	552 AEW&C Wg	19.10.55	—	552 AEW&C Wing	Scr. DM AFB
4372	RC-121D		53-557	552 AEW&C Wg	16.11.55	—	552 AEW&C Wing	Scr. DM AFB
4373	RC-121D		53-558	552 AEW&C Wing	7.10.55	—	79 AEW&C Wing	Scr. DM AFB
4374	RC-121D		53-559	552 AEW&C Wg	12.10.55		552 AEW&C Wing	Scr. DM AFB

C/N	Ordered as	Built as	1st Reg.	For	Del Date	Other Reg	Last user	Fate
4375	RC-121D		53-560	552 AEW&C Wg	9.3.55	—	551AEW&C Wing	Last noted DM AFB 1982
4376	RC-121D		53-561	551 AEW&C Wg	9.2.56	—	551AEW&C Wing	Scr. DM AFB
4377	RC-121D		53-562	551 AEW&C Wg	9.2.56	—	551AEW&C Wing	Scr. DM AFB
4378	WV-3		137891	VW-4	29.4.56	—	VW-4	w/o 23.8.64
4379	WV-3		137892	VW-4	8.4.55	—	VW-4	Scr. DM AFB
4380	WV-3		137893	VW-3	8.4.55	—	VW-3	w/o 17.9.56
4381	WV-3		137894	VW-4	18.4.55	—	VW-4	Scr. DM AFB
4382	WV-3		137895	VW-4	26.4.55	—	552 AEW&C Wing	Scr. DM AFB
4383	WV-3		137896	VW-3	26.4.55	—	VW-4	Scr. DM AFB
4384	WV-3		137897	VW-4	2.6.55	—	VW-4	Scr. Litchfield Park, AZ
4385	WV-3		137898	VW-3	8.6.55	67-21472	552 AEW&C Wing	Scr. DM AFB
4386	RC-121D		54-2304	552 AEW&C Wg	9.2.56	—	552 AEW&C Wing	Scr. DM AFB
4387	RC-121D		54-2305	551 AEW&C Wg	9.2.56	—	551 AEW&C Wing	Scr. DM AFB
4388	RC-121D		54-2306	552 AEW&C Wg	9.2.56	—	552 AEW&C Wing	Scr. DM AFB
4389	RC-121D			552 AEW&C Wg	9.2.56	—	79 AEW&C Wing	Scr. DM AFB
4390	RC-121D			552 AEW&C Wg	9.2.56	—	552 AEW&C Wing	w/o 22.3.58
4391	RC-121D			552 AEW&C Wg	1.3.56	—	79 AEW&C Wing	Last noted DM AFB 1982
4392	RC-121D			552 AEW&C Wg	9.2.56	—	551 AEW&C Wing	Scr. DM AFB
4393	RC-121D			552 AEW&C Wg	5.11.56	—	552 AEW&C Wing	Scr. DM AFB
4394	RC-121D			552 AEW&C Wg	3.7.56	—	79 AEW&C Wing	w/o 15.3.78
4395	RC-121D			552 AEW&C Wg	4.5.56	—	79 AEW&C Wing	Last noted DM AFB 1982
4396	RC-121D			552 AEW&C Wg	8.5.56	—	79 AEW&C Wing	w/o 8.5.56
4397	RC-121D			552 AEW&C Wg	14.5.56	—	552 AEW&C Wing	Last noted DM AFB 1982
4398	RC-121D			551 AEW&C Wg	15.5.56	—	551 AEW&C Wing	Scr. DM AFB
4399	RC-121D			551 AEW&C Wg	28.5.56	—	551 AEW&C Wing	Scr. DM AFB
4400	RC-121D			552 AEW&C Wg	19.5.56	—	79 AEW&C Wing	Scr. DM AFB
4401	RC-121D			552 AEW&C Wg	9.6.56	—	552 AEW&C Wing	Scr. DM AFB
4402	RC-121D			551 AEW&C Wg	12.6.56	—	79 AEW&C Wing	Scr. DM AFB
4403	RC-121D			551 AEW&C Wg	18.6.56	—	551 AEW&C Wing	Scr. DM AFB
4404	RC-121D			552 AEW&C Wg	13.7.56	—	552 AEW&C Wing	Scr. DM AFB
4405	RC-121D			552 AEW&C Wg	10.8.56	—	79 AEW&C Wing	Scr. DM AFB
4406	RC-121D			551 AEW&C Wg	13.7.56	—	552 AEW&C Wing	Scr. DM AFB
4407	RC-121D			552 AEW&C Wg	9.8.56	—	551 AEW&C Wing	Scr. DM AFB
4408	RC-121D			79 AEW&C Wg	14.8.56	—	79 AEW&C Wing	Scr. DM AFB
4409	RC-121D			551 AEW&C Wg	10.8.56	—	79 AEW&C Wing	w/o 11.7.56
4410	RC-121D			552 AEW&C Wg	28.8.56	—	552 AEW&C Wing	Scr. DM AFB
4411	RC-121D			552 AEW&C Wg	28.8.56	—	79 AEW&C Wing	Scr. DM AFB
4412	RC-121D			552 AEW&C Wg	26.10.56	—	79 AEW&C Wing	Scr. DM AFB
4413	WV-2		141289	VW-13	24.2.56	55-5262	551 AEW&C Wg	w/o 11.11.66
4414	WV-2		141290	VW-13	24.2.56	—	VW-2	Scr. Litchfield Park AZ
4415	WV-2		141291	VW-15	24.2.56	55-5263	VW-13	Scr. DM AFB
4416	WV-2		141292	VW-11	26.2.56	—	VAQ-33	Florence Air Museum. Scr. 1998
4417	WV-2		141293	VW-11	24.2.56	—	VW-13	Scr. DM AFB
4418	WV-2		141294	VW-11	24.2.56	—	VW-15	w/o 18.10.58
4419	WV-2		141295	AEWMATRON 2	24.2.56	—	VW-13	Scr. Litchfield Park AZ
4420	WV-2		141296	VW-2	24.2.56	67-21473	553 RW	Scr. DM AFB
4421	WV-2		141297	NADU South Weymouth	24.2.56	—	NRL Patuxent	Pres. Museum of Aviation Robins Warner-Robins AFB GA
4422	WV-2		141298	VW-13	24.2.56	—	VW-13	Scr. Litchfield Park AZ

C/N	Ordered as	Built as	1st Reg.	For	Del Date	Other Reg	Last user	Fate
4423	WV-2		141299	VW-13	24.2.56	—	VW-13	Scr. DM AFB
4424	WV-2		141300	VW-11	24.2.56	55-5264	551 AEW&C Wing	Scr. DM AFB
4425	WV-2		141301	VW-11	24.2.56	—	VW-13	Scr. Litchfield Park AZ
4426	WV-2		141302	VW-11	24.2.56	55-5265	551 AEW&C Wg	Scr. DM AFB
4427	WV-2		141303	VW-11	25.5.56	—	VW-13	w/o 2.4.59
4428	WV-2		141304	VW-11	25.5.56	—	Pac Missile Range	Scr. DM AFB
4429	WV-2		141305	VW-11	11.6.56	—	VW-11	Scr. Litchfield Park AZ
4430	WV-2		141306	VW-11	22.6.56	67-21474	553 RW	Scr. DM AFB
4431	WV-2		141307	VW-11	2.7.56	—	VW-13	Scr. DM AFB
4432	WV-2		141308	VW-13	2.8.56	—	VW-11	Scr. Litchfield Park AZ
4433	WV-2		141309	VW-13	1.8.56	—	PMTC	Pres. McClellan Air Museum Sacramento CA
4434	WV-2		141310	VW-15	22.8.56	—	VW-15	w/o (missing) 20.2.58
4435	WV-2		141311	VW-13	20.8.56	—	PMTC	Pres. Octave Chanute Museum Rantoul IL
4436	WV-2		141312	VW-13	20.8.56	67-21475	552 AEW&C Wing	Scr. DM AFB
4437	WV-2		141313	VW-13	21.8.56	—	VW-2	Scr. Litchfield Park AZ
4438	WV-2		141314	VW-15	19.9.56	—	VW-15	w/o 17.4.57
4439	WV-2		141315	VW-15	19.9.56	—	VW-13	Scr. Litchfield Park AZ
4440	WV-2		141316	VW-2	12.9.56	—	VW-13	Scr. DM AFB
4441	WV-2		141317	VW-13	26.9.56	67-21476	AFSC	w/o 24.1.69
4442	WV-2		141318	VW-11	8.10.56	55-5267	551 AEW&C Wing	Scr. DM AFB
4443	WV-2		141319	AEWMATRON 2	4.12.56	—	VW-13	Scr. DM AFB
4444	WV-2		141320	VW-2	23.10.56	67-21477	553 AEW&C Wing	Scr. DM AFB
4445	WV-2		141321	VW-15	23.10.56	—	VW-13	w/o 11.6.65
4446	WV-2		141322	VW-15	30.10.56	—	VW-11	Scr. DM AFB
4447	WV-2		141323	VW-15	30.10.56	—	VW-4	Scr. DM AFB
4448	WV-2		141324	AEWMATRON 2	8.11.56	—	AEWTULANT	w/o 9.8.62
4449	WV-2		141325	AEWMATRON 2	9.11.56	—	VXN-8	Scr. DM AFB
4450	WV-2		141326	AEWMATRON 2	9.11.56	—	VW-11	Scr. DM AFB
4451	WV-2		141327	AEWMATRON 2	20.11.56	55-5268	551 AEW&C Wing	Scr. DM AFB
4452	WV-2		141328	AEWMATRON 2	23.11.56	67-21478	553 AEW&C Wing	Scr. DM AFB
4453	WV-2		141329	AEWMATRON 2	5.12.56	—	VW-13	w/o 30.7.53
4454	WV-2		141330	AEWMATRON 2	12.12.56	67-21479	553 AEW&C Wing	Scr. DM AFB
4455	WV-2		141331	Navy CIC Officers Cllge	17.12.56	—	VW-4	Scr. DM AFB
4456	WV-2		141332	AEWMATRON 2	2.1.57	—	VW-11	w/o ?.3.59
4457	WV-2		141333	Navy CIC Officers Cllge	4.1.57	—	551 AEW&C Wing	Scr. DM AFB
4458	WV-2		143184	Navy CIC Officers Cllge	7.2.57	57-143184	USAF	Scr. DM AFB
4459	WV-2		143185	AEWMATRON 2	15.1.57	67-21480	553 AEW&C Wing	Scr. DM AFB
4460	WV-2		143186	AEWMATRON 2	17.1.57		VQ-1	Scr. DM AFB
4461	WV-2		143187	AEWMATRON 2	18.1.57		VW-1	Scr. Litchfield Park AZ
4462	WV-2		143188	AEWMATRON 2	22.1.57	67-21481	553 AEW&C Wing	Scr. DM AFB
4463	WV-2		143189	AEWMATRON 2	13.2.57	57-143189	USAF	Scr. DM AFB
4464	WV-2		143190	VW-2	13.2.57	—	USN	Scr. DM AFB
4465	WV-2		143191	AEWMATRON 2	5.3.57	67-21482	553 Recon Wing	Scr. DM AFB
4466	WV-2		143192	Navy CIC Officers Cllge	7.3.57	—	VT-86	Scr. DM AFB
4467	WV-2		143193	AEWMATRON 2	13.3.57	—	AEWBARRON PAC	w/o 22.1.61

C/N	Ordered as	Built as	1st Reg.	For	Del Date	Other Reg	Last user	Fate
4468	WV-2		143194	AEWMATRON 2	1.3.57	—	AIR BARSRON 2	Scr. Litchfield Park AZ
4469	WV-2		143195	AEWMATRON 2	1.3.57	67-21483	553 Recon Wing	Scr. DM AFB
4470	WV-2		143196	AEWMATRON 2	1.3.57	—	US Army	Scr. DM AFB
4471	WV-2		143197	AEWMATRON 2	1.3.57	—	AIR BARSRON 2	w/o 32.12.57
4472	WV-2		143198	AEWMATRON 2	1.3.57	—	VW-4	Scr. DM AFB
4473	WV-2		143199	AEWMATRON 2	1.3.57	57-143199	USAF	Scr. DM AFB
4474	WV-2		143200	AEWMATRON 2	1.3.57	57-143200	USAF	Scr. DM AFB
4475	WV-2		143201	AEWMATRON 2	1.3.57	N671NA	NASA	Scr. DM AFB
4476	WV-2		143202	AEWMATRON 2	9.5.57	67-21484	553 Recon Wing	Scr. DM AFB
4477	WV-2		143203	AEWMATRON 2	20.5.57	67-21485	553 Recon Wing	Scr. DM AFB
4478	WV-2		143204	AEWMATRON 2	29.5.57	67-21486	553 Recon Wing	Scr. DM AFB
4479	WV-2		143205	AIRBASRON 2	7.6.57	—	VQ-1	Scr. DM AFB
4480	WV-2		143206	AIRBASRON 2	28.6.57	67-21487	553 Recon Wing	Scr. DM AFB
4481	WV-2		143207	AIRBASRON 2	2.7.57	67-21488	553 Recon Wing	Scr. DM AFB
4482	WV-2		143208	AIRBASRON 2	12.7.57	67-21489	553 Recon Wing	Scr. DM AFB
4483	WV-2		143209	AIRBASRON 2	17.7.57	—	VQ-2	Scr. Rota, Spain
4484	WV-2		143210	AIRBASRON 2	8.8.57	67-21490	553 Recon Wing	Scr. DM AFB
4485	WV-2		143211	AIRBASRON 2	31.7.57	—	AEWBARRON PAC	Scr. Litchfield Park AZ
4486	WV-2		143212	AIRBASRON 2	7.8.57	—	AEWBARRON PAC	Scr. Litchfield Park AZ
4487	WV-2		143213	AIRBASRON 2	21.8.57	67-21491	553 Recon Wing	Scr. DM AFB
4488	WV-2		143214	AIRBASRON 2	26.8.57	67-21492	553 Recon Wing	Scr. DM AFB
4489	WV-2		143215	AIRBASRON 2	29.8.57	67-21493	553 Recon Wing	w/o 25.4.69
4490	WV-2		143216	AIRBASRON 2	4.9.57	67-21494	553 Recon Wing	Scr. DM AFB
4491	WV-2		143217	AIRBASRON 2	26.8.57	67-21495	553 Recon Wing	w/o 6.9.69
4492	WV-2		143218	AIRBASRON 2	19.9.57	67-21496	553 Recon Wing	Scr. DM AFB
4493	WV-2		143219	AIRBASRON 2	19.9.57	67-21497	553 Recon Wing	Scr. DM AFB
4494	WV-2		143220	Navy CIC	3.10.57	—	Navy Test Off's Clge	Scr. DM AFB
4495	WV-2		143221	Navy CIC Officers Cllge	10.10.57	—	VT-86	Stored for NMNA Pensacola FL
4496	WV-2		143222	AIRBASRON 2	10.10.57	67-21498	553 Recon Wing	Scr. DM AFB
4497	WV-2		143223	AIRBASRON 2	4.11.57	67-21499	553 Recon Wing	Scr. DMAF
4498	WV-2		143224	AIRBASRON 2	13.11.57	67-21500	553 Recon Wing	Scr. DM AFB
4499	WV-2		143225	VW-3	2.12.57	—	VW-1	Scr. Litchfield Park AZ
4501	L-1049C-55-81		PH-TFP	KLM	12.12.53	PH-LKP	KLM	Scr. Amsterdam NL 1963
4502	L-1049C-55-81		PH-TFR	KLM	11.6.53	PH-LKR	KLM	Scr. Amsterdam NL 1963
4503	L-1049C-55-81		PH-TFS	KLM	23.6.53	PH-LKS	KLM	Scr. Amsterdam NL 1963
4504	L-1049C-55-81		PH-TFT	KLM	30.6.53	PH-LKT	KLM	w/o 15.7.57
4505	L-1049C-55-81		PH-TFU	KLM	17.7.53	PH-LKU	KLM	Scr. Amsterdam NL 1963
4506	L-1049C-55-81		PH-TFV	KLM	27.7.53	PH-LKV	KLM	Scr. Amsterdam NL 1963
4507	L-1049C-55-81		PH-TFW	KLM	1.8.53	PH-LKW	KLM	Scr. Amsterdam NL 1963
4508	L-1049C-55-81		PH-TFX	KLM	6.8.53	PH-LKX	KLM	Scr. Amsterdam NL 1963
4509	L-1049C-55-81		PH-TFY	KLM	27.8.53	PH-LKY	KLM	w/o 5.9.54
4510	L-1049C-55-81		F-BGNA	Air France	19.6.53	—	Air France	w/o 15.7.53
4511	L-1049C-55-81		F-BGNB	Air France	26.7.53	—	Aviasol	Scr. Landes France 1979. Zoo attraction
4512	L-1049C-55-81		F-BGNC	Air France	22.8.53	—	CATAIR	w/o 9.8.69
4513	L-1049C-55-81		F-BGND	Air France	31.8.53	F-BRNH	CATAIR	Scr. Cormeilles France 1974
4514	L-1049C-55-81		F-BGNE	Air France	16.9.53	'5N-07G'	Biafran Govt	Scr. Lisbon Portugal 1971
4515	L-1049C-55-81		F-BGNF	Air France	19.9.53	—	Aviasol	Disco, Marquise France.Presumed scrapped after 1981

C/N	Ordered as	Built as	1st Reg.	For	Del Date	Other Reg	Last user	Fate
4516	L-1049C-55-81		F-BGNG	Air France	29.9.53	—	CATAIR	Scr. Nîmes France 1979
4517	L-1049C-55-81		F-BGNH	Air France	23.10.53	—	Air France	Scr. Paris-Orly 1967
4518	L-1049C-55-81		F-BGNI	Air France	23.10.53	—	Air Cameroun	Scr. Nîmes France 1976
4519	L-1049C-55-81		F-BGNJ	Air France	4.11.53	F-BRAD	Air Fret	Pres. Nantes, France
4520	L-1049C-55-81		AP-AFQ	Pakistan Int.	1.2.54	—	PIA	Scr. Karachi Pakistan after 1973
4521	L-1049C-55-81		AP-AFR	Pakistan Int.	18.2.54	T-1043	Indonesian AF	Stored 1978, prob scr.
4522	L-1049C-55-81		AP-AFS	Pakistan Int.	7.4.54	—	Lebanese Air Charter	Scr. Karachi India after 1970
4523	L-1049C-55-83		N6215C	Eastern Air Lines	23.11.53	—	Eastern	Scr. Miami FL 1968
4524	L-1049C-55-83		N6216C	Eastern Air Lines	7.11.53	—	Eastern	Scr. Fox Field CA 1971
4525	L-1049C-55-83		N6217C	Eastern Air Lines	16.11.53	—	Eastern	Scr. Fox Field CA 1971
4526	L-1049C-55-83		N6218C	Eastern Air Lines	20.11.53	—	Eastern	w/o 4.12.65
4527	L-1049C-55-83		N6219C	Eastern Air Lines	30.11.53	—	Eastern	Scr. Miami FL 1967
4528	L-1049C-55-83		N6220C	Eastern Air Lines	13.12.53	—	Eastern	w/o 3.8.61
4529	L-1049C-55-83		N6221C	Eastern Air Lines	19.12.53	—	Eastern	Scr. Miami FL 1968
4530	L-1049C-55-83		N6222C	Eastern Air Lines	23.12.53	—	Eastern	Scr. Fox Field, CA 1972
4531	L-1049C-55-83		N6223C	Eastern Air Lines	31.12.53	—	Eastern	Scr. Fox Field, CA 1971
4532	L-1049C-55-83		N6224C	Eastern Air Lines	10.1.54	—	Eastern	Scr. Fox Field, CA 1971
4533	L-1049C-55-83		N6225C	Eastern Air Lines	22.1.54	—	Eastern	Scr. Fox Field, CA 1972
4534	L-1049C-55-83		N6226C	Eastern Air Lines	24.1.54	—	Eastern	Scr. Ft Lauderdale FL 1974
4535	L-1049C-55-83		N6627C	Eastern Air Lines	11.2.54	—	Air Cargo Support	Scr. Miami FL 1981
4536	L-1049C-55-83		N6628C	Eastern Air Lines	19.2.54	HI-329	Aerotours	Scr. Santo Domingo after 1984
4537	L-1049C-55-83		N6629C	Eastern Air Lines	25.2.54	—	Eastern	Scr. Fox Field, CA 1971
4538	L-1049C-55-83		N6630C	Eastern Air Lines	28.2.54	—	Eastern	Scr. Miami FL 1967
4539	L-1049C-55-81		VH-EAG	Qantas	29.3.54	—	Qantas	Scr. Burbank CA 1965
4540	L-1049C-55-94		CF-TGA	Trans-Canada A/l	26.2.54	—	TCA	Scr. Burbank CA 1966
4541	L-1049C-55-94		CF-TGB	Trans-Canada A/l	17.3.54	N9739Z, N189S	Standard Airways	w/o 29.5.63
4542	L-1049C-55-94		CF-TGC	Trans-Canada A/l	9.4.54	—	TCA	Scr. Montreal Canada after 1965
4543	L-1049C-55-94		CF-TCD	Trans-Canada A/l	1.5.54	N8473R, N4715G	Capitol International	Scr. Wilmington DE 1969
4544	L-1049C-55-94		CF-TGE	Trans-Canada A/l	10.5.54	N8742R, CF-RNR	World Wide Airways	Pres. Bar, near Pearson Airport, Toronto Canada
4545	L-1049C-55-81		VH-EAH	Qantas	26.4.54	N9716C	Capitol Airways	Scr. Wilmington DE 1967
4546	L-1049C-55-81		VH-EAI	Qantas	20.5.54	N9717C	American Flyers	Scr. Fox Field CA 1972
4547	L-1049C-55-87		VT-DGL	Air-India	26.4.54	BG 581, IN-318	312 Sqn Ind.Navy	In storage Goa 1994
4548	L-1049C-55-87		VT-DGM	Air-India	18.6.54	BG 582, IN-319	312 Sqn Ind.Navy	In storage Goa 1994
4549	L-1049E-55-89	'E-55-81	VH-EAJ	Braathens	5.7.54 (del Qantas)	N9718C	Midair Inc	Scr. Barstow CA after 1977
4550	L-1049C-55-81	'E-55-89	EC-AIN	Iberia	23.6.54	—	Iberia	w/o 5.5.65
4551	L-1049C-55-81	'E-55-89	EC-AIO	Iberia	23.7.54	N8023, HP-475	Biafran Govt	Scr. Abidjan Ivory Coast 1971
4552	L-1049C-55-81	'E-55-89	EC-AIP	Iberia	21.7.54	—	Iberia	w/o 6.3.61
4553	L-1049C-55-81	'E-55-108	PH-LKA	KLM	26.5.54	4R-ACH, EC-AQL	KLM	Scr. Amsterdam NL 1963
4554	L-1049C-55-92		HK-175	Avianca	23.8.54	—	Avianca	Scr. Bogota 1969
4555	L-1049C-55-92		HK-176	Avianca	8.9.54	—	Avianca	Playground, Bogota — scr.!
4556	L-1049C-55-92		HK-177	Avianca	29.9.54	—	Avianca	w/o 21.1.60
4557	L-1049E-55-89	'E-55-115	CU-P573	Braathens (del Cubana)	8.11.54	N1005C	Capitol	Stored Dover AFB, DE for museum
4558	L-1049E-55-90	'E-55-107	PH-LKB	KLM	11.8.54	—	KLM	Scr. Amsterdam NL 1964

C/N	Ordered as	Built as	1st Reg.	For	Del Date	Other Reg	Last user	Fate
4559	L-1049E-55-90	'E-55-107	PH-LKC	KLM	23.9.54	—	KLM	Scr. Amsterdam NL 1964
4560	L-1049E-55-90	'E-55-107	PH-LKD	KLM	21.10.54	—	KLM	Scr. Amsterdam NL 1963
4561	L-1049E-55-81		YV-C-AMR	LAV	23.10.54	—	LAV	w/o 20.6.54
4562	L-1049E-55-81		YV-C-AMT	LAV	11.11.54	YV-C-ANF, N58921	VIASA	Scr. Fox Field CA 1966
4563	L-1049E-55-94		CF-TGF	Trans-Canada A/l	23.6.54	N9742Z	American Flyers	Scr. Fox Field CA 1970
4564	L-1049E-55-94		CF-TGG	Trans-Canada A/l	10.7.54	—	TCA	w/o 17.12.54
4565	L-1049E-55-94		CF-TGH	Trans-Canada A/l	31.8.54	N9639Z	American Flyers	Scr. Fox Field CA 1971
4572	L-1049E-55-102	N5172V		Northwest Orient	19.4.55	YV-C-ANB	LAV	Scr. Fox Field CA 1966
4573	L-1049E-55-102	L-1049E-55-118	VH-EAK	N'west O. (d Qantas)	18.1.55	—	TEAL	Scr. Burbank CA 1969
4574	L-1049E-55-102	L-1049E-55-118	VH-EAL	N'west O. (d Qantas)	31.1.55	N9719C, OB-R-741	American Flyers	w/o 20.9.65
4575	L-1049E-55-102		N5173V	Northwest Orient	22.1.55	N5173V, YV-C-ANC	LAV	w/o 14.10.58
4576	L-1049E-55-102		YV-C-AND	Northwest Orient	31.1.55	YV-C-AND, N9745Z	LAV	Scr. Fox Field CA 1966
4577	L-1049E-55-102		N5175V	Northwest Orient	12.2.55	YV-C-ANE, N9748Z	LAV	Scr. Fox Field CA 1966
4578	L-1049E-55-81	L-1049E-55-118	VH-EAE	Qantas	6.2.55	N9720C	Int A/C Services	Scr. Wilmington, DE 1970
4579	L-1049E-55-118		VH-EAF	Qantas	18.2.55	—	TEAL (lease)	Scr. Burbank CA 1964
4580	L-1049E-55-81	'L-1049E-55-119	VH-EAA	Qantas	4.3.55	N9714C, CF-PXX, LV-IXZ	AER (Argentina)	Scr. Buenos Aires 1970
4581	L-1049E-55-81	L-1049E-55-119	VH-EAB	Qantas	4.3.55	N93164, ZP-TVB, N4192A, N442LM, N11SR	PM Leasing	Scr. Kuwait 1982
4582	L-1049E-55 'G-82-110		PP-VDA	Varig (del TWA)	19.9.55	N7101C	TWA	w/o 29.2.60
4583	L-1049E-55 'G-82-110		PP-VDB	Varig (del TWA)	16.3.55	N7102C	TWA	Scr. Kansas City MO 1965
4584	L-1049E-55 'G-82-110		PP-VDC	Varig (del TWA)	14.3.55	N7103C	TWA	Scr. Tuscon, AZ 1971
4585	L-1049G-82-110		N7104C	TWA	16.3.55	—	TWA	Scr. Tuscon, AZ 1970
4586	L-1049G-82-110		N7105C	TWA	14.3.55	—	TWA	Scr. Fox Field CA 1971
4587	L-1049G-82-110		N7106C	TWA	21.4.55	—	TWA	Scr. Fox Field CA 1971
4588	L-1049G-82-110		N7107C	TWA	4.4.55	—	TWA	Scr. Kansas City MO 1963
4589	L-1049G-82-110		N7108C	TWA	30.3.55	—	TWA	Scr. Tuscon AZ 1970
4590	L-1049G-82-110		N7019C	TWA	19.4.55	—	TWA	Scr. Burbank CA 1963
4591	L-1049G-82-110		N7020C	TWA	6.5.55	—	TWA	Scr. Kansas City MO 1965
4592	L-1049G-82-110		N7021C	TWA	6.5.55	—	TWA	Scr. Fox Field CA 1970
4593	L-1049G-82-110		N7022C	TWA	10.5.55	—	TWA	Scr. Fox Field CA 1971
4594	L-1049G-82-110		N7023C	TWA	10.5.55	—	TWA	Scr. Fox Field CA 1971
4595	L-1049G-82-110		N7024C	TWA	31.5.55	—	TWA	Scr. Tuscon AZ 1965
4596	L-1049G-82-110		N7025C	TWA	27.5.55	—	TWA	Scr. New York-JFK NY 1967
4597	L-1049G-82-110		N7026C	TWA	2.6.55	—	TWA	Scr. Kansas City MO 1965
4598	L-1049G-82-110		N7027C	TWA	3.6.55	—	TWA	Scr. Tuscon, AZ 1970
4599	L-1049G-82-110		N7028C	TWA	7.6.55	—	TWA	Scr. Kansas City MO 1965
4600	L-1049G-82-110		N7029C	TWA	30.6.55	—	TWA	Scr. Kansas City MO 1965
4601	L-1049G-82-110		N7030C	TWA	16.6.55	—	TWA	Scr. Kansas City MO 1965
4602	L-1049G-82-105		D-ALAK	Lufthansa	29.3.55	—	Lufthansa	w/o 11.1.59
4603	L-1049G-82-105		D-ALEM	Lufthansa	19.4.55	—	Lufthansa	Scr. Hamburg Germany 1967
4604	L-1049G-82-105		D-ALIN	Lufthansa	29.4.55	—	Lufthansa	Pres. Hermeskeil Museum Germany
4605	L-1049G-82-105		D-ALOP	Lufthansa	28.5.55	—	Lufthansa	Café, Neu-Wulmstorf. Scr 1975
4606	L-1049E-55	L-1049E-82-140	VH-EAC	Qantas	25.10.55	—	Qantas	w/o 24.8.60
4607	L-1049E-55	L-1049E-82-140	VH-EAD	Qantas	26.11.55	N9751C	Capitol Airways	Scr. Fox Field CA 1970
4610	L-1049G-82-81		PP-VDA	Varig	29.4.55	—	Varig	w/o 16.8.57

C/N	Ordered As	Built As	1st Reg.	For	Del Date	Other Reg	Last User	Fate
4611	L-1049G-82-81		PP-VDB	Varig	18.6.55	—	Varig	Scr. Porto Alegre Brazil 1967
4612	L-1049G-82-81		PP-VDC	Varig	27.6.55	—	Varig	Scr. Porto Alegre Brazil 1967
4613	L-1049E-55-87		VT-DHL	Air-India	26.1.55	BG-580, IN-317	312 Sqn Ind. Navy	In storage Goa 1994
4614	L-1049E-55-87		VT-DHM	Air-India	17.2.55	BG-575, IN-315	312 Sqn Ind. Navy	At Goa for Indian Navy Museum
4615	L-1049E-55-87		VT-DHN	Air-India	25.2.55	BG-577	6 Sqn Indian AF	Derelict, Pune 1994. Prob scr.
4616	L-1049G-82-81		CS-TLA	TAP	15.7.55	N8838, 5N-83H	Phoenix Air Trans.	Restaurant, Faro Portugal — destroyed by arsonists
4617	L-1049G-82-81		CS-TLB	TAP	28.7.55	—	TAP	Restaurant Miami. Scr. 1978
4618	L-1049G-82-81		CS-TLC	TAP	15.9.55	'5T-TAF'	Nth Am A/c Trading	Restaurant, Kirkop Malta. Burnt by arsonists 1997
4619	L-1049G-82-110		none	Hughes Tool Co	24.2.56	N4903C, N6696C	Capitol International	Scr. Wilmington, DE 1970
4620	L-1049G-82-98		F-BHBA	Air France	7.7.55	—	Aviasol	Playground, scr. 1976
4621	L-1049G-82-98		F-BHBB	Air France	29.7.55	—	Air Fret	Scr. Nîmes France 1973
4622	L-1049G-82-98		F-BHBC	Air France	9.8.55	—	Air France	w/o 29.8.60
4623	L-1049G-82-98		F-BHBD	Air France	22.8.55	—	Air France	Scr. Toulouse after 1967
4624	L-1049G-82-98		F-BHBE	Air France	31.8.55	—	CATAIR	Scr. Cormeilles France 1973
4625	L-1049G-82-98		F-BHBF	Air France	3.10.55	—	Air France	Scr. Paris-Orly 1967
4626	L-1049G-82-98		F-BHBG	Air France	10.10.55	—	Aviasol	Bar, Quimper France
4627	L-1049G-82-98		F-BHBH	Air France	5.12.55	—	Aviasol	Scr. Paris-Orly 1967
4628	L-1049G-82-92		HK-184	Avianca	27.10.55	—	Avianca	Scr. Barranquilla Colombia 1969
4629	L-1049G-82-132		PH-LKE	KLM	22.12.55	—	KLM	Scr. Amsterdam NL 1964
4630	L-1049G-82-98		PH-LKF	KLM	5.1.56	—	KLM	Scr. Amsterdam NL 1964
4631	L-1049G-82-98		PH-LKG	KLM	20.1.56	—	KLM	Scr. Amsterdam NL 1965
4632	L-1049G-82-112		CU-T601	Cubana	20.2.56	—	Cubana	Scr. Havana Cuba after 1961
4633	L-1049G-82-112		CU-T602	Cubana	15.3.56	—	Cubana	Scr. Havana Cuba after 1961
4634	L-1049G-82-98		F-BHBI	Air France	23.2.56	—	Phoenix Air Trans.	Stored Lanzarote later scr.
4635	L-1049G-82-132		PH-LKH	KLM	1.2.56	—	KLM	Scr. Amsterdam NL 1962
4636	L-1049G-82-134		YV-C-AME	LAV	17.2.56	N9749Z, N174W	North Slope Supply.	w/o 5.5.70
4637	L-1049G-82-105		D-ACED	Lufthansa	22.7.55	D-ALAP	Lufthansa	Scr. Frankfurt Germany 1967
4639	L-1049G-82-98		F-BHBJ	Air France	4.5.56	—	Air France	Scr. Paris-Orly 1967
4640	L-1049G-82-105		D-ACID	Lufthansa	22.7.55	D-ALEC, 'N8025',' 5T-TAK'	Nth Am. A/c Trad.	Derelict, then scr. Lisbon Portugal 1981
4641	L-1049G-82-109		CF-TEU	Trans-Canada A/l	22.4.56	N9640Z	Douglas Aircraft Co.	Scr. Fox Field CA 1966
4642	L-1049G-82-105		D-ALOF	Lufthansa	18.8.55	'5T-TAG', 'N8025'	Nth Am. A/c Trad.	w/o 1.7.68
4643	L-1049G-82-105		CF-TEV	Trans-Canada A/l	15.5.56	N9641Z	Douglas Aircraft Co.	Scr. Fox Field, CA 1966
4644	L-1049G-82-124	L-1049-82-151	PH-LKI	Thai Airways (del. KLM)	20.7.56	EC-AQM, N8024	Aviaco	Scr. Miami FL 1971
4645	L-1049G-82-124	L-1049-82-151	PH-LKK	Thai Airways (del. KLM)	28.6.56	EC-AQN, 'N8025', '5T-TAC'	Nth Am. A/c Trad.	w/o 1.68
4646	L-1049G-82-105		VT-DIL	Air-India	5.6.56	BG-578	6 Sqn Indian AF	Scr. India, 1976
4647	L-1049G-82-106		D-ACOD	Lufthansa	22.7.55	D-ALID, '5T TAH', 'N8025'	Nth Am. A/c Trad.	Derelict Abidjan 1978
4648	L-1049G-82-114	L-1049G-82-144	N7121C	Hughes Tool Co.	21.6.56	N468C	F&B Livestock Co	Scr. Miami FL 1973
4649	L-1049G-82-105	L-1049G-82-144	D-ACUD	Lufthansa	22.7.55	D-ALOF, N7122C	TWA	Scr. Tucson after 1960
4650	L-1049G-82-114	L-1049G-82-144	N7123C	TWA	20.7.56	N137X, N137XR	Oxnard Aviation	Scr. after 1970
4651	L-1049G-82-114	L-1049G-82-144	N7124C	TWA	31.7.56	—	TWA	Scr. Fox Field CA 1971
4652	L-1049G-82-114	L-1049G-82-144	N7125C	TWA	27.8.56	—	Iberia (lease)	w/o 8.11.60

C/N	ORDERED AS	BUILT AS	1ST REG.	FOR	DEL DATE	OTHER REG	LAST USER	FATE
4653	L-1049G-03-142		N6231G	Eastern Air Lines	26.10.56	—	Eastern	Scr. Fox Field CA 1971
4654	L-1049G-82-114		N71216C	TWA	30.8.56	—	TWA	Scr. Fox Field CA 1971
4655	L-1049G-03-142		N6232G	Eastern Air Lines	14.9.56	—	Eastern	Scr. Fox Field CA 1971
4656	L-1049G-82-114	L-1049G-82-144	N7127C	TWA	26.9.56	—	TWA	Scr. Fox Field CA 1971
4657	L-1049G-03-142		N6233G	Eastern Air Lines	1.10.56	—	Eastern	Scr. Fox Field CA 1971
4658	L-1049G-82-114	L-1049G-82-144	N7128C	TWA	28.9.56	—	TWA	Scr. Tuscon AZ 1970
4659	L-1049G-03-142		N6234G	Eastern Air Lines	12.10.56	—	Eastern	Scr. Fox Field CA 1971
4660	L-1049G-03-142		N6235G	Eastern Air Lines	18.10.56	—	Eastern	Scr. Fox Field CA 1971
4661	L-1049G-03-142		N6236G	Eastern Air Lines	29.10.56	—	Eastern	Scr. Fox Field CA 1970
4662	L-1049G-03-142		N6237G	Eastern Air Lines	2.11.56	—	Eastern	Scr. Fox Field CA 1970
	L-1049G-03-142		N6328G	Eastern Air Lines	9.11.56	—	Eastern	Scr. Fox Field CA 1970
4664	L-1049G-03-142		N6329G	Eastern Air Lines	15.11.56	—	Eastern	Scr. Miami FL 1967
4665	L-1049G-03-142		N6240G	Eastern Air Lines	30.11.56	—	Eastern	Scr. Fox Field CA 1971
4666	L-1049G-82-106		VT-DIM	Air-India	6.12.56	BG 576, IN-316	Indian Navy	Stored, damaged 1983
4667	L-1049G-82-106		VT-DIN	Air-India	12.12.56	—	Air-India	w/o 19.7.59
4668	L-1049G-82-98		F-BHMI	Air France	26.12.56	—	CATAIR	Scr. Cormeilles France 1975
4669	L-1049G-82-98		F-BHMJ	Air France	27.12.56	—	Aviasol	Bar, Strasbourg France. Burnt 1978
4670	L-1049G-82-98		F-MHMK	Air France	22.1.57	—	Air France	w/o 6.12.57
4671	L-1049G-82-98		F-BHML	Air France	4.2.57	D-ADAM,' 'D-ALAP	Air Fret	Pres. Munich Int Airport
4672	L-1049G-03-124		HS-TCA	Thai Airways	22.7.57	XA-NAC, CS-TLF	TAP	Scr. Salisbury Rhodesia 1967
4673	L-1049G-82-99		EC-AMP	Iberia	8.7.57	N8021	unknown (smugglers)	w/o 6.6.70
4674	L 1049G-82-134		YV-C-AMI	LAV	21.8.57	N9746Z, N173W	Aviation Specialties	w/o 9.6.73
4675	L-1049G-82-112		CU-T-631	Cubana	27.7.57	—	Cubana	Scr. Havana Cuba after 1961
4676	L-1049G-82-99		EC-AMQ	Iberia	12.8.57	N8022	International Aerodyne	Scr. Miami FL 1970
4677	L-1049G-03-124		HS-TCB	Thai Airways	27.8.57	XA-NAD, HP-280, CS-TLE, N833D	Ronald Adimey	Scr. Buffalo NY 1977
4678	L-1049G-03-124		HS-TCC	Thai Airways	24.9.57	XA-NAF, EC-WRN, EC-ARN, N8026, HP-467	RAPSA (Panama)	w/o 30.3.68
4679	L-1049G-82-153		VH-EAO	Qantas	25.10.57	N9722C, N86682	American Flyers	Scr. Fox Field, CA 1970
4680	L-1049G-82-153		VH-EAP	Qantas	20.11.57	N9723C	Stereo Vision Int.	Scr. Burbank CA 1974
4681	L-1049G-03-158		PP-VDD	Varig	18.11.57	—	Varig	Scr. Sao Paulo Brazil 1967
4682	L-1049G-82-109		CF-TEW	Trans-Canada	22.11.57	N7772C	TCAL Air Lines	Scr. Burbank 1962
4683	L-1049G-82-109		CF-TEX	Trans-Canada	20.12.57	N9642Z, 9G-28, N964	Transocean Air Lines	Scr. Fox Field, CA 1971
4684	L-1049G-03-158		PP-VDE	Varig	11.12.57	—	Varig	Scr. Porto Alegre Brazil 1967
4685	L-1049G-03-158		PP-VDF	Varig	17.1.58	ZS-FAA, VP-WAW, TR-LNY	Afro-Continental	Clubhouse, Harare Zimbabwe Scr. 1990
4686	L-1049G-82-106		VT-DJW	Air-India	26.7.58	BG583	No.6 Sqn Indian AF	Poss. stored for Indian AF Museum
687	L-1049G-82-106		VT-DJX	Air-India	12.8.58	BG579	No.6 Sqn Indian AF	Last noted stored Pune, India
4801	L-1049H-82-133		VH-EAM	Qantas	13.10.58	N7776C, LV-PJU, LV-JHF, CP-797	Leasing Consultants	Scr. Columbus, OH 1972
4802	L-1049H-82-147		N1006C	Air World Leases	5.12.56	—	Berliner Flug Ring (lease)	Scr. Sebring FL 1975
4803	L-1049H-82-133		VH-EAN	Qantas	15.11.56	N7777C	Alaska Airlines	Bar, Kotzebue, AK. Scr. 1980
4804	L-1049H-82-148		N6911C	Flying Tiger Line	1.2.57	—	Flying Tiger	w/o 15.3.62
4805	L-1049H-82-147		N1007C	Air World Leases	10.1.57	CP-998	Aeromar (Dominica)	Scr. Opa Locka 1988
4806	L-1049H-82-147		N1008C	Seaboard & Western	28.1.57	—	Capitol	Scr. Sebring FL 1975

C/N	Ordered as	Built as	1st Reg.	For	Del Date	Other Reg	Last user	Fate
4807	L-1049H-82-147		N1009C	Seaboard & Western	13.2.57	YV-C-LBP, CP-797, LV-JJO	AER	Scr. Miami FL 1973
4808	L-1049H-82-147		N1010C	Seaboard & Western	18.2.57	CS-TLD, YV-C-LBI, LV-JIO	AER	Scr. Miami FL 1972
4809	L-1049H-82-148		N6912C	Flying Tiger Line	25.3.57	C-FBDB	Downair	Scr. Stephenville Canada 1979
4810	L-1049H-82-148		N6913C	Flying Tiger Line	4.3.57	—	Flying Tiger	w/o 14.12.62
4811	L-1049H-82-148		N6914C	Flying Tiger Line	8.3.57	—	Quicktrans	w/o 15.12.65
4812	L-1049H-82-148		N6915C	Flying Tiger Line	15.3.57	—	Flying Tiger	w/o 4.3.60
4813	L-1049H-82-149		N6931C	California Eastern	18.4.57	—	Sky Truck Int	Scr. Guadeloupe 1979. Nose to Musée de L'Air
4814	L-1049H-03-156		N6916C	Flying Tiger Line	4.4.57	—	Flying Tiger	Scr. Kingman AZ 1974
4815	L-1049H-03-156		N6917C	Flying Tiger Line	9.4.57	HP-526	ANDES	w/o 15.12.73
4816	L-1049H-03-156		N6918C	Flying Tiger Line	15.4.57	HL4006	Nusantara	Scr. Anchorage AK 1972
4817	L-1049H-03-143		N6921C	United States Overseas A/L	27.5.57	—	Flying Tiger	Missing 15.3.62
4818	L-1049H-82-148		N101R	Resort Airlines	1.5.57	CX-BEM, N7023C	Sky Lines International	Scr. Miami 1974
4819	L-1049H-03-150		N6919C	Flying Tiger Line	20.5.57	HL4002	North Slope Supply Co.	Fire trainer Anchorage, Burnt by 1978
4820	L-1049H-82-148		N1880	Dollar Lines	16.5.57	CF-WWH	F.A. Conner	Fire trainer Miami FL last noted 1994
4821	L-1049H-03-154		N1927H	Air Finance Corp	17.7.57	CF-AEN	Joint Church Aid	Scr. St. Hubert Canada 1974
4822	L-1049H-03-150		N6920C	Flying Tiger Line	11.5.57	—	Flying Tiger Line	w/o 9.9.58
4823	L-1049H-03-148		N6932C	California Eastern	7.6.47	HI-254	Balair	Scr. Miami FL 1979
4824	L-1049H-03-148		N102R	Resort Airlines	10.6.57	—	TWA	w/o 24.11.59
4825	L-1049H-03-143		N6922C	US Overseas A/L	24.6.57	CF-BFN, EC-ARN, HI-524CT	AMSA	Stored Borinquen Puerto Rico
4826	L-1049H-03-148		N6933C	California Eastern	9.7.57	—	Slick	Scr. Miami FL 1975
4827	L-1049H-03-148		N5409V	Flying Tiger Line	20.2.58	—	Flying Tiger	w/o 23.9.62
4828	L-1049H-03-152		N7131C	National Airlines	11.9.57	CF-NAJ	CanRelief Air	w/o 3.8.69
4829	L-1049H-03-152		N7132C	National Airlines	16.9.57	CF-NAK	CanRelief Air	w/o 17.12.69
4830	L-1049H-03-148	L-1049H-03-152	N5400V	Slick Airways	17.9.57	N6937C	Aircraft Specialties	Airworthy, Airline Historical Foundation, Kansas City Apt
4831	L-1049H-03-152		N7133C	National Airlines	28.10.57	CF-NAL	CanRelief Air	Derelict Sao Tomé
4832	L-1049H-03-152		N7134C	National Airlines	28.10.57	CF-NAM	CanRelief Air	Derelict Sao Tomé
4833	L-1049H-03-159		PP-YSA	REAL Aerovias Brasil	17.2.58	N563E	Balair	Scr. Miami FL 1976
4834	L-1049H-03-159		PP-YSB	REAL Aerovias Brasil	17.2.58	N564E	Balair	w/o 20.10.71
4835	L-1049H-03-157		AP-AJY	Pakistan International A/L	11.2.58	T-1042 or T-1041	Indonesian AF	Scr. 1970s
4836	L-1049H-03-157		AP-AJZ	Pakistan International A/L	1.3.58	T-1042 or T-1041	Indonesian AF	Scr. 1970s
4837	L-1049H-03-159		PP-YSC	REAL Aerovias Brasil	20.2.58	N565E	Carolina Aircraft Corp	Scr. Ft. Lauderdale FL 1973
4838	L-1049H-03-159		PP-YSD	REAL Aerovias Brasil	18.3.58	N566E	Holy Nation of Islam Inc	w/o 24.9.74
4839	L-1049H-06-166		N5401V	TWA	23.4.58	—	Capitol International	Scr. Miami FL 1974
4840	L-1049H-06-166		PH-LKL	KLM	14.4.58	N45516	Aircraft Specialties	w/o 11.5.75
4841	L-1049H-06-162		PH-LKM	KLM	22.4.58	—	KLM	w/o 14.8.58
4842	L-1049H-06-166		N5402V	TWA	3.5.58	—	Capitol International	Scr. Sebring FL 1975
4843	L-1049H-06-162		PH-LKN	KLM	5.5.58	N45515	North Slope Supply Co	Displayed Kingman AZ. Scr. 1977
4844	L-1049H-06-166		N5403V	TWA	29.5.58	—	Capitol International	Scr. Sebring FL 1975
4845	L-1049H-06-166		N5404V	TWA	24.7.58	—	Capitol International	Scr. Sebring FL 1975
4846	L-1049H-06-167		N6635C	California Eastern	24.7.58	LV-FTU, N486C	F & B Livestock	Chicken Coop, Blue Creek Belize
4847	L-1049H-06-167		N6636C	California Eastern	21.7.58	LV-FTV	Aerolessors Inc	Maintenance trainer Sebring FL. Scr. after 1968

C/N	ORDERED AS	BUILT AS	1ST REG.	FOR	DEL DATE	OTHER REG	LAST USER	FATE
4848	L-1049H-06-160	L-1049H-06-167	N5407V	Slick Airways	30.9.59	N6935C	Slick	Scr. Oakland CA 1969
4849	L-1049H-06-160	L-1049H-06-160	N5408V	TWA	5.8.59	N6936C	Airlift International	w/o 22.6.67
4850	L-1049H-03-168	L-1049H-06-170	CF-TEY	Trans Canada A/Ls	21.1.59	N74CA	Air Traders Int	w/o 22.6.80
4851	L-1049H-03-168	L-1049H-06-170	CF-TEZ	Trans Canada A/Ls	13.12.58	N9740Z	Quicktrans	w/o 3.2.56
4852	L-1049H-03-168		N6924C	Flying Tiger Line	1.10.58	—	unknown	w/o 15.10.78
4853	L-1049H-03-168		N6925C	Flying Tiger Line	29.9.58	B-1809	China Airlines	Scr. Taipei 1972
5500	WV-2		143226	VW-1	2.12.57	56-6956	USAF AFSC-ASD	Scr. DM AFB
5501	WV-2		143227	VW-1	5.12.57	—	VW-1	Scr. Litchfield Park
5502	WV-2		143228	VW-1	9.5.57	—	VW-1	Scr. Litchfield Park
5503	WV-2		143229	NADC, Johnsville	13.12.57	—	VW-3	Scr. Litchfield Park
5504	WV-2		143230	VW-1	24.1.58	—	VW-1	Scr. Litchfield Park
5505	WV-2		145924	VW-3	13.3.58	—	VXN-8	Scr. DM AFB
5506	WV-2		145925	VW-3	28.1.58	—	VXN-8	Scr. DM AFB
5507	WV-2		145926	VW-1	30.1.58	—	Pacific Missile Range	Scr. Point Mugu CA
5508	WV-2		145927	VW-3	20.2.58	—	VQ-1	w/o 16.3.70
5509	WV-2		145928	VW-3	25.2.58	—	VW-1	w/o 25.8.70
5510	WV-2		145929	VW-3	13.3.58	—	VW-4	Scr. DM AFB
5511	WV-2		145930	VW-1	13.3.58	—	VW-1	Scr. DM AFB
5512	WV-2		145931	VW-3	3.3.58	—	VW-1	Scr. DM AFB
5513	WV-2		145932	VW-3	27.3.58	—	VQ-1	Scr. DM AFB
5514	WV-2		145933	VW-3	16.4.58	—	VW-1	Scr. DM AFB
5515	WV-2		145934	VW-1	6.5.58	—	VW-1	Scr. DM AFB
5516	WV-2		145935	VW-1	12.5.58	—	VQ-1	Scr. DM AFB
5517	WV-2		145936	VW-2	16.5.57	—	VQ-1	Scr. Agana, Guam
5518	WV-2		145937	VW-2	27.5.57	N670NA	NASA	Scr. DM AFB
5519	WV-2		145938	VW-2	19.6.58	—	VQ-1	Scr. DM AFB
5520	WV-2		145939	VW-2	27.7.58	—	VAQ-33	Scr. DM AFB
5521	WV-2		145940	VW-2	8.8.58	—	VQ-1	Scr. DM AFB
5522	WV-2		145941	VW-2	10.8.58	—	VW-11	Scr. DM AFB

STARLINERS

C/N	ORDERED AS	BUILT AS	1ST REG.	FOR	DEL DATE	OTHER REG	LAST USER	FATE
1001	L-1649A-98-01		N1649	Lockheed	10.10.56	N60968, N1102	Restaurant, Japan.	Prob scr. 1990s
1002	L-1649A-98-15		N7301C	TWA	4.9.57	—	Aerocondor	w/o 18.12.66
1003	L-1649A-98-09		N3702C	TWA	11.5.57	—	Flying Ambassadors	Scr. Ft. Lauderdale FL 1968
1004	L-1649A-98-15		N3703C	TWA	26.5.57	—	TWA	Scr. Kansas City MO after 1962
1005	L-1649A-98-15		N7304C	TWA	12.6.57	—	Bush Aviation	Scr. Ft. Lauderdale FL 1968
1006	L-1649A-98-09		N7305C	TWA	10.5.57	LV-PXM, LV-GLH	Trans Atlantica Argentina	Scr. (damaged) Rio de Janeiro Brazil after 1961
1007	L-1649A-98-09		N7306C	TWA	4.5.57	—	TWA	Cocktail lounge Kansas City. Scr. 1970s
1008	L-1649A-98-09		N7307C	TWA	7.5.57	LV-PXL, LV-GLI, N7307C	Trans Atlantica Argentina	Dest FAA safety test 1964
1009	L-1649A-98-22		N7308C	TWA	18.5.57	LV-PHW, LV-HCU	TWA	Scr. Arizona 1966
1010	L-1649A-98-22		N7309C	TWA	28.5.57	—	TWA	Scr. Arizona 1966
1011	L-1649A-98-11		F-BHBK	Air France	30.6.57	TU-TBB	Air France	Fire trainer Paris-Orly. Burnt 1980s
1012	L-1649A-98-22		N7310C	TWA	28.5.57	—	TWA	Scr. Seattle WA 1966
1013	L-1649A-98-20		N7311C	TWA	31.5.57	—	Trans American Leasing	L/n derelict but complete, Isluga Chile

C/N	ORDERED AS	BUILT AS	1ST REG.	FOR	DEL DATE	OTHER REG	LAST USER	FATE
1014	L-1649A-98-20		N7312C	TWA	14.6.57	—	TWA	Scr. Arizona 1966
1015	L-1649A-98-20		N7313C	TWA	30.5.57	—	TWA	w/o 26.6.59
1016	L-1649A-98-20		N7314C	TWA	22.6.57	—	Fly By Night Safaris	Scr. (damaged) Las Vegas NV 1969
1017	L-1649A-98-20		N7315C	TWA	27.6.57	—	TWA	Fire trainer Anchorage AK. Burned 1980s
1018	L-1649A-98-20		N7316C	TWA	26.6.57	—	Burns Aviation?	Maine Coast Airways. Stored Auburn ME
1019	L-1649A-98-20		N7317C	TWA	30.6.57	—	Willair International	Scr. Honolulu HI 1973
1020	L-1649A-98-11		F-BHBL	Air France	5.7.57	—	Air France	Scr. Paris-Orly France 1967
1021	L-1649A-98-20		N7318C	TWA	10.7.57	—	Bush Aviation	Scr. Ft. Lauderdale FL 1968
1022	L-1649A-98-20		N7319C	TWA	24.7.57	—	TWA	Scr. Kansas City MO 1968
1023	L-1649A-98-20		N7320C	TWA	26.7.57	LV-PHV, LV-HCD	Trans Atlantica Argentina	Scr. Ft. Lauderdale 1970
1024	L-1649A-98-20		N7321C	TWA	31.7.57	—	World Samplers	Scr. Houston-Travel Hobby after 1974
1025	L-1649A-98-20		N7322C	TWA	29.7.57	—	Trans American Leasing	Scr. Miami FL 1973
1026	L-1649A-98-16		N8081H	TWA	5.6.58	—	Willair International	Scr. Stockton CA (damaged) 1969
1027	L-1649A-98-11		F-BHBM	Air France	23.7.57	—	Air France	w/o 10.5.61
1028	L-1649A-98-11		F-BHBN	Air France	8.8.57	—	Air France	Scr. Paris-Orly France 1967
1029	L-1649A-98-20		N7323C	TWA	15.8.57	—	Bush Aviation	Scr. Ft. Lauderdale FL 1970
1030	L-1649A-98-20		N7324C	TWA	22.8.57	—	Trans American Leasing	Scr. Paramaribo Surinam 1988
1031	L-1649A-98-11		F-BHBO	Air France	22.8.57	TU-TBA	Air France	Scr. Paris-Orly France 1967
1032	L-1649A-98-11		F-BHBP	Air France	24.8.57	—	Air France	Scr. Paris-Orly France 1967
1033	L-1649A-98-11		F-BHBQ	Air France	29.8.57	—	Air France	Scr. Paris-Orly France 1967
1034	L-1649A-98-17		D-ALUB	Lufthansa	25.9.57	N45511	Lufthansa	Cafe, Hartenholm Germany. Burnt 1975
1035	L-1649A-98-20		N7325C	TWA	15.9.57	—	TWA	Scr. Arizona NV 1966
1036	L-1649A-98-11		F-BHBR	Air France	24.9.57	LX-LGY, N4796, TF-ERA, HP-501	Nittler Air Transport	Scr. Douala Cameroon 1980
1037	L-1649A-98-16		N8082H	TWA	29.3.58	HL4003	Air Korea	Scr. Korea 1970s
1038	L-1649A-98-16		N8083H	TWA	16.4.58	N8083H	Canary Leasing	Maine Coast Airways. Stored Auburn, ME
1039	L-1649A-98-16		N8084H	TWA	25.3.58	—	TWA	Scr. Kansas City MO 1968
1040	L 1649A-98-17		D-ALAN	Lufthansa	20.12.57	N45512, N179AV, N974R	Aeroborne Enterprises	Maine Coast Airways Restoration Sanford FL
1041	L-1649A-98-17		D-ALER	Lufthansa	9.1.58	N45517, ZS-DTM, LX-LGZ, ZS-FAB	Trek	Scr. Johannesburg SA 1970
1042	L-1649A-98-17		D-ALOL	Lufthansa	17.1.58	N45520, ZS-DVJ, LX-LGX	Trek	SAAF Museum Johannesburg SA Ex boardroom
1044	L-1649A-98-17		D-ALER	Air France	8.2.58		Air France	Scr. Paris-Orly France 1967
1045	L-1649A-98-11		F-BHBT	Air France	16.2.58		Air France	Scr. Paris-Orly France 1967

4 In Service

THE CHOICE OF THE STARS

The Constellation opened up new air routes and made air travel possible for tens of thousands (if not millions) for whom it had been just a dream. From the outset, with help from Howard Hughes, the Connie was associated with film stars and celebrities, and this encouraged business people and aspirational tourists to follow. Connies made incidental appearances in many films — Marilyn Monroe travels in a TWA Super Connie in 'How to Marry a Millionaire' (1953) for example even if the exterior shots actually show an unconvincing model!

TWA's large fleet and Lockheed's wide choice of interiors allowed aircraft to be configured to cater for different routes. For example: by 1951, the airline offered an 18-berth sleeper 'Ambassador' and a 49-seat first class service to London and Paris, while 32-berth sleepers and a 60-seat 'Sky Tourist' class were available on flights to Rome and Lisbon. This latter service was the first time that low-cost air travel was available on the Atlantic.

TWA advertising emphasised the comforts of its cabins, including sleeper berths wider than those on the railways: 'The most restful way to hurry', 'The most comfortable way to get there fast' were typical advertising slogans of the mid-1950s.

Eastern Air Lines adopted a different approach in the early 1960s by operating low-cost 'turn up and go' services under the Eastern Shuttle banner. More akin to a Greyhound bus service, the Shuttle offered one-way fares from as low as $12 from New York to Boston, with services every two hours. Unlike today's 'no frills' services, these were not high-density aircraft, but 32-seat L-1049s (as well as some DC-7s).

Approximately 80 airlines had fleets of five or more Constellations, and there were at least as many owners, operators or just brokers who had smaller numbers. Space precludes listing them all, but descriptions of the operations of a couple are included.

Air France was one of the biggest non-US Constellation operators, taking delivery of 52 Constellations and 10 Starliners between 1947 and 1957. The Connies were put to hard use on the transatlantic routes and to France's various colonies in north and West Africa and the Far East. In fact, there were few regions of the world not visited, especially after the Super Constellation entered service in 1953. Mexico and South America, Rome and Moscow were all linked to Paris-Orly by Air France Connies at one time.

ABOVE: Thai Airways were one of many airlines the world over to operate a small number of Constellations, often as their first international equipment. Several airlines found the Connie a step too far and passed them on to other carriers after a short career. The original Thai Airways (as opposed to today's Thai International) went out of business after less than a year of operations with its two L-1049Gs. *Author's Collection*

BELOW: Another Asian user was Air Ceylon which operated two leased KLM Connies in its own colours and used other KLM aircraft from time to time on its services to London, Singapore and Bangkok. The first aircraft, L-749A PH-LDP *Mahadevi* is seen at Amsterdam at the time it entered service in February 1956. *John Stroud Collection/The Aviation Picture Library*

LEFT: BOAC's L-049s served the airline for nearly a decade after 1946. G-AHEN was an exception, suffering damage at Bristol Filton and being sold as an insurance write-off. After being rebuilt, an eventful career followed including service in Israel and Hawaii before a return to the UK register with Britannia in 1963 and eventual scrapping in 1965. Sadly, no ex-BOAC Connie survives today — excluding one or two leased briefly. *Flight/Aviation Picture Library*

From November 1959, jets began to replace Air France's Connies — first the Sud-Est Caravelle, and later the Boeing 707, but the airline converted a number to freighters and operated them on transatlantic and cross-Channel routes and to Morocco until September 1967, ending 20 years of service.

Qantas Empire Airways Ltd, the national airline of Australia, was a natural Constellation customer. Prior to the arrival of L-749s in 1947, the airline had operated Lancastrians and Liberators (both converted bomber designs) and Empire Class flying boats. The Connies opened up the 'Kangaroo route' to London. The Sydney–Darwin–Calcutta–Karachi–Cairo–Rome–London service was the longest at that time without a change of aircraft (although it still took three days).

In 1951, L-1049C Super Constellations arrived and opened up the Pacific route to the USA (as well as cutting a day off the

kangaroo route). In December 1957 Qantas offered the first true round-the-world services, in both directions (Australia–Pacific–USA–London–Middle East–Asia–Australia and reverse), with its new 'Super G' L-1049G Constellations.

As with many airlines, Boeing 707s began to enter service at the end of the 1950s and the Connies were mainly relegated to regional routes or converted to freighters. Racehorses were a speciality and many a Melbourne Cup winner arrived from New Zealand aboard a Qantas L-1049H. In all, Qantas operated 23 Constellations of five models between 1947 and 1963, losing one in a non-fatal crash at Mauritius.

ABOVE AND BELOW: South African Airways' four L-749As served through the 1950s on 'Springbok' services to Europe and some internal routes. The fleet was later sold to ACE Freighters of the UK, ZS-DBR (above) becoming G-AYST and -DBU (below in later colour scheme) becoming, G-ASYU, both eventually being scrapped in 1967-69. *Stephen Piercey Collection/The Aviation Picture Library*

From the outset, the Constellation proved popular in South America. For the first time, cities like Rio de Janeiro, Caracas and Lima could be linked to major cities in the USA, and directly to Europe. The first foreign aircraft to land at London-Heathrow Airport was a Constellation of Panair do Brasil. Panair, Aerovias Guest Mexico, and Linea Aeropostal

ABOVE: The first Constellation also became the first Super Connie and appeared as such in this smart colour scheme in October 1950. Known unofficially as 'Old 1961' and even less so as 'the Beast of Burbank' due to its many Frankenstein's monster-like patches and non-standard additions, this veteran later tested many new engines, propellers and radars. Eventually, this famous aircraft was sold for spares and broken up at Burbank. *Michael Stroud Collection*

Venezolana were among the first Connie operators anywhere, later followed by many others in the region, such as Cubana, CAUSA (Compania Aeronautica Uruguya SA) and COPISA (Compania Peruana Internacional de Avicion SA). These airlines operated a mix of new Super Constellations and second-hand earlier models. Cubana's Connies did not long survive the 1959 Communist revolution and subsequent US trade embargo. COPISA and CAUSA ceased trading themselves at the end of the 1960s.

In North and South America, the national airlines moved up to 707s, DC-8s and Lockheed Electras in the early 1960s, passing their Connies on to the often struggling private operators. When, in turn they acquired new equipment (or went bust), the Connies that were not scrapped went to smaller companies offering charters and local passenger or freight services.

Lockheed Aircraft Services had begun converting Connies and Super Connies to freighters and mixed passenger/cargo configuration at its Ontario, California, base in 1960. Many freighters had already been built as C-121s and R7Vs for the military. Other companies and airlines (notably Air France)

ABOVE: The second production Super Constellation makes a maximum climb take-off during testing. Together with its predecessor, N6202C was retained for development work by the manufacturer. Delivered to Eastern Air Lines, she saw her final service with the Happy Hours Travel Club and was written off after a forced landing short of Fort Lauderdale airport in 1973.
John Stroud Collection/The Aviation Picture Library

ABOVE: Unlike TWA who put all its faith in the Constellation for many years, Pan Am also bought Boeing Stratocruisers, and later, DC-7s. By early 1957, the Connies were gone. PAA adoped a white-topped colour scheme in 1951. *John Stroud Collection/The Aviation Picture Library*

LEFT: Eastern Air Lines was the first customer for the L-1049 Super Constellation, introducing them in December 1951 on domestic services. In 1961 the Super Connies inaugurated the low-fare 'turn-up-and-go' Air Shuttle service. *Author's Collection*

made their own conversions. A strengthened metal floor with tie-downs was invariably fitted, as was a rear freight door. Those operated by Eastern, Lufthansa, Air France and others also had a forward door. Payloads were in the order of 30,000lb (13,600kg), although some Flying Tiger Line aircraft were further strengthened to lift up to 45,000lb (20,414kg).

Many of the last Constellations in service on freight runs between Miami and the Caribbean (notably the Dominican Republic) were not actually freighters, but passenger aircraft with seats removed or replaced as needed. Most of the cargo carried was in the nature of packet freight and live animals (such as chickens) before the Connies were effectively grounded by FAA prohibition on their use in US airspace in 1993.

HERE COMES THE COMET — BIRTH OF THE SUPER CONNIE

By Christmas 1949, the writing for the piston-engined airliner appeared to be on the wall. Kelly Johnson recalled getting a Paul Revere-themed Christmas card from a friend: 'The British were coming — with the Comet!' 'The question was, how soon?', he later recalled in a paper given to the Society of Automotive Engineers. Lockheed's response was not to develop its own jet airliner (something it would not do until the late 1960s with the L-1011 TriStar), but to further refine the Constellation to carry more passengers at lower cost. This would help stimulate the expected demand in air travel that was being suppressed by high fares.

ABOVE: Transocean was an American charter operator with four L-749As in service by 1958. They also ran two L-1049Hs at different times. In summer 1958 they flew a number of charter services between the Caribbean and London, but much of their work was on contract services to the US forces.
Flight/The Aviation Picture Library

BELOW: CF-TGB was the second in an eventual fleet of 14 Super Constellations for Trans-Canada Air Lines (TCA). Services from Vancouver were mainly to Canada's eastern cities, extending to Europe (via Winnipeg) in 1960.
John Stroud Collection/The Aviation Picture Library

ABOVE: TWA's first L-1049 N6901C is seen over the Grand Canyon in a well-known publicity photo. TWA's early Super Connies lacked the nose radar and the wingtip tanks of the later 'Super Gs'. Sadly, this aircraft's sister ship (N6902C) was to crash into the Grand Canyon after a collision with a United Airlines DC-7 in 1956. *Author's Collection*

The original Constellation fuselage had become 'volume limited' — in other words, the useable space was filled well before the useable weight. The new turbo-compound engines promised even more power at a cost per seat mile competitive with the new jetliners. However, before they were available, Lockheed chose to get the maximum out of the normal R-3350 engines by undertaking one of the first 'stretches' of an airliner design. The Model 849, a same-length version of the L-749 with more powerful engines (the CA-1 version of the R-3350) and the 949, a 12ft (3.66m) stretched freighter, were abandoned and the L-1049 'Super Constellation' was born. The L-1049 was longer by an impressive 18ft 4.75in (5.64m), brought about by the addition of barrel sections forward and aft of the wing. Apart from the extra length, the civil Super Connie could be identified by the square, as opposed to round cabin windows. Engines were the 2,700hp R-3350-956C18CA-1. A technical description of the different Constellation variants is in Chapter 2.

Many of the features of the Super Constellation were tested on 'Old 1961' as the prototype C-69/L-049 was known around

Burbank. Given the new construction number 1961S (for 'Stretched'), the prototype Super Connie first flew on 13 October 1950. The first two production aircraft, part of an initial Eastern order for 14, were retained by Lockheed for the development programme and the initial milestone of CAA certification was achieved in only ten weeks, being granted on 29 November 1951. Six airlines, Eastern, TWA, Seaboard and Western, KLM, Air France and Pakistan Airlines, had ordered 62 L-1049s before the prototype had flown. The value of these orders, just over $96 million was the largest in Lockheed's history to that time.

ABOVE: TWA's L-749A *Star of Delaware* had a long but uneventful career (1950-1967) with the airline. Sold to the World Citizens International travel club and then to freight operators CIM, it was eventually impounded and abandoned at Lomé, Togo in the late 1970s. *John Stroud Collection/The Aviation Picture Library*

LEFT AND BELOW: Noted designer Henry Drefuss and his organisation designed the interior of TWA's Super Connies with wood-panelled bulkheads to avoid the 'Midtown Tunnel' effect of the long fuselage. Other airlines such as KLM (left) adopted similar styling. The murals in the lounge area were widely featured in TWA publicity. *Author's Collection*

Delivery of civil Super Constellations suffered due to the Korean War, Lockheed having to divert resources to C-121/R7V-1 production for the Navy and Air Force, as well as to other programmes such as the F-80 and F-94 fighters and the P2V Neptune patrol plane. On the other hand, the war brought much needed money to Lockheed and re-opened a somewhat moribund order book. Military development of the Super Constellation also saved Lockheed much R&D money, most notably by sponsoring and testing the turbo-compound engine.

ABOVE: Delta Air Lines is one of the most successful US airlines today, but is not widely known as a Constellation operator. In fact Delta had Connies only between 1953 and 1958, six L-649As inherited after taking over Chicago and Southern and four L-049s (as seen here) acquired from Pan Am in 1956. *Aeroplane*

BELOW: L-1049 N6906C *Star of the Rhine* roars off the ground, the gear coming up smartly. Its full designation was an L-1049-54-80 which meant it was built with the CB-1 version of the R-3350 engine as a 75-seater. TWA mainly used this model in an all First Class 67-seat, eight berth layout for domestic services. *John Stroud Collection/The Aviation Picture Library*

ABOVE: Seen taxying in to New York's Idlewild Airport (today's John F. Kennedy International) is one of Cubana's three L-1049Gs. The Cuban airline replaced its three earlier Connies with 'Super Gs' in 1956, but the 1959 revolution led to a US embargo and they were grounded for lack of parts. *Stephen Piercey Collection/The Aviation Picture Library*

BELOW: Back in the days when most airports were not trying their hardest to prevent anyone laying eyes on an aircraft, New Yorkers would make a Sunday afternoon trip to Idlewild to enjoy their wonderful viewing gallery. TWA L-749s in old and new schemes can be seen here as can an Eastern 649 or 749. *John Stroud Collection/The Aviation Picture Library*

ABOVE: The first L-1049H was delivered to Qantas as VH-EAM *Southern Spray*. This version was designed for easy conversion between passenger and freight configuration, and could also carry a mixed load of cargo and people. Qantas later converted two other Super Connies to L-1049H standard.
John Stroud Collection/The Aviation Picture Library

LEFT: VH-EAG *Southern Constellation* was Qantas's first Super Connie and made its inaugural Sydney–San Francisco service on 15 May 1954.
John Stroud Collection/The Aviation Picture Library

BELOW: Varig of Brazil ordered three L-1049Es in 1953 but later delayed its order until the newer L-1049G was available. Three more Gs (including PP-VDE) and four L-1049Hs followed. *Stephen Piercey Collection/The Aviation Picture Library*

KLM was one of the airlines to experience unwanted and costly delays, and despite having been the first to order Super Connies in late 1950 its first L-1049Cs did not arrive until August 1953. In the spirit of the Atomic Age, the 13 Super Connies were named (in Dutch) after aspects of nuclear physics: *Atoom, Electron, Proton, Neutron, Photon, Meson, Dueteron, Nucleon, Triton, Isotoop, Positon, Negaton* and *Ion*, the last four being 1049Es delivered in 1954.

Faced with the threat from the new jet airliners, both the De Havilland Comet and the Avro Canada Jetliner having flown in July and August 1949 respectively, Lockheed also explored turboprop power to close the gap with jet speeds. Four turbo Super Connies were built, all for the military – two R7V-2s for the Navy and two YC-121Fs for the USAF. The latter were distinguished by their wingtip fuel tanks but were otherwise the same with T-34-P-6 turboprops, a powerplant also tested on the YC-97J Stratofreighter and the YC-124B Globemaster. Despite the performance improvements (an R7V-2 was dived to 479mph (771km/h) and another carried 166,400lb (75,480kg)), and Eastern Air Lines' interest in re-engining 30 of its L-1049As and Cs, there were no further turbo Constellations. Proposals by British engine maker Napier to offer an Eland turboprop version never reached the hardware stage (although Napier had claimed that Panair do Brasil were on the brink of ordering 11).

STARLINER

The ultimate development of the Constellation series was the L-1649. It was larger, faster and longer-ranged than all previous models. A contemporary TWA brochure described it, somewhat breathlessly, thus: 'TWA's latest, greatest airliner, (it) introduces a new era of air travel . . . superb luxury, incomparable elegance and dependability. For this is the largest and most luxurious airliner ever built in America!'

ABOVE: Seaboard & Western changed its name to Seaboard World in 1961 and leased most of its fleet to other airlines (including Eastern, Sabena and BOAC) at one time or another, which helps explain the minimal colour scheme, seen on L-1049H N1006C at New York, probably in that year.
Stephen Piercey Collection/The Aviation Picture Library

For Lockheed it was also the only unprofitable version of the Constellation family. The decision to proceed with the L-1649 in 1955 was taken at a time when jets were only a few years away, and the airlines had some trouble marketing the Starliner, as it was called to distinguish it from its predecessors. TWA took to calling their L-1649s 'Jetstreams', and even registered this as a serial mark, hoping that this would attract some of the cachet of the new jet transports. The Starliner was launched with a 24-aircraft order from TWA (later joined by five others). Air France took 10, and Lufthansa four, and together with one retained by Lockheed made a grand total of 44. An order for four by Linee Aeree Italiane was cancelled when this airline was taken over by Alitalia in 1957.

The Starliner emerged as a version of the proposed L-1549, with that design's new wing but without its fuselage stretch or Pratt & Whitney PT-2 turbo props. P&W had withdrawn these engines in 1955 arguing that Lockheed's proposed maximum weight of 190,000lb (86,180kg) was too great and would overstrain them. Having built the tooling, Lockheed went ahead with the 'compromise' L-1649 design using the EA-2 version of the Wright turbo-compound engine rated at 3,400hp. The prototype first flew from Burbank on 11 October 1956, and the type entered service with TWA on 1 June 1957 on the New York–London–Frankfurt route.

The Starliners were certainly magnificent aircraft. TWA made much of their luxurious (four-abreast) seating, sophisticated air conditioning that would change the air every two-and-a-half minutes, in-flight galley and spacious 'Starlight Lounge' in which passengers were invited to 'linger over a highball'. Radar, aerodynamics and mechanical refinements sped and smoothed the journey and included the 'electronically synchrophased' propellers that eliminated the annoying harmonic throb of the engines for a more restful flight.

The range of the Starliner was greater than any contemporary airliner at 5,650 miles (9,090km) with a 10,000lb (4,536kg) payload. The endurance was even more impressive. In October 1957, TWA introduced a non-stop over-the-Pole service between London and San Francisco, a flight that lasted over 23 hours! Even with today's fuel-efficient turbofans, there are no scheduled services approaching that flight time today.

Starliner production finished in June 1958, but Super Constellations for the military kept rolling off the line until November. Air France scrapped all its Starliners in the late 1960s, and TWA scrapped a few but the majority, including Lufthansa's, went on to second and third-tier operators in the way of most Constellations. Trek Airways of South Africa operated three on profitable charter services to Luxembourg, one of which was also operated by South African Airways (SAA) in 1965 on services to Perth, Australia. This aircraft survives today with the SAA Museum at Johannesburg.

THE END OF THE LINE

On 6 April 1967, an era ended when L-749A N6020C Star of Kentucky flew the final passenger service for TWA from New York (JFK) to St. Louis via Philadelphia, Pittsburgh, Columbus, and Louisville. Among those aboard were four long-term TWA employees who had been on the record-breaking Burbank-Washington flight of 17 April 1944, including Captain Orville Olson, who had been co-pilot on that day. With the retirement of the last 'Super G', TWA became the first major airline to have an all-jet passenger fleet. The last freight Starliner was retired on 11 May.

Eastern's last Super Connie passenger flight (with N6232G) took place on 14 February 1968. Pan American's had gone long before, in 1957, replaced by DC-7s.

The last scheduled US passenger flight by a member of the Connie family was flown by an Alaska Airlines Starliner in September 1968. The L-1649s had technically been withdrawn

ABOVE: Western were a Los Angeles-based passenger and cargo airline with routes to several towns in Alaska. They acquired Speedpak freight panniers along with their L-749As and flew the last (unscheduled) US Connie passenger services in November 1968.
John Stroud Collection/The Aviation Picture Library

LEFT: At one time Capital Airlines of Washington DC — not to be confused with Capitol or Capitol International — was one of the most successful US domestic airlines. N86531 was one of 12 L-049s they operated during the 1950s.
Author's Collection

ABOVE: After the false start with the L-749s in 1947-48, Aerlinte Eireann tried again in 1958 with the lease of Super Constellations from Seaboard and Western. The inaugural flight (on L-1049H N1009C) left Dublin for New York amid much fanfare on 28 April 1958. *John Stroud Collection/The Aviation Picture Library*

BELOW: Another view of N1009C at Dublin. Although remaining on the US register, the Aerlinte (later Aer Lingus) Super Connies wore full colours and names: N1009C was ***St Patrick/Padraig***. The aircraft were all returned by the end of 1960 as the first Boeing jetliners arrived.
John Stroud Collection/The Aviation Picture Library

on 14 May 1967 when Alaska Airlines' N7316C flew a service between Anchorage and Kotzebue, Alaska, but one of the grand old ladies was kept on as a backup to the new Boeing 727s for another 16 months.

After retirement from Alaska, this aircraft passed on through a couple of users as a bulk oil carrier, changed hands again, made a visit to Paris in 1976 and returned to the US where it became embroiled in a legal argument over airport fees. Although her future looked bleak at one time, N7136C, one-time TWA's *Star of the Tigris* lives on as one of the three Starliners in the care of Maurice Roundy of Auburn, Maine, and perhaps may one day fly again.

ABOVE: Air France's F-BGNC was an L-1049C, later converted to L-1049G standard. Although lacking the tip tanks or radar of production Gs, the owners felt it warranted the 'Super G' markings. Sold to CATAIR in 1968, it crashed in Cameroon the following year. *Stephen Piercey Collection/The Aviation Picture Library*

TOP: Although one might be forgiven for thinking that CATAIR (Compagnie d'Affrètements et de Transport Aériennes) was a subsidiary of Air France, it was in fact a separate company that made minimal colour-scheme changes to the ex-Air France aircraft it bought, six L-1049Gs in total. F-BRAD (formerly F-BGNJ) survives today with a preservation group at Nantes. *Stephen Piercey Collection/The Aviation Picture Library*

TOP: COPISA (Compania Peruana Internacional de Aviacion S.A.) of Lima operated a number of Connies, all L-749As, in its short existence. Usually these were flown in a mixed passenger/freight layout with Miami being a common destination. COPISA ceased trading circa 1970.
Stephen Piercey Collection/The Aviation Picture Library

ABOVE: Koreanair, predecessor of today's Korean Air Lines was a tiny affair in the late 1950s with some DC-3s, a DC-4 and a single ex-KLM and BOAC L-749A, seen here. This aircraft was sold on to a Dutch company in 1962. In 1966-7 the company leased two L-1049Hs from Flying Tiger Line.
Stephen Piercey Collection/The Aviation Picture Library

ABOVE: ACE (Aviation Charter Enterprises) Freighters was a pioneer in the all-freight market operating mainly from Southend, England from 1965. Four L-749As were operated including G-ALAL. This was a former BOAC aircraft which before that briefly belonged to Aerlinte Eireann. *Aeroplane*

BELOW: Seen elsewhere in this volume, G-ASYS was originally sold to South African Airways as ZS-DBR in 1950. It is seen here in reduced circumstances at Coventry-Baginton airport where it remained from 1964 to 1967. ACE added G-ASYS to its collection of L-749As but never flew her before they ceased trading after less than two years of operations in September 1966.
Austin J. Brown/The Aviation Picture Library

ABOVE: The L-1649 Starliner promised much, but in the end was the only Constellation version not to make a profit for Lockheed. Air France operated ten Starliners, making it the second-largest user after TWA with F-BHBK, delivered in July 1957 being the first, although it was damaged the day after delivery when an engine exploded. *Author's collection*

BELOW: From many angles, the Starliner looked little different from a late model Super Constellation. Like TWA with its 'Jetstreams' and Air France with its 'Super Starliners', Lufthansa adopted a new marketing identity for its four L-1649s, as 'Super Stars'. D-ALUB was the first delivered, in 1957 and ended its days as a café near Hamburg, burnt out in 1975. *Lufthansa/TheAviation Picture Library*

ABOVE: Linee Aeree Italiane (LAI) ordered four Starliners in 1955 for the Rome–New York direct route, but merged with Alitalia in 1957 and the order was cancelled. This artist's impression is slightly stylised, but serves to emphasise the new wing of the L-1649 and the different spacing of the engines.
John Stroud Collection/The Aviation Picture Library

BELOW: A beautiful night scene of an Air France 'Super Starliner' being turned around for another flight to Chicago, Moscow, Mauritius or even to Tokyo via Anchorage. F-BHBL *Rochambeau* served all of its brief career with Air France. After four years' storage and no buyers, she was broken up at Orly.
Flight/The Aviation Picture Library

ABOVE, RIGHT AND BELOW: About a dozen Constellations were converted to aerial sprayer configuration in the early 1970s for companies such as Aircraft Specialties of Arizona and Christler Flying Service of Wyoming. Three of the latter company's aircraft were sold to Beaver Air Spray who operated them under the Conifair name at St. Jean and a forward base at Rivière du Loup, Quebec. Tanks of over 3,000 gallons were fitted to spray liquid or dry pesticides against budworm and other pests. One was lost, but the other two survive today at Avra Valley, Arizona including C-GXKO, right, now N749TW 'The MATS Connie' and C-GXKR stored for a Dutch group.
Stephen Piercey/The Aviation Picture Library

ABOVE: This most unusual and attractive-looking Super Connie is a veteran of Transocean Airlines and Capitol International Airways and of the Biafran airlift when it carried aid (rather than arms, unlike some of its bretheren) to the beleagured airstrip at Uli under the Joint Church Aid and Canairelief banners. On its return it was stored at various airfields in Canada including Dorval, Montreal where it received Hellenic Air titles, although the identity of this company is unclear. It was eventually scrapped in 1974.
Stephen Piercey Collection/The Aviation Picture Library

BELOW: Pacific Air Transport were one of many small operators who sought work here and there with one or two aircraft in the 1960s and 1970s. This aircraft was slightly special in that it is thought to be the last L-049 to fly, this was in Florida as late as 1981, although this picture dates from the West Coast a decade earlier.
Austin J. Brown/The Aviation Picture Library

ABOVE: The last scheduled Constellation passenger flights were flown by Quisqueyana of the Dominican Republic in 1978. *Stephen Piercey Collection/The Aviation Picture Library*

RIGHT: The sad fate of many a Constellation was to gradually rot away at Miami's 'corrosion corner' or at other Florida airfields such as Opa Locka or Fort Lauderdale. *Austin J. Brown/The Aviation Picture Library*

BELOW: Former KLM and Flying Tiger Line L-1049H Super Connie N45515 wound up as a billboard at Mohave County Airport, Kingman, Arizona. It was later scrapped. *Author's Collection*

BELOW RIGHT: This L-1049G owned by California Airmotive was entered in an 'Unlimited' air race at Brown Field, near San Diego in July 1971. Protests from the warbird fighter fraternity led to its withdrawal after one qualifying session. *Author's Collection*

ABOVE AND BELOW: AeroChago's HI-422, one-time TWA's *Star of West Virginia* roars into life and gets airborne from San Juan, Puerto Rico in 1987. This L-749A had a colourful career after leaving TWA in 1968 including drug running, impounding, repossession and at least ten further owners, the last being Dominican freight operator AeroChago S.A. who acquired her in 1983. In 1988, this veteran reportedly made a heavy landing at Santo Domingo and was withdrawn from service. later to be broken up for spare parts.
Austin J. Brown/The Aviation Picture Library

5 CUSTOMERS

'LUXURY COMES LATER'

The Constellation's great fame was due to its impact on airline services in the post-war world, but before it carried a single paying passenger it was the USAAF that introduced it to service and proved its reliability in operations. Shortly after the first 10 TWA aircraft that were to be built had been re-assigned to the USAAF in September 1942, the Army made its own order for 150 more as C-69As and Bs. Before long, a total of 313 had been ordered — 11 C-69s, 30 C-69As and 210 C-69Bs, alongside the nine TWA aircraft and the prototype. The A model was to be a high-density troop transport and the B a long-range version with the fuel tankage of the Pan Am intercontinental aircraft, but in fact neither of these variants or three heavier C-69D transports were ever built.

In the rush to build up the armed forces' mobility before D-Day, the Army had ordered large numbers of the Douglas DC-4 (as the C-54 Skymaster and a different design to the DC-4E) which was, like the Constellation, hijacked from production destined for the airlines. The C-54 was a less advanced and less capable design, but flew nearly a year before the C-69, completed its test programme with few troubles and was suited to both intercontinental and front-line troop and cargo duties. By the end of the war nearly 840 were in service with the USAAF alone, and another 180 served with the US Navy.

The Army simply didn't need as many C-69s as it had thought, but needed more P-38s and B-17s, types that made better use of Lockheed's shop floors. Almost all the C-69 orders were cancelled in favour of more production of combat aircraft and only 15 C-69s were ever completed as such. The USAAF used most of their C-69s for testing, destroyed one in the static rig at Wright Field, lost one in a non-fatal crash at Topeka, Kansas, only flew to Europe when the war there was over (the first transatlantic Connie flight), and disposed of them all quickly after hostilities ended.

BELOW: NC86505 was configured as a 47-seater for international routes when delivered to TWA in November 1945. Its career was brief, however for it crashed 13 months later on approach to Shannon Airport in Ireland, partly because of a faulty altimeter. Note that international-service TWA Connies wore 'Trans World' titles for several years before the airline changed its name from Transcontinental and Western Air. *John Stroud Collection/The Aviation Picture Library*

ABOVE: L-749A VT-DAR *Maratha Princess* joined the three L-749s already serving with Air-India in January 1950. Traded in when Air-India bought Super Connies in 1950, it was later converted to a freighter using parts from one of the two Navy R7V-2 turbo Connies. Used for some dubious purposes in South America, it was eventually impounded and scrapped in Uruguay. *Author's collection*

The later, much more successful military history of the Constellation is covered in Chapter 6.

One event stood out in the C-69's service however, although it was hardly of a military nature. On 17 April 1943, while the first Constellation was still grounded pending the arrival of modified engines, Howard Hughes somehow circumvented officialdom and flew the second aircraft (c/n 1962/ 43-10310) with a group of VIP passengers, including actress Ava Gardener (then his current girlfriend), to Washington DC. Alongside him in the co-pilot's seat was Jack Frye. Ostensibly, this was a delivery flight to hand the aircraft to General 'Hap' Arnold, but it happened to be wearing TWA's colours, broke the coast-to-coast record and took in a display tour of politicians and civil aviation officials in Washington before the Army got anywhere near it. There were grumblings that Hughes was using a government contract to promote his airline and himself at a time when the war situation was difficult. The record, however was impressive — six hours 58 minutes from Burbank to DC — and it was to be followed by many more for the Constellation, if not for Hughes himself.

It seems remarkable that Hughes was allowed to fly the Constellation at all after an incident that had happened not long before. Trying out the pilot's seat for the first time on a test flight with Milo Burcham and Kelly Johnson, Hughes lowered the flaps at high speed. This put the Connie into a deep stall from which they only just recovered, and at one point the airspeed read '0' with the nose pointing vertically downwards. To top this, he let the aircraft drift further and further to the left in successive practice landings until he nearly hit the Burbank tower and Burcham had to wrest control from his hands. On the record-breaking flight Hughes shut down two engines and was about to cut off a third to show his confidence in the design when TWA vice-president Jack Nichols brought him to his senses.

Although Lockheed and TWA were disappointed that their new design had become an army troopship and was not making money in service ('luxury comes later' said Lockheed's house journal), the war had definite benefits. The Army had taken over much of the flight-testing from Lockheed and the many problems the testing showed up were fixed at government expense. Likewise, Wright had to make the R-3350 safe for the top-priority B-29, and Lockheed was a beneficiary of this work as well.

With the end of the war and the cancellation of the bulk of C-69 orders, Lockheed kept the production line open, bought back as many aircraft from the military as it could and began to

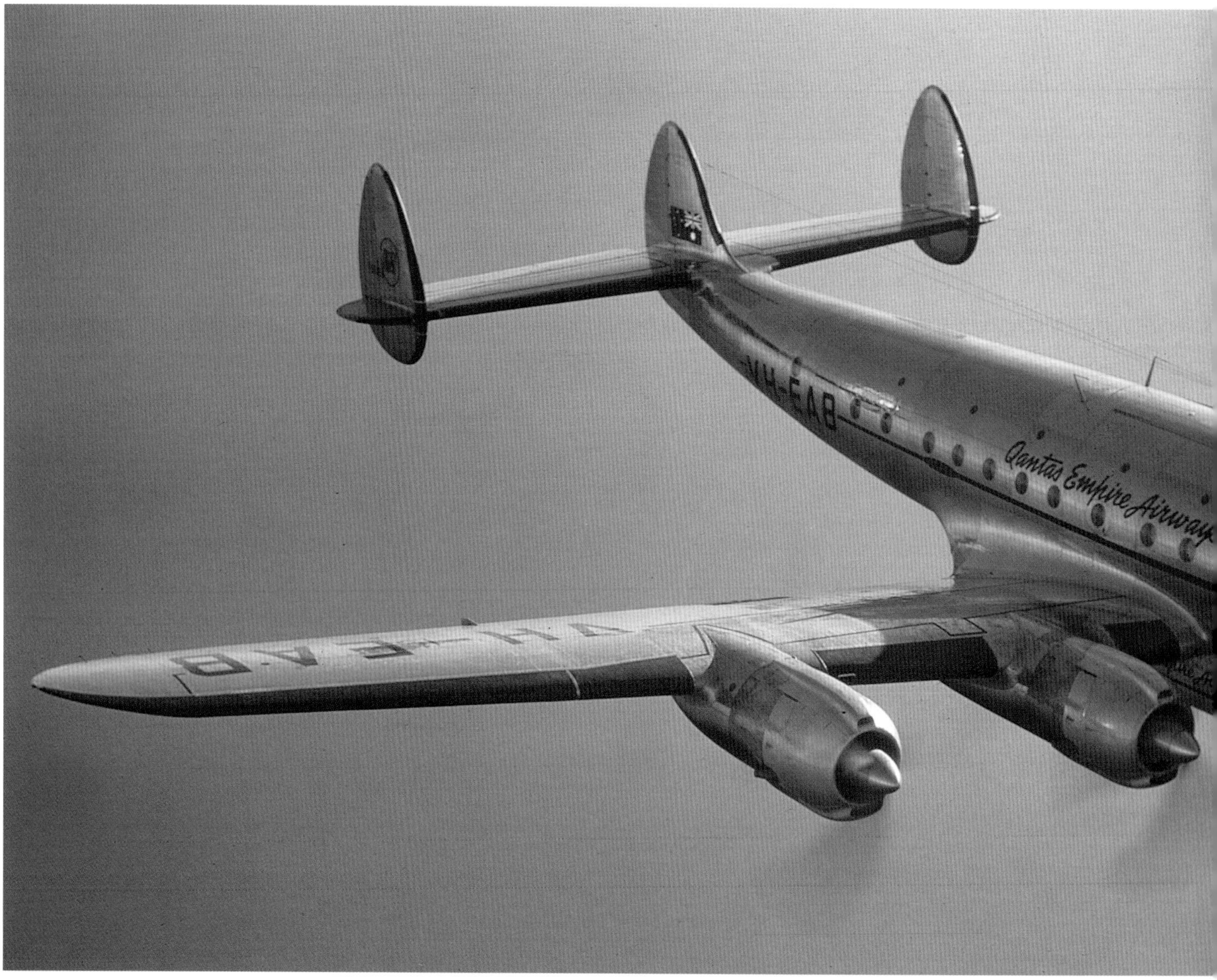
VH-EAB
Qantas Empire Airways
VH-EAB

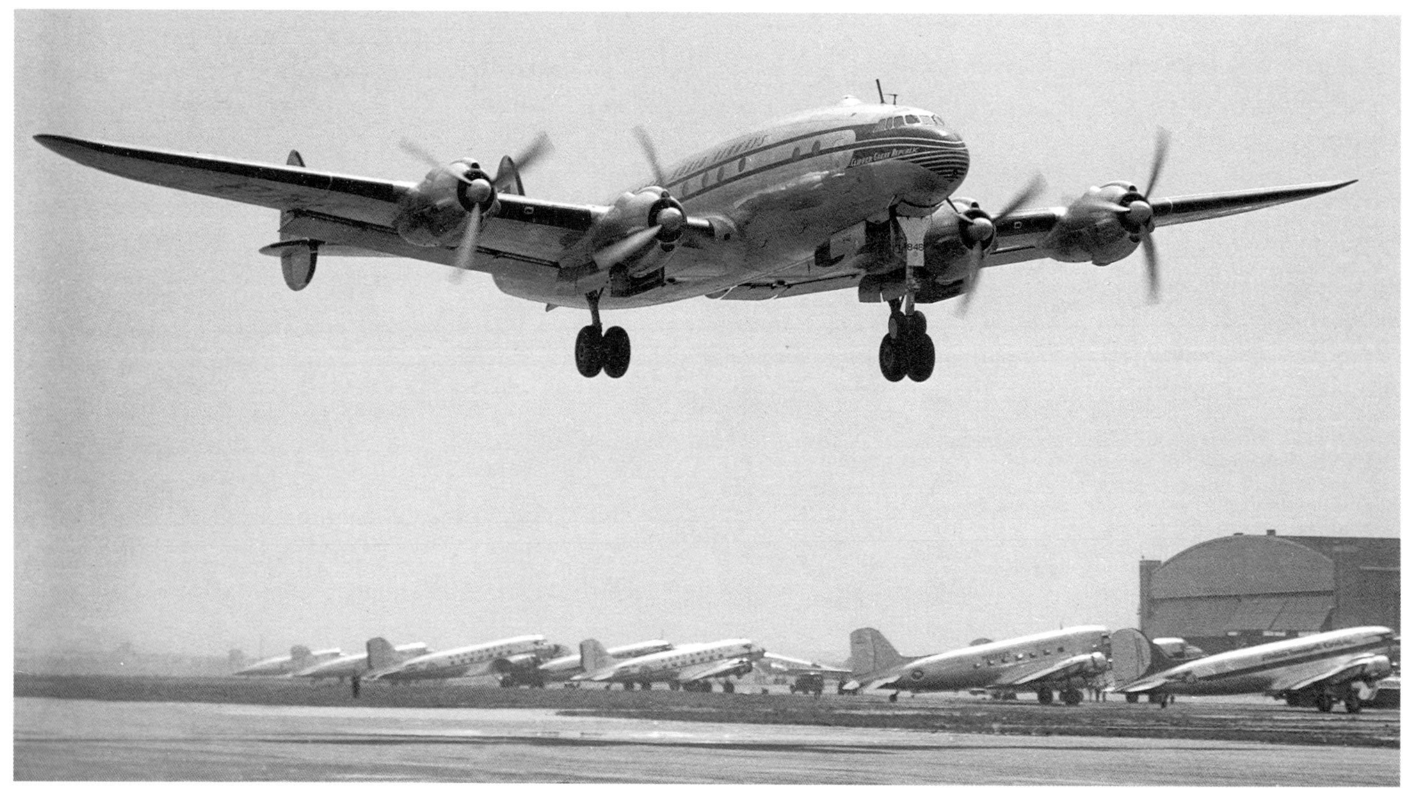

ABOVE: Qantas started its long association with the Constellation in 1947 when the first of an eventual 23 aircraft of six models arrived. Two of these, the L-749 seen here and an L-1049E delivered in 1955 were registered VH-EAB, Qantas traditionally re-uses the VH-EA- block of registrations with the flagship aircraft in their fleet. *Author's Collection*

LEFT: The crash-landing of a Pan Am L-049 in Connecticut led to the grounding of all Constellations for several months. NC88846 *Clipper Bermuda* was renamed *Clipper Great Republic* during the hiatus and is seen here making the first flight after the grounding was lifted. In 1951 it crashed near Sanoyea, Liberia with the loss of all on board. *John Stroud Collection/The Aviation Picture Library*

refurbish them to civil standards. The first C-69 equipped to airline standards was certificated by the Civil Aeronautics Administration (CAA) with Approved Type Certificate (ATC) A-763 on 14 October 1945. Among the changes deemed necessary for civil operations by the CAA and Lockheed were more windows, a galley, crew rest bunks, engine fire detectors and extinguishers, and better air conditioning and heating systems. A major visible difference was the replacement of the large and vulnerable nose landing light and its hemispherical cover with a twin unit on the nosewheel leg. The 'eyebrow' windows over the cockpit also disappeared.

Of course, the major change from troop transport to civil airliner was the installation of a luxury passenger interior. The enforced delay in delivery of the Constellation to the airlines was used by Lockheed and TWA to refine the interior, but not without some false starts. Howard Hughes had rejected Lockheed's proposed interior for TWA and called in top designer Raymond Loewy. Hughes showed Loewy a picture of an earlier TWA interior and told him 'do it like this'. Loewy went for an open cabin and colours designed to reassure the traveller most used to long distance train journeys and as yet unsure of air travel. Later Henry Dreyfuss, another noted designer, was to design the interiors for export Super Constellations.

TWA's first L-049 was delivered to Kansas City on 15 November 1945 wearing 'Trans World Airlines' titles, although the airline did not officially change its name from Transcontinental and Western Air until May 1950.

It fell to Pan Am to make the first revenue flight in the L-049, on 3 February 1946, with a flight from New York to Bermuda. TWA was only three days behind with a New York–Paris service. It seems odd that over water flights began before trans-continental services, but these were inaugurated in grand style on 15 February with a flight from Los Angeles to New York. The star-studded passenger list included Cary Grant, Gene Tierney (yet another of Hughes myriad celebrity girlfriends') and Veronica Lake. This was the first non-stop commercial flight across the USA and touched down in New York after eight hours and 30 minutes. However, ten days earlier, a proving flight had broken the trans-continental speed record with a Burbank–New York flight lasting six hours and seventeen minutes.

EARLY ROUTES

Despite this leap forward in performance, the arrival of the L-049 did not immediately signal an explosion of air travel. Development of US post-war air travel was hindered by wartime restrictions that reserved most seats for government and military passengers and which took some time to be relaxed. The much-touted 'non-stop' transcontinental service was only true in one direction. East-west services still required an intermediate stop at Chicago due to prevailing headwinds, a situation that continued well into the Super Constellation era.

Pan Am's first Constellation was delivered on 5 January 1946 and on the international front, the carrier was quickly introducing new services. The first commercial international service was from New York to Lisbon on 20 January.

The first to the United Kingdom arrived at Hurn Airport, Bournemouth, on 3 February. London-Heathrow Airport was still under construction at this time and direct services to the British capital did not begin until 1 June that year.

While TWA's agreement with Lockheed prevented Pan Am competing on inter-continental services, nothing stopped TWA flying to Europe, initially with a New York to Paris service via Gander and Shannon that began on 5 February 1946. Despite this new international focus, TWA did not change its name to Trans World Airlines until 1950.

ABOVE AND BELOW: The first foreign aircraft to land at London's new Heathrow Airport was an L-049 of Pan Am subsidiary Panair do Brasil which arrived on a proving flight on 16 April 1946, having flown from Rio de Janeiro via Recife and Dakar. PP-PCF served with Panair until it was damaged in 1962. The airline itself ceased trading in 1965. *John Stroud Collection/The Aviation Picture Library*

Despite the extensive testing and many modifications, the early Constellations were not really ready for airline service and many teething troubles were experienced in early operations. For one thing, the air conditioning and heating system was not particularly satisfactory, leading to extremes of temperature at different parts of the cabin. Lockheed had reduced demands on the engines by using a system that re-circulated much of the air, an arrangement that worked fine in the test rig, but less so in service. The extraction of cigarette smoke and defrosting of windows were two areas of difficulty that took time to set right.

The first accident to befall an airline Connie occurred on 18 June 1946 and involved Pan Am's *Clipper Empress of the Skies* on the first leg of a trans-atlantic flight from New York. The starboard outer engine caught fire and could not be extinguished. To the horror of the passengers, who are said to have included two well-known film stars, the engine mount burned through and the power unit fell off. This proved to be a blessing in disguise, as the plummeting engine took the fire with it. The aircraft was still in a bad way, however, and diverted to the small airfield at Willimantic, Connecticut, where a successful belly landing was made beside the runway with no injuries to passengers or crew and little airframe damage. While awaiting assistance, a steward reportedly served tea picnic-style on the grass to the shaken passengers. Replacement propellers

were brought in and a patch was fitted over the hole where engine No.4 had once been, a few other minor repairs were made and the Connie was ferried back to Lockheed on (literally) three engines.

Lockheed was thus able to assuage some of the public's concern by publicising the strength and excess power of the Constellation (others were to joke that, in the early years, the Constellation was 'the world's best tri-motor'). The cause of the fire was said to be the failure of one of the drives for the pressurisation system. Lacking lubrication, a bearing failed, the shaft oscillated and fractured a hydraulic pipe causing the fluid to be ignited by the hot engine.

As a result of this incident, cabin pressurisation and air conditioning was disabled for a number of weeks while blower shaft modification kits were delivered and installed. This restricted flights to no more than 10,000ft (3,050m), adding extra time to the trans-atlantic journey and reducing the payload.

Before Constellation operations returned to normality, however, another accident was to lead to the grounding of all

ABOVE: Qantas made its first proving flight to Heathrow in November 1947 with L-749 VH-EAA *Ross Smith* (named for an Australian aviation pioneer). Passed to BOAC in 1955 as G-ANUP, and later to Caledonian Airways, it was wrecked in a crash landing in Ethiopia in 1964. *Flight/The Aviation Picture Library*

L-049s. A TWA Connie, *Star of Lisbon*, was on a training flight near Reading, Pennsylvania when electrical arcing in the baggage compartment caused a fire that spread to the cabin insulation and filled the cabin and cockpit with smoke. The crew were blinded and choked and flew the aircraft into powerlines and trees while trying to land. Only one of the six crew survived the crash. The accident happened on 11 July, and all aircraft were grounded until 23 August. The Type Certificate remained revoked until 14 October. The result of the following investigation was a change in procedures for clearing smoke from the cabin and a modification to cable runs where they entered the fuselage from the wing.

Deliveries to foreign airlines had begun apace with acceptance of the first aircraft (converted C-69s) by the British Overseas Airways Corporation (BOAC) in May 1946. Technically, the

ABOVE: XA-GOQ (c/n 2503) began its working life as Pan Am's first L-749 *Clipper America* in June 1947. Within a year it was sold to Aerovias Guest of Mexico who operated it for only four months before going bust (although they reformed as Guest Aerovias in 1954). A long period of service with Air France and the French Air Force test centre followed. Finally retired as an engine testbed in 1974, 2503 is preserved at the Musée de L'Air. *Michael Stroud Collection*

first non-US operator had been Panair Do Brasil, a subsidiary of Pan Am that was operating a London service as early as 27 April. One of its aircraft, PP-PCF, had already made the first landing by a non-British airline at the new London–Heathrow Airport on 16 April as part of a proving flight.

The interior layouts of Connies varied between customer airlines and often within their fleets, with different configurations for domestic and international routes. Interior configuration for a BOAC L-049 was a 42-seat passenger cabin with seats in pairs astride a central aisle. Each of the outboard seats had a circular window. The crew consisted of a pilot, first officer, navigation officer, two engineers and a radio officer. On initial services, the cabin crew was all male, consisting of three stewards. Between the cockpit and the cabin was a crew rest area with four seats and windows, and a windowless galley. There was a desk for the head steward at the rear of the cabin as well as a wardrobe for coats and two toilet compartments.

BOAC's first Constellation service took place on 1 July 1946 with a London–Shannon–Gander–New York flight. This was scheduled to be thrice-weekly although it was suspended on 11 July following the accident to the Pan Am aircraft. BOAC began a service to Montreal on 15 April 1947, and services to Montreal and to Sydney on 1 December 1948 via Rome, Cairo, Karachi, Calcutta, Singapore and Darwin. They were flown with second-hand L-749s which supplemented the five original aircraft.

BOAC's purchase of Constellations and, soon afterwards, Boeing Stratocruisers, was controversial at a time when Britain was trying to rebuild its own civil aircraft industry and conserve precious foreign exchange, of which dollars, especially, were scarce. In 1946, however, the converted Lancaster and Halifax bombers available were not up to servicing the trans-atlantic or Empire routes with any meaningful load, and the American products were the only realistic choice in 1946 while Britain got back on its feet and looked towards the Comet.

KLM of the Netherlands was one of the next operators, having ordered the type as early as 1939. Deliveries began in May 1946 and by November the L-049s were in service on routes from Amsterdam to New York and to Batavia in the Dutch East Indies.

Other early users included Air France, whose first L-049 arrived in June 1946 but did not enter service until January 1947; Qantas, who inaugurated the 'Kangaroo Route' to London in December 1947; Aerlinte Eireann of Ireland, whose three L-749s were delivered in formation in September 1947, but which were sold to BOAC the following year amid some controversy; and American Overseas Airlines (AOA).

American Overseas Airlines which only existed for five years before being bought by Pan Am, ordered L-049s in September 1945 and began services to London from New York on 23 June 1946. The following year, services to London from Boston and Washington were introduced, as was a service to Frankfurt via Prestwick.

The C-69/Model 49, of which 88 were built, was seen as an introductory type pending delivery of a pure commercial model known as the Model 749 or 'Gold Seal' Constellation. Prior to that, Lockheed introduced the L-649, an interim model based around Wright's development of a commercial version of the Duplex Cyclone engine designated the R-3350 BD-1.

Eastern Air Lines was the launch customer, changing its September 1945 order for 14 L-O49s for the new model. As it happened, Eastern was the only customer to obtain 649s from the production line. All other orders for this variant were converted to L-749s on the production line including those for Air France and TWA. Six of the higher-weight L-649As were delivered to Chicago and Southern Airlines in 1950 and these became part of the Delta fleet when the airlines merged in 1953.

The first L-749 was delivered to Air France in April 1947. This model had additional fuel tanks in the outer wings and new 'jet stack' exhausts gave some extra thrust at the expense of increased cabin noise. (More details of the differences between Constellation models are given in Chapter 2).

The first 749As were actually built as C-121A transports for the USAF, helping Lockheed out of an orders slump and beginning the Connie's real military career, described in detail in Chapter 6. As with the L-649A, the 749A was an increased gross weight version. Fifty-nine were built for the civil market, of which TWA took 26.

An out-of-sequence designation was the L-149, which was not built as such but signified L-049s that were converted with the outer wing fuel tanks of the L-749 by Lockheed Air Service at Burbank.

As early as 1947 Lockheed was proposing that surplus or new L-149 and L-749s could be converted to deluxe executive transports or photo-survey aircraft for oil exploration. Used 149s and 749s were costed at $720,000 and $820,000 respectively without engines ($160,000 more in each case). An annual operating cost including fuel, flight crew, technical

TOP: Four of the crew of an Air-India Constellation. The captain and the radio operator sat to the left, while the first officer and flight engineer are on the right. Overwater flights required a navigator as well, seated in the next compartment behind the [illegible] cockpit. *John Stroud Collection/The Aviation Picture Library*

ABOVE: Passengers board VT-CQP, Air-India's *Malabar Princess* which made the inaugural Bombay–London Constellation service, leaving on 9 June 1948 and arriving on the 15th. The first services went via Cairo and Geneva, but the later fast service, stopped only at Cairo. This aircraft was lost with 48 fatalities on 3 November 1950 when it flew into Mont Blanc. *John Stroud Collection/The Aviation Picture Library*

personnel and maintenance of $1.25 million for a 149 and $1.153 million for a 749 was estimated. In the late 1940s the market for executive aircraft was small, but there was no shortage of potential airframes suitable for conversion including some of Lockheed's own products such as Harpoon and Ventura bombers. It is not surprising that Lockheed's plans were shelved and it was to be another two decades before 'private' Connies appeared, and then only in small numbers.

It may be of interest here to list some of the cost that were current in the immediate post-war years for US Connie operators, as calculated by Lockheed after the first 10,000 hours of operations. Aviation gasoline was 40 cents/US gal and oil was 80 cents, with approximate rates of consumption of 390gals and 8.3gals/hour respectively. Pre-first flight publicity had promised fuel consumption of less than one gallon per mile. Spares and labour were $47 and $91/hour. An experienced pilot could expect to earn $15,600/annum with expenses, while his navigator and radio operators might make $9,000 each. Insurance was usually $8 for each $1,000 of coverage with public liability and property damage cover adding another 13 cents for every 100 miles (161km) flown.

ABOVE: The airline of the nascent Israeli state, EL AL ordered three L-049s in 1950. The aircraft were second hand and among the first Connies built — 4X-AKA, seen here with temporary US registration N90827 after upgrade to L-149 standard, was the fifth off the line. Sister ship 4X-AKC was shot down by Bulgarian anti-aircraft fire in 1955 after straying off course.
John Stroud Collection/The Aviation Picture Library

BELOW: *Clipper Flora Temple* was Pan Am's second L-049 and was delivered in February 1946. The Pan Am colours of the day masked the perspex landing light cover that stood out against the metal finish of many other early Constellations. This aircraft was passed to Pan Am subsidiary Panair do Brasil in 1951 and crashed into a hillside near Asuncion, Paraguay in June 1955. *Author's Collection*

ABOVE: A number of Pan Am's first Connies were passed directly to the airline's South American subsidiary Panair do Brasil. L-049 PP-PCG, delivered in May 1946, seen here at Rio's Santos Dumont airport, had a brief career, crashing with heavy loss of life in July 1950 after colliding with power lines at Porto Allegre, Brazil. *John Stroud Collection/The Aviation Picture Library*

BELOW: Qantas Empire Airways' VH-EAA *Ross Smith* with Speedpak attached comes over the fence somewhere in California rather than the Australian Outback. The large flap area of the Constellation contributed to its good short-field capability. *John Stroud Collection/The Aviation Picture Library*

In April 1944 when the Constellation made its first record-breaking flight to Washington, it was said that the design had the following performance margins over its nearest competitor: 25 percent greater power, 24 percent higher speed, 24 percent range advantage, 14 percent payload advantage and 23 percent better cost/seat mile per hour. By 1948, however, there were new competitors and these margins had been considerably eroded. Other innovative features such as pressurisation, Fowler flaps, hydraulically boosted controls and a flight engineer's position, although not necessarily Lockheed inventions, had also been adopted by Boeing for its Model 377 Stratocruiser, Douglas for its DC-6 and on the British Bristol Brabazon.

In 1939, as war loomed, Lockheed had been last in the race in a generation of new airliners behind the Boeing 307 and the Douglas DC-4. With the Constellation, the company had taken the wise decision to make a leap forward rather than a timid step and was able to exploit this quickly when the war was over. Now, with the competition delivering airliners that directly challenged the Constellation, another leap was needed, and this would come in the form of the L-1049 Super Constellation.

ABOVE AND BELOW: Aerlinte Eireann ordered five L-749s for transatlantic services in 1946. The first three aircraft, EI-ACR, -ACS and –ADA were delivered in formation to Shannon on 16 September 1947. While plans for services to the US were being made, and the first Dublin–New York proving flight was flown by EI-ADA in October 1947, the Aerlinte Connies were operated on routes to London and Rome. Unfortunately, a change of government led to a review of the whole project, and its eventual cancellation. The aircraft were all sold to BOAC in May 1948. *John Stroud Collection/The Aviation Picture Library*

ABOVE: KLM ordered Constellations as early as 1941, but cancelled them in war time. Re-ordered in 1943, four L-049s were delivered in May 1946. PH-TAV seen here with a fine selection of KLM Douglas and Convair types, ended its days as a restaurant in Santiago in the 1970s. *John Stroud Collection/The Aviation Picture Library*

BELOW: Paris Charles de Gaulle Airport in the early 1950s. F-BAZL was ordered as an L-649, completed as an L-749 and then later converted to an L-749A. In 1966 it became a VIP transport with the government of Senegal and was scrapped in France in 1979. *John Stroud Collection/The Aviation Picture Library*

6 MILITARY CONNIES

The Constellation's use as a military aircraft was almost as extensive as its civil career. There was an enormous number of military versions, many of them one-offs, and to catalogue them all and their uses is really outside the scope of this work. This chapter summarises the most important military roles of the Connie and describes the main variants.

The US military was a major user of the Constellation, ordering 330 new examples between 1948 and 1957 in addition to the C-69s commandeered from the airlines during the war. A small number of Connies served with the air forces and governments of India, France, Indonesia, Ethiopia and Senegal.

The many variants are described separately, but a note on US military designations may be in order. The basic Air Force model designation for L-749s and above was C-121, to which various prefixes (such as 'R' for reconnaissance and 'E' for electronic) and suffixes (marking successive variants) were added. The Navy system was more complicated. The original USN variant was the R7O-1 where 'R' was used to signify cargo, 'O' was the letter designator for the manufacturer (Lockheed-Burbank), and '7' indicated that the Connie was the seventh cargo aircraft type from this builder to enter service. The '-1' indicated the first service model. Before delivery, Lockheed's designator changed to 'V' (as in the PV-2 Harpoon, built by Lockheed-Vega), resulting in the R7V-1. The other major naval usage of the Connie was for special patrol ('P'), which worked fine as the PO-2W ('W' standing for electronic), but not as the PV-2 (taken), so this model became the WV-2, again before delivery. This nonsense ended with the introduction of the tri-designation system by Defense Secretary McNamara in October 1962. Navy Connies joined their USAF brethren in becoming C-121s, with the aforementioned PO-2W/ WV-2 being re-christened the EC-121K, to cite one example.

BELOW: The USAAF's Air Transport Command (ATC) used C-69s for repatriating troops from Europe and the Pacific among other tasks. This example (c/n 1966) is thought to have ditched in the Mediterranean with some parts being salvaged and used by Air France. *John Stroud Collection/The Aviation Picture Library*

ABOVE: General Dwight Eisenhower used this VC-121A (L-749) *Columbine* (named for the state flower of his wife's home state of Colorado) between 1950 and 1952. It was assigned to SHAPE and based at Paris-Orly, but is seen here at a wet Soesterberg AB, Holland in September 1951. *Flight/The Aviation Picture Library*

SERVING THE AIR FORCE AND NAVY

The first major use of the C-121/R7V-1 was by the US Military Air Transport Service (MATS) which was formed in June 1948 in an early example of 'joint' (inter-service) operations by combining the USAF's Air Transport Command and the Naval Air Transport Service. As soon as the first C-121As joined MATS they were pressed into urgent service supporting the Berlin Airlift. Although they did not fly into Berlin themselves, the seven aircraft initially available flew nearly six million miles in their first month taking cargo and passengers from the US to Frankfurt for onward transit to Berlin by C 54s and other types of aircraft. This reduced the strain on the smaller aircraft and allowed more to be allotted to flying the air corridor into the beleaguered city.

Constellations of the MATS became frequent visitors to Europe from then on, increasingly in VIP passenger form as larger transport aircraft such as the Douglas C-73 Globemaster became available to take on the bulk freight mission.

The Constellation became the main personal transport of high-ranking US politicians and military men throughout the 1950s, notably General (and President) Dwight Eisenhower and General Douglas MacArthur. The unit responsible for the VC-121 VIP transports of various kinds was the 1254th Air Transport Squadron (later Group, then Wing) based mainly at Washington National Airport. In his role as Supreme Commander, Allied Forces Pacific (SCAP), General MacArthur used a VC-121A named *Bataan* from 1950 to 1951, during the early days of the Korean War. This was the first Connie to have APS-10 weather radar installed.

As Supreme Commander, Headquarters, Allied Powers, Europe (SHAPE), General Eisenhower used a VC-121A named *Columbine* (after the state flower of Colorado, his wife's home state). As President-elect and President, Eisenhower used a VC-121A and a VC-121E (*Columbine* II and III). Replaced as presidential aircraft by a VC-137 (Boeing 707) shortly after the term 'Air Force One' came in to use, the VC-121s served on through the 1960s transporting lesser VIPs as part of the 89th Military Airlift Wing at Andrews AFB, Maryland.

EARLY WARNING CONNIES

The Kamikaze attacks faced by the US Pacific fleet in World War 2 showed the need for carrier-based airborne early warning (AEW). An offshoot of this was the development of land-based AEW for detection of attacks on shore bases and anchorages. Initially this mission was fulfiled by modified B-17G (PB-1W) bombers carrying a ventral APS-20 radar.

In 1949 two L-749s were constructed with large ventral and dorsal radomes to explore the use of the Constellation as an early-warning platform. In the upper position APS-45 height-finding radar was installed, and underneath a smaller radome contained APS-20 search radar. These two airframes, which were designated PO-1Ws, were used for research and tactics development and were successfully used in a series of NATO exercises beginning in 1951. By this time the Navy had seen the worth of the AEW Connie and begun to order them in large numbers. Production aircraft were based on the Super Constellation airframe and had a larger ventral radome, space for 28 crew (including 12 relief crew bunk spaces), increased fuel tankage under the wing centre section and, most noticeably, wingtip fuel tanks containing 600 US gals (2,271l) of fuel. This model was officially designated the WV-2 Warning Star, but was commonly called the 'Willie Victor', even when it became the EC-121K after 1962. Another nickname

was 'Careless Connie' in reference to the bulbous ventral radome. October 1954 saw Early Warning Squadron One (VW-1) trade in its PB-1Ws for WV-2s, becoming the first Warning Star squadron. The USN purchased WV-2s in large numbers not only to support fleet activities, but also to equip the so-called barrier squadrons. These were established to extend radar coverage as far from the coasts of the US as possible at a time when America was fearful of another Pearl Harbor surprise attack, this time launched by the Soviet Union. The Atlantic Barrier was commissioned July 1955 and activated a year later, while the Pacific Barrier was slightly later in formation.

The idea of the barriers was to maintain a 24-hour watch of the approaches to the US at a distance that would detect and prevent a sneak attack. To this end, two WV-2s from Barrier Force Atlantic (BARFORLANT) and two from the Barrier Squadron Pacific (BARONPAC) would be constantly airborne on patrols off each coast.

As well as the Willie Victors of early warning squadrons VW-11, VW-13 and VW-15 at NS (Naval Station) Argentia, Newfoundland, and at NAS (Naval Air Station) Patuxent River, Virginia, the barrier included a Destroyer Escort Squadron providing a screen of radar picket ships. In the Pacific, the task was performed by VW-12 and -14 and Destroyer Escort Squadron Seven and the barrier was in place in July 1958. The ships maintained station along a 1,500 mile (2,414km) line between Kodiak at the base of the Alaskan 'panhandle' and Midway Island. The Connies patrolled the length of this line from their bases on Midway, Kodiak and at Barber's Point, Hawaii.

At the time, the major fear was a surprise attack by Soviet bombers, and despite the construction of the Distant Early Warning (DEW) and Pinetree radar networks in Canada and Alaska, land-based radar coverage was inadequate and had many gaps. The navy early warning squadrons flew countless miles (23 million in the first five years of Atlantic barrier operations alone) on missions of up to 16 hours duration searching on their radar screens for 'bogeys' (unidentified aircraft) and 'skunks' (unidentified ships).

ABOVE: The test instrumentation boom on the port wing suggests that this otherwise anonymous Navy Super Connie may in fact be the first R7V-1, which was delivered in 1955. Note the strengthening around the rear freight door. Many of these early R7Vs were later passed to the USAF. *Aeroplane*

ABOVE RIGHT: One of the most remarkable looking Connies was the WV-2E which was the first early-warning WV-2 modified with a 40ft (12.1m) rotating radome (or rotodome) to detect airborne targets. The belly radome was not fitted but the support pylon contained the original APS-45, allowing a direct comparison with the new APS-70 in the rotodome. The WV-2E was not adopted, the Navy choosing the carrier-based Grumman Tracker instead. *Michael Stroud Collection*

BELOW RIGHT: The two PO-1Ws were the prototype early warning Connies, based on the L-749A airframe. Production 'Willie Victors' (WV-2s) were L-1049s and had a reshaped lower radome. The two aircraft later served as calibration aircraft with the FAA (without radomes) and one is preserved at Salina, Kansas. *Aeroplane*

In winter and summer above 40° latitude, the crews wore immersion suits in case of ditching in the sea. These were usually donned in flight where possible as the heat from the electronics, which were powered by 3,000 vacuum tubes, made the cabin warm enough as it was. Power for the electronics and their air conditioning system was said to equal that needed for a city of 20,000 people.

The least favourite piece of equipment was a World War 2-vintage radio transmitter called the ART-13. Many of the newer hands on the squadrons never really got to grips with it. One radioman planning to go water skiing when his WV-2 returned to Barber's Point after a patrol found himself rushed straight on to a transport Connie bound for Adak, Alaska, because he was the only man available who could tune the ART-13, which was common to both variants. He certainly got some funny looks at Adak when he revealed the swimming trunks under his flight suit.

A subsidiary mission that even the crews did not know about was for the PacBar Connies to collect particles in filters exposed to the outside air. These were tested for the presence of radiation that would signify a Soviet atomic test. Another was to direct Fairchild C-119 transports to an air pick-up of capsules dropped by spy satellites and others carried by unmanned balloons overflying the USSR.

The dangers of maintaining a 24-hour, seven-day-a-week barrier on both coasts in all weathers are illustrated by the number of WVs lost in landing accidents, in-flight fires and which simply disappeared over the years (see the military accidents table on page 107). In addition, five aircrewmen vanished without trace on a snorkelling trip to the Midway Atoll reef and were rumoured to have been snatched by a Soviet submarine for interrogation. It was known that subs sometimes waited outside the three-mile limit around Midway to monitor PacBar take-offs and landings.

An amazing incident that was luckily non-fatal occurred when a WV-2 of WV-12 lost its upper radome in flight out of Midway. The 7ft (2.13m) high unit removed the centre vertical stabiliser on its way aft, causing the Connie to roll completely and go into a vertical dive. Only the strength of the pilot, Cdr Bogdanovich, who braced his feet on the instrument panel to get extra leverage on the control wheel, enabled the aircraft to pull out. The radio operator was pinned to the ceiling and could not send a mayday signal. After a safe landing at Midway, the Connie was said to have gained several extra degrees of wing dihedral. Despite or perhaps because of this 'adjustment', the repaired aircraft was said to fly faster than other WV-2s.

Improved land-based radar and the development of the intercontinental ballistic missile (ICBM) saw the ending of the barriers and the retirement of the WVs from their original role in 1965. The last squadron, VW-11, that had moved to Iceland, was replaced by USAF EC-121s in November of that year.

In 1961 VW-1 which had been permanently detached to NAS Agana, Guam, to provide AEW support to the 7th Fleet, was switched over to weather reconnaissance as its primary mission. They soon earned the title of 'Typhoon Trackers' as the Pacific counterpart to VW-4, the 'Hurricane Hunters'. Before satellites became common, the only way to achieve a 'fix' on the centre of a tropical storm and get an accurate idea of its speed, strength and heading was to penetrate its centre. A specific Warning Star version, the WV-3 (later WC-121), was later built for this role, which often involved flying at wave-top height at night in the worst weather imaginable. The first WV-3, BuNo. 137891 flew into the heart of Hurricane 'Cleo' in August 1964 and suffered such strong updraughts during the initial penetration of the storm that the port wingtip tank and part of that wing were torn off. While trying to exit the storm, a downdraught ripped away the starboard tank and a larger portion of that wing. The battered Connie made a successful

ABOVE: This C-121G was a former R7V-1 (as can be seen by its 'porthole' windows) and was passed to the Air Force in 1958. It took part in 'Deep Freeze' Antarctic operations, became a trainer with an early warning and control wing and was retired in 1978. Selected from desert storage for civil conversion, it served as a freighter in the Dominican Republic and now belongs to the Swiss-based 'Super Constellation Flyers' group. *Stephen Piercey Collection/The Aviation Picture Library*

ABOVE RIGHT: There were four Navy R7V-2 turboprop Super Constellations, two of which were later given to the USAF as YC-121Fs, one of which is seen here. The engines used were the Pratt & Whitney T-34s and Lockheed also tested the Allison T-56 for the C-130 on 'Old 1961', the prototype Connie. *Michael Stroud Collection*

BELOW: This innocuous-looking Connie is an EC-121S 'Coronet Solo' broadcast platform, seen somewhere in Southeast Asia probably in 1970. The EC-121Ss were operated by the Pennsylvania Air National Guard transmitting television signals into Cambodia. Other EC-121S roles included radar monitoring and electronic warfare simulation. *Stephen Piercey Collection/The Aviation Picture Library*

landing at its base, NS Roosevelt Roads, Puerto Rico, but was declared damaged beyond repair. The cause of this mishap was partially attributed to the tip tanks being full, a prohibited practice for storm penetration.

As part of its role supporting the 7th Fleet, the Willie Victors of VW-1 flew AEW patrols for aircraft carriers on Yankee Station off North Vietnam from 1965 to 1971. Shore bases included Da Nang and Chu Lai in South Vietnam.

Another USN Connie variant used in Vietnam was the NC-121J that featured large 'TV' aerials rather than radomes. These 'Project Jenny' aircraft broadcast propaganda programmes to US-supplied televisions in villages in the Mekong Delta (and baseball games to US servicemen). Three of the four aircraft were damaged in a mortar attack on their base in April 1966, but the operation continued until 1970.

NAVAL ELECTRONIC PATROL SQUADRONS

From 1960, two Fleet air reconnaissance squadrons, VQ-1 and VQ-2 operated WV-2Q (EC-121M) Warning Stars on Electronic Counter Measures (ECM) and Electronic Intelligence (Elint) missions in Southeast Asia and Europe, North Africa and the Middle East.

The most serious Cold War incident to befall a military Constellation was the shoot-down of an EC-121M of VQ-1 over the Sea of Japan on 15 April 1969. The aircraft, BuNo 135749, was seven hours into a patrol mission from Atsugi, Japan, with a crew of 31 when it was attacked by a pair of North Korean MiG fighters 95 miles south Ch'ongjin, North Korea. The Koreans claimed to have shot the aircraft down over its own territory with a 'single shot', suggesting a surface-to-air missile. At the time a senator from South Carolina

suggested that nuclear weapons should be used in response. The Secretary of Defense's response was that 'the weak can be rash, the powerful must be restrained'. At the time, VQ-1 had been flying about two surveillance missions a month in the area, eavesdropping on North Korean radars and communications and monitoring Chinese-Russian fighting that was reported along the Ussuri River. Another source states that 190 such flights had taken place since 1 January 1969. Despite a massive search, only two bodies and a small amount of wreckage were ever recovered.

Numerous USN units and programmes made use of small numbers of Connies for a wide variety of tasks. These included the 'Blue Angels' aerobatic team (support aircraft), Projects Magnet, Birdseye and ASWEPS, which mapped the Earth's magnetic field, ice caps and sea temperatures respectively, and Antarctic Development Squadron Six (VX-6) supporting Antarctic research. One of the last users was the Pacific Missile Test Center (PMTC) at Point Mugu, California, who retired its last EC-121K from missile tracking duties in May 1979. The very last was Tactical Electronic Warfare Squadron 33 (VAQ-33) at Key West, Florida, who retired its single EC-121K (BuNo 141292), in June 1982, thus bringing to an end 38 years of United States military Connie operations.

AIR FORCE EARLY WARNING SQUADRONS

Use of the Constellation by the USAF paralleled that of the Navy in that the primary task, other than transport, was early warning. The RC-121C and RC-121D (EC-121D after 1962) were essentially the same as the WV-2, but with Air Force communications equipment and revised accommodation. They were assigned to the 551st and 552nd AEW&C Wings, based at Otis AFB, Maine, and McClellan AFB, California, respectively. These units used their Connies to monitor areas beyond coverage of the DEW Line, particularly the Greenland–Iceland–UK (GIUK) gap and the Cuban corridor. Again these flights were flown in all weathers with a duration of up to 17 hours, added to which was a three-hour pre-flight and briefing and two hours of post-flight work and debriefing.

In 1965 air force EC-121s were sent to Vietnam to provide co-ordination, control, early warning and communications relay to aircraft and ground bases conducting combat operations. On 24 October 1967, history was made when a US fighter was guided by an EC-121 to shoot down an enemy MiG-21 fighter, the first such success by airborne controllers. The Connie involved, 53-555, is now in the USAF Museum. In general, the EC-121D's radar was not ideal for picking up air targets against ground clutter and equipment was added that could detect and track the MiGs' own identification friend or foe (IFF) equipment. These missions operated under the codename 'Big Eye'. (later renamed 'College Eye').With radomes removed and a camouflage coat applied, the EC-121Rs of the 553rd Reconnaissance Wing flew 'Batcat' missions from Korat in Thailand, listening for signals from the thousands of motion sensors dropped all the way along the Ho Chi Minh Trail.

The air force EC-121s went through a variety of upgrades until the last EC-121Ts were retired by the 79th AEW&CS at Keflavik in November 1978. One of the last roles for the EC-121 was to test various avionics for its successor, the Boeing E-3A AWACS.

OTHER MILITARY USERS

In addition to the US military, a small number of Connies were used by the air forces and governments of other nations.

India was the largest foreign military user. The Indian Air Force (IAF) converted at least six of the nine L-1049Gs it acquired from Air-India in 1961 and 1962 to maritime patrol aircraft with ASV-21 search radar in a ventral 'dustbin' radome. The IAF Connie unit was No.6 Squadron based at Poona. Two were used as freighters and were retained by the air force when the navy took over the maritime patrol tasking and five of the Super Connies in 1976. The navy aircraft served on from Goa

TOP: The US air components of the North American Air Defense (NORAD) system of the late 1950s are seen in formation (left to right F-94C Starfire, F-86D Sabre and F-89 Scorpion). *Michael Stroud Collection*

ABOVE: A VQ-1 EC-121M lands at NAS Atsugi, Japan. This aircraft was the last to serve with the squadron, being retired in September 1974. VQ-1's mission during the Vietnam war was to 'sniff out' electronic signals such as those used by North Vietnamese SAM guidance radars. *Author's Collection*

with No.312 Squadron until they were withdrawn from service one-by-one between 1981 and 1983 after more than 6,500 naval flying hours.

France operated seven L-749 Constellations with civil registrations for search and rescue missions with L'Escadron Aérien de Recherche et de Sauvetage (EARS) 99 between 1960 and 1969. Flown by military crews, the aircraft were equipped with a comprehensive communications suite and a variety of air-droppable survival packages. A single L-749 was used as an engine test-bed from 1963 to 1974 with a large pylon mounting above the centre fuselage.

Indonesia was given two ex-Pakistan Airlines L-1049Hs and an L-1049C in 1969 as thanks for military assistance (MiG-19 fighters) supplied for use against India. Based at Halim, these were used on transport duties for a relatively short time and mostly, it would seem, on internal routes.

Senegal operated a single ex-Air France L-749A on Presidential transport duties between 1966 and 1969.

Ethiopia briefly used a C-121C until it was lost in a non-fatal forced landing near Khartoum in July 1957.

Military Constellation variants

US C-121 production broke down as follows:

9 C-121A, 33 C-121C, 50 C-121J, 10 RC-121C, 72 RC-121D, 142 WV-2, 2 WV-1, 8 WV-3, 4 R7V-2 (YC-121F). *Total*: 330

ABOVE: An EC-121of an unknown navy unit takes on fuel from a Royal Navy bowser at RNAS Lossiemouth sometime in the 1960s. The overall blue colour scheme gave way to gull grey and white slowly during the 1960s. *The Aviation Picture Library*

The major military variants are described below.

USAF

C-69

As related earlier, the original L-049s ordered for TWA were taken over by the USAAF as C-69s. These were joined by ten more ordered directly from Lockheed, of which one (42-94550) became the VIP C-69C and four (42-94554–4294557) which were not finished by war's end and were delivered to BOAC in 1946. One C-69 (42-94551) was lost in a non-fatal accident in September 1945 and another (42-94552) was tested to destruction at Wright Field. Interior accommodation was for either 60 passengers on a mix of conventional seats and benches or 22 sleepers. Contracts for the C-69A, which was a troop transport/ freighter variant, were cancelled at war's end. The C-69B was an unbuilt high-altitude variant for flying freight such as B-29 engines over the 'Hump' in China, and the C-69D was to have been a higher gross weight version of the C-69C. The very first Constellation, 43-10309, briefly became the XC-69E when re-engined with R-2800-83 engines and fitted with thermal de-icers being developed for the C-69D.

C-121A/B

Following less than happy experiences with the C-69, and a long delay before a second major order, the USAF chose to designate all further Constellations C-121s.

The C-121B actually preceded the C-121A into service, being ordered as a single VIP (VC-121B) presidential transport in the expectation that Thomas Dewey would win the 1948 election. When Harry S. Truman was re-elected, he chose to stick with the C-118 (DC-6) *Independence*. The VC-121B (48-808) did serve as a VIP transport for many years at Andrews AFB, Maryland. C-121As were based on the Model 749 with strengthened floor and port-side cargo door, although a plush 44-seat VIP interior could be fitted.

Delivered from November 1948 and initially assigned to MATS, the nine C-121As were involved in the Berlin Airlift, transporting supplies to Rhein Main AB in West Germany, where other aircraft shipped them on to the blockaded city. Later, six were fitted as VC-121 transports and used for the Special Air Mission (SAM) or VIP role from Andrews AFB. General Dwight Eisenhower used a VC-121A (48-614, *Columbine*) as his personal transport. When he became President, Eisenhower used 48-610 as 'Air Force One' (although this actual term was not in use until c.1962) and named it *Columbine II*. Another famous VC-121A was 48-613, used by General Douglas MacArthur as *Bataan*.

C-121 serials: 48-608–48-617

Converted to VC-121As: 48-610–48-614 and 48-617

C-121C

The main USAF transport model of the Constellation was originally ordered on a navy contract. 33 C-121Cs based on the L-1049D were delivered. Like the navy's R7V-1s, the C-121Cs had cargo doors forward and aft of the wing, but featured 20 square windows rather than eight 'portholes'. C-121Cs were converted to a number of roles and had other designations as follows:

JC-121C 54-0160 and -0178 converted to electronic test-beds
EC-121C Redesignation of above
NC-121C Redesignation of 54-0160 (-0178 retired)
EC-121S Six (54-0155, -0159, -0164, -0173, -0180, -0183) converted to Coronet Solo TV broadcast platforms
VC-121C.Two (54-0168 and -0174) used by the ANG Bureau as staff transports

Serials: 54-0151–54-0183

ABOVE: The Navy's Connies played a major role in Antarctic exploration by transporting supplies and people to 'The Ice' as well as undertaking photographic and air sampling missions. *Phoenix* was an R7V-1P (for Photo) with Antarctic Development Squadron VXE-6 and is seen at Christchurch, New Zealand. After ice flights with Connies stopped in 1970s, *Phoenix* (Bu No 131624) was mainly kept on SAR standby and was sent to the 'boneyard' in 1971 and later scrapped. *Author's Collection*

BELOW: *El Coyote* was converted from a WV-2 to (eventually) an NC-121K with special equipment for measuring the Earth's magnetic field. This aircraft replaced *El Paisano*, a similarly configured and painted WV-2 which crashed in Antarctica in October 1960. *Stephen Piercey Collection/The Aviation Picture Library*

The C-121C designation was also applied to a completely separate batch of aircraft which were designated as follows:

RC-121C The Air Force version of the WV-2, the RC-121C differed mainly in terms of internal layout, but also lacked tip tanks. Based on the L-1049B.

Serials: 51-3836–51-3845. TC-121C Nine RC-121Cs (all except 51-3840) redesignated for use as trainers.

A note about designation prefixes: 'J' stood for temporary test status, 'N' permanent test status, 'R' reconnaissance (search), replaced by 'E' electronic from 1962. Prior to then, 'E' stood for 'exempt', meaning the aircraft was on a special test status and exempt from most technical orders affecting others of the same basic type.

RC-121D/EC-121

More capable USAF versions of the WV-2 with internal changes. Later fitted with APS-95 in place of APS-20. Seventy-

two were built and the survivors later became EC-121Ds. Others were converted as follows:
EC-121H. Twenty-seven EC-121Ds and seven WV-2s modified with SAGE (Semi-Automatic Ground Environment) electronics for AEW&C role. Identifiable by new dorsal radome atop forward fuselage. APS-103 radar in main dorsal radar and APS-95 in ventral radome.
EC-121Q. Six Ds upgraded with dorsal APS-103 and ventral APS-95 and other advanced electronics.
EC-121T. Increased weight upgrade of 22 EC-121Ds and 1 EC-121H. Fifteen had dorsal radar and radome removed. New processing computer.
NC-121D. Converted WV-2/EC-121K 143226/56-6956 with dorsal cameras for recording radiation on space re-entry vehicles.

VC-121E

Ordered as an R7V-1 for the Navy, this aircraft, BuNo 131650, was completed as a presidential transport for the Air Force, complete with rectangular windows. Named *Columbine III*, it served Presidents Eisenhower and Kennedy until replaced by a VC-137 as 'Air Force One' in October 1962.

YC-12F

Two of the Navy's R7V-2 turboprop Connies were transferred to the USAF for their investigations into turbine power. BuNo 131660 became 53-8157 and 131661 became 53-8158.

C-121G

Designation for 32 R7V-1s transferred from the navy. Assigned the serial block 54-4048–4079. Four (54-4050–4052 and -4048) became TC-121G trainers and one of these later became a VC-121G.

EC-121R

Thirty EC-121Ks and EC-121Ps transferred from the Navy for use as airborne relay stations in Vietnam. These aircraft lost their radomes, gained camouflage paint and were used to monitor transmissions from air-dropped seismic sensors on the Ho Chi Minh Trail.

EC-121S

Five C-121Cs converted for electronic reconnaissance and ECM missions as per the EC-121Q. All operated by the Pennsylvania ANG.

C-121G/R7V-1

The Navy transferred to the Air Force 32 of its 51 R7V-1s. The Air Force assigned the designation C-121G.
Serials: a single block 54-4048–4079.

US NAVY

PO-1W (WV-1)

Based on the C-121C (strengthened-floor L-749A) airframe, two PO-1Ws were ordered in 1948 to fulfil the Navy's AEW role. The first Connies to have the large ventral and dorsal radomes containing APS-45 (above) and APS-20 (below), they were effectively prototypes for the Navy and Air Force versions to follow. During testing, the central fin and rudder was enlarged to give more control authority to counteract the stabilising effects of the radomes. Both were in service by 1951 and served with VW-1 'Typhoon Trackers' and VW-4 'Hurricane Hunters' before transfer to the FAA in 1958 and 1959.
Serials: 124437 and 124438.

R7V-1 (C-121J)

The USN ordered 11 transport models of the L-1049 in August 1950 and another 39 in February 1951 under the designation R7O-1. By the time they entered service with transport squadrons VR-1, VR-7 and VR-8 from 1952, the designation had become R7V-1. These were the Navy equivalent of the USAF C-121C, with a strengthened wing and large freight door. In true naval fashion, they had circular windows (portholes) unlike the Air Force freighters.

32 R7V-1s were later transferred to the USAF as C-121Gs. Those still in Navy service in October 1962 became C-121Js.

Serials: 128434–444, 131621–629, 131632–649, 131651–659, 140311–140313.

PO-2W (WV-2, EC-121K) Warning Star

The PO-2W was the same basic package as the PO-1W in a Super Constellation airframe. N67900, the first C-69 (and first 1049) served as the prototype. The first of 142 were delivered in 1954 and the remaining 123 were re-designated as EC-121Ks in 1962. Improvements over the PO-1W included a larger crew capacity with better amenities, and wingtip fuel tanks. The 5.5 tonnes of electronic equipment could be loaded and unloaded through a large freight door as found on the C-121.

The USAF later received 35 EC-121Ks from the Navy and used many in Vietnam, some in a Communications Intelligence (ComInt) or eavesdropping role. One such aircraft was used under the codenames 'Sea Trap' and 'Rivet Top' to gather real-time data on SAM and MiG radar emissions and was based in Thailand from 1967 to 1970. Some Navy aircraft were upgraded as EC-121Ps with modified APS-20 for use in a limited anti-submarine role.
Serials: 126512–513, 128323–326, 131387–392, 135746–135761, 137887–137890, 141289–333, 143184–230, 145924–941.

WV-2E (EC-121L)

This was a single aircraft (the first WV-2, 126512) modified before completion with a 40ft rotating dome (rotodome) antenna above the fuselage. The rotodome contained APS-70 search radar, and its pylon retained the APS-45 of the standard WV-2, but the ventral APS-20 dish was removed. Although this concept is used on today's E-3 AWACS, at the time (1956), the WV-2E lost out to the carrier-based Grumman W2F-1 Tracker with a fixed radar dome. The WV-2E was retained for research purposes and was later designated the EC-121L. Two W2V-1s based on the L-1649 Starliner airframe but with T-56-A-7 turboprops and auxiliary J34 turbojets on the wingtips were ordered but cancelled, partly because of advances in ground-based radar.

ABOVE: As well as their own new-build RC and EC-121s, the USAF received a number of WV-2s from the Navy which they modified to their own standard. EC-121H 55-2567 was formerly WV-2 141318 and served for most of the 1960s with the 551st Airborne Early Warning and Control Wing at Otis AFB, Maine.
The Aviation Picture Library

WV-2Q (EC-121M)

At least 13 WV-2s became WV-2Q (later EC-121M) ECM platforms. They included 131390-392, 135747, 135749 (shot down by North Korean MiGs, April 1969), 135751–752, 135747, 143186, 143209, 145927, 145936 and 145940.

WV-3 (WC-121N)

A batch of eight WV-2s (137891–898) was completed as weather reconnaissance aircraft, and another (141323) was converted after delivery. These 'Hurricane Hunter' aircraft flew in the most atrocious weather gathering data on storm conditions.

R7V-2

The last two R7O-1s (131630 and 131631) were completed as R7V-2s with Pratt & Whitney YT-34 turboprops. Additional changes to the R7V-1 included larger tailfins and wingtip fuel tanks. They were later joined by two more (131660 and 131661), but despite their much higher cruise speed (410mph/660km/h), were not adopted as production models and were used mostly as test-beds. One, 133661, was used for trials of the Allison Model 501 (T56) as used on the Lockheed Electra and Orion before reverting to T-34 power and becoming an Air Force YC-121F.

MILITARY CONSTELLATION LOSSES AND MAJOR INCIDENTS

Date	Serial	c/n	Model	Location	P.O.B/Fatal	Unit	Circumstances
1946	43-10314	1966	C-69	Mediterranean (or Iceland!)	?/?	War Assets Administration	Ditched but later repaired (or had cabin fire — to Air France)
18/9/45	43-94551	1972	C-69	Near Topeka, KS	?/0	USAAF/TWA	Engine fire, made belly landing in cornfield
7/7/53	128440	4107	R7V-1	Chesterton MD	?/0	NATC	Flaps stuck in opposite position, tail broke off, crashed
21/11/53	51-3838	4114	RC-121C	San Pablo Bay, San Francisco CA	?/0	8th AD, Air Defense Com	Ditched on GCA approach in fog
30/10/54	128441	4108	R7V-1	Atlantic	42/42	VR-1	Vanished between Bermuda and the Azores
9/12/54	131387	4307	WV-2	Johnsville NAS, PA	?/0	NADU	Hard landing, turned over, skidded and burned
17/1/55	131639	4140	C-121J	Newfoundland NAS,	crew k	VR-1	Two engines failed, crashed in Gulf of St Lawrence
1956	131638	4139	R7V-1	en route USA–Japan	?/0	VR-8	Engine fire, aircraft landed with engine hanging by cables
17/9/56	137893	4380	WV-3	100 miles south of Guam	?/0	USN	Ditched due to fuel mismanagement. Sunk by USAF jets to avoid shipping hazard
30/12/56	54-0165	4184	C-121C	Dhahran, Saudi Arabia	41/15	1608 ATW	Struck sandbank on approach, burst into flames
17/4/57	141314	4438	WV-2	Argentia NAS, Canada	24/0	VW-15	Overheated brake caused fire in port wing, No.2 engine fell off, aircraft crashed after wheels-up landing
10/7/57	ET-T-35	2608	C-121A	30 miles from Khartoum	?/0	Ethiopian Government	Fire in Nos ? and 2 engines, made successful belly landing, burnt out

DATE	SERIAL	C/N	MODEL	LOCATION	P.O.B/FATAL	UNIT	CIRCUMSTANCES
7/10/57	137897	4384	WV-3	NAS Jacksonville, FL	?/0	VW-3	Aborted take-off, struck sewer pipe and ditch. Repaired, but later retired
23/12/57	143197	4471	WV-2	25 miles off Kahuku Point, Oahu HI	23/19	VW-2/ VW-14 crew	Four engines failed at 1,500ft, ditched in heavy seas
14/1/58	128437	4104	R7V-1	NAS Patuxent River, MD	9/9	VW-11	Crashed into forest while practising instrument landings in foggy, wet weather
28/2/58	141310	4434	WV-2	100m west of Corvo Island, Portugal	22/22	VW-15	Disappeared between checkpoints
22/3/58	55-0118	4390	RC-121D	McClellan AFB, CA	?/0	552 AEW &C Wing	Engine failed, crashed six minutes after take-off
14/5/58	131652	4153	R7V-1	Taft, CA	?/0	USN	Crashed. 'Substantial damage'
25/5/58	55-0123	4396	RC-121D	Otis AFB, ME (USA)	0/0	551 AEW&CW	Burned out on ramp during preflight check
18/10/58	141294	4418	WV-2	Placentia Bay, Canada	29/11	VW-15	Crashed into Placentia Bay, 1000 feet short of the Argentia NAS runway during a GCA approach.
28/2/59	54-4069	4149	C-121G	Prescott, AZ	?/?	MATS	Crashed (details unknown)
29/3/59	141332	4456	WV-2	Argentia NAS	/0	VW-11	Crash landed when one main gear collapsed on touchdown. Aircraft hit snowbank and burned
2/4/59	141303	4427	WV-2	Argentia NAS	29/1	VW-13	Hard landing with one engine out, starboard wing broke off and aircraft flipped over and burned
1960s	Unknown		WV-2	Barbers' Point, HI	?/0	USN WV-12	Upper radome broke off, took starboard stabiliser (or centre fin) with it. Aircraft rolled, but recovered safely
1960	143211	4485	WV-2	Midway Island	?/0	USN	Lost right landing gear on take-off, returned and made belly landing repaired but flown to boneyard
9/3/60	141305	4429	WV-2	NAS Argentia	?/0	VW-11	Right main gear damaged in practice landing, collapsed on landing. Repaired but did not return to service
31/10/60	126513	4302	WV-2	McMurdo, Antarctica	23/0	VXN-8 'Paisano'	Landing gear struck snowbank, collapsed, port wing ripped off
22/1/61	143193	4467	WV-2	Midway Island	22/6	AEW BARRONPAC	Struck seawall short of runway, cartwheeled, struck a crash truck killing three
22/3/61	51-3482	4118	TC-121C	Butte Sink, Marysville CA	crew k	551 AE W&C Wing	Crashed into swampwhile on test flight
12/4/62	54-4066	4146	C-121G	Guam	?/?	4066 MATS	Crashed (details unknown)
22/5/62	131390	4310	WV-2Q	Near Markt Schwaben, W Germany	26/26	VQ-2	Empennage fell off, aircraft rolled several times and crashed
9/8/62	141324	4448	WV-2	Patuxent River, MD	19/5	AEWTULANT	Crashed on approach in heavy rainstorm
31/8/62	51-4057	4138	C-121G	Oakland, CA	1?/0	MATS	Ran over ground power unit, damaged beyond repair by fire
31/7/63	141329	4453	EC-121K	Gander, Newfoundland	?/0	VW-13	Ran off runway into mud during touch-and-go, broke in half
1/8 1964 or 23/8	137891	4378	WC-121N	NS Roosevelt Rds, PR	?/0	VW-4	Both tip tanks and parts of wing ripped off in hurricane penetration. Damaged beyond repair
3/11/64	131625	4126	C-121J	NAS Patuxent River, MD	?/0	AEWTULANT	Damaged beyond repair when gear raised on landing
11/6/65	141321	4445	EC-121K	Keflavik	0/0	VW-13	Landing gear retracted inside hangar, crushing groundcrewmen
11/7/65	55-0136	4409	EC-121H	Nantucket	?/0	551st AEW&C Wing	Overheated brake caused fire in port wing, No.2 engine fell off. Crashed after wheels-up landing (another source says crashed at sea, 3 survivors)
11/7/65	Unknown		EC-121H	Atlantic Ocean off Nantucket	19/16	551st Wing	Engine fire, another failed, ditched at sea. Survivors rescued by helicopter and warships
20/8/65	135747	4314	EC-121M	NAS Atsugi, Japan	?/0	VQ-1	Starboard landing gear failed to extend, aircraft slid into building in subsequent emergency landing
27/1/66	135751	4318	EC-121M	NAS Atsugi, Japan	0/0	VQ-1	Heat lamps ignited radome on ground, burnt out
11/11/66	55-5262	4413	EC-121H	125 miles east of Nantucket	19/19	551st AEW &C Wing	Crashed into Atlantic 40 minutes after take-off
25/4/67	53-0549	4364	EC-121H	Off Nantucket	16/15	551st AEW &C Wing	A starboard engine caught fire after take-off, aircraft struck sea soon after
24/1/69	67-21476	4441	EC-121R	Otis AFB, Maine	?/0	AFSC-ADTC	Damaged beyond repair in landing accident
14/4/69	135749	4316	EC-121M	s-e of Chongjin, N.Korea	31/31	VQ-1	Shot down by two North Korean MiG fighters over the Sea of Japan
25/4/69	67-21493	4489	EC-121R	Korat RTAB	18/18	554RS 553 Wg	Crashed into rice paddy after take-off
6/9/69	67-21495	4491	EC-121R	Korat RTAB	4/18	554RS 553 Wg	Crashed on approach in rain, four Thais on ground also killed
16/3/70	145927	5508	EC-121K	Da Nang, South Vietnam	28/23	VQ-1	Landed with No.3 engine out on shortened runway, cartwheeled into hangar area
25/8/70	145928	5509	EC-121K	NAS Atsugi, Japan	?/0	VW-1	Accidental gear retraction on ground. Aircraft scrapped
8/10/70	131644	4145	C-121J	McMurdo Sound, Antar'a	80/0	VXE-6 'Pegasus'	Struck snowbank in blizzard, abandoned
19/7/73	145936	5517	EC-121K	NAS Agana, Guam	0/0	VQ-1	Internal fire. Written off
15/3/78	55-0121	4394	EC-121T	Keflavik, Iceland	?/0	79 AEW&CW	Port landing gear collapsed while taxying, burnt out
?/1/83	IN-316	4666	L-1049G	Goa?	?/0	Indian Navy	Damaged beyond repair in taxying accident

7 Accidents and Incidents

ATTRITION — 'FALLEN STARS'

In regular airline service, the Constellation was one of the safest of the post-war propliners, but there were many accidents and incidents. Some of these were due to design faults or mechanical problems, and many others that were the result of what today are called 'human factors'.

Early Constellations suffered particularly from engine fires and hydraulic failures, but Lockheed had the twin luxuries of time and government money to apply to the problems thrown up in USAAF use before the airlines got their hands on the Connie. The loss of a C-69 due to a nacelle fire resulted in modifications to the fuel system, and the more serious crash of a TWA L-049 on a training flight (while passenger operations were suspended due to another accident) brought about improved electrical routing and cabin smoke evacuation drills. Elimination of the carburettors in favour of direct injection of fuel, combined with better fire extinguishers, allowed fires to be started and extinguished at will (at least in Lockheed tests) without spreading to the surrounding structure.

Super Constellation problems included nozzle-box cracking on the turbo-compound engines. The problem was eventually fixed by 1953 and an extra layer of armour fitted around the turbine wheel to protect the structure in the event of failure, something which was all too common. Over-speeding propellers that could not be feathered resulted in several accidents, including one that resulted in huge damages being awarded against propeller manufacturer Hamilton Standard.

Of 95 losses between 1946 and 1966 — the heyday of the Constellation in airline service, engine fires, engine failures and propeller failures were the primary cause of 16. Hydraulic failures were directly behind two, and other mechanical failures, five. Accidents that appear to have been primarily weather related accounted for 14 Connies and Super Connies and nine were lost to indeterminate causes, but 34 losses could be ascribed to pilot or crew error, although many of these had weather or technical failure as a contributing factor. Three aircraft were destroyed by terrorists, and another was shot down, four were involved in mid-air collisions (although one landed safely and one crash-landed with few fatalities) and there were three fatal accidents without loss of the aircraft. These included a steward killed by a disintegrating propeller and a passenger sucked out of a Super Connie by an explosive decompression. Undercarriage collapses destroyed five, and three more were wiped out by collisions on the ground. 19 aircraft were repaired after undercarriage collapse or belly landings brought about by a range of mechanical and human factors, and one returned to service after a serious ground collision.

The apparently low figure for losses due to hydraulic failure masks the contribution of this complex system to other accidents that were eventually attributed to crew mishandling of the emergency or to other related mechanical failures. An example is the loss of a Northwest Super Connie (on lease to Eastern at the time) at McChord AFB in September 1953. With the two starboard engines feathered, there was not enough pressure in the secondary system to fully extend the right main gear before a forced landing was made. Fortunately all the passengers were able to escape the subsequent blazing wreck when the aircraft swerved off the runway.

Below: HI-515, seen here leaving Miami under threatening skies is an ex-USAF C-121J and ANG EC-121S that was retired to desert storage in 1978 and selected for civil freighter conversion in 1987. Bought by Aerolineas Mundo S.A (AMSA), its subsequent career was a short one, ended by a crash into the sea off Levittown, Puerto Rico on 5 May 1990. *Austin J. Brown/The Aviation Picture Library*

ABOVE: C-69 43-10310 was the second Constellation built and is seen here in TWA livery but wearing its Army radio call letters. In these markings this aircraft broke the transcontinental speed record in April 1944. The aircraft became a 'hangar queen' and was never actually part of the TWA fleet. After being rebuilt for the Flying Tiger Line, the aircraft was being used for pilot training at Burbank when an unintentional wheels-up landing was made, the crew escaped, but fire broke out and the aircraft was totally destroyed. *Michael Stroud Collection*

Without 'a cockpit full of snakes' or compounding problems, ingenuity could prevent a disaster. A TWA L-1049 crew found themselves circling Kansas City for five hours with the left gear stuck down, the right gear up and the nose gear partially retracted. Eventually the source of the leak was traced, and it was repaired with the aid of a penny coin. The lost fluid was replaced with all the coffee and water that could be found aboard, allowing the recalcitrant left and nose gears to be raised. A belly landing was then made on foam without injury to the occupants.

Several aircraft were involved in more than one incident. The first airline Constellation to be involved in a serious incident in passenger service was Pan Am's NC88858 which belly-landed at Willimantic, Connecticut, with three engines attached. This famous 'Trimotor Connie' was sadly lost with 30 passengers two years later when it crashed short of Shannon Airport in Ireland.

Two of the most famous and tragic accidents befell TWA Connies and both involved collisions with United Air Lines (UAL) Douglas aircraft, each with the loss of the same number of passengers.

On 30 June 1956, TWA's *Star of the Seine*, a four-year-old L-1049, collided with a UAL DC-7 and fell into the Grand Canyon with the loss of 128 lives from both aircraft, the worst US airline disaster to that time. Both aircraft had taken off from Los Angeles, bound for Kansas City and Chicago, respectively, each taking the scenic route via the canyon. The faster Douglas caught up with the Super Connie and struck it from behind, it is thought, while both crews were concentrating on giving the passengers a good view. At this time, en route separation was dependent mainly on visual lookout and this tragedy led to

ABOVE: This Panair do Brasil Connie is unidentified but its feathered no.4 (starboard outer) engine is a reminder why the Constellation was sometimes called 'the best trimotor in the world'. Panair do Brasil itself had five fatal Connie and Super Connie accidents and wrote off several others. Flying Tiger Line lost nine, including two on the same day, but TWA, who after all had the biggest fleet, lost over 30 in fatal crashes alone. *Panair do Brasil/The Aviation Picture Library*

greater regulation of the airways and funding for more navigational aids.

The second major collision happened on 16 December 1960 when TWA's L-1049 *Star of Sicily* was struck from behind by a United DC-8 over Staten Island, New York. Poor weather, a faulty beacon and an ambiguous ATC handover contributed to the collision, as did the excessive speed of the DC-8, which was travelling at 380mph (610km/h) when it entered the pattern for Idlewild airport. The Super Connie fell onto Miller Army Airfield and the DC-8 carried on to crash into Park Slope, Brooklyn, where six residents lost their lives in addition to the 128 passengers and crew on both aircraft.

An early Connie tragedy illustrates how much facilities, procedures and technology have improved since the early post-war years. On 19 June Pan Am's *Clipper Eclipse* (formerly *Clipper Dublin*) was on the inaugural westbound journey of the airline's new around the world service with 36 aboard when the port outer engine gave trouble and had to be feathered. The aircraft was in the cruise at 18,500ft (5,639m) over Iraq, and due to closed airports (it was 2am) and a lack of repair facilities en route, the pilot elected to continue to Istanbul, the scheduled destination, rather than making a landing at the nearby RAF base at Habbaniya. Having descended to 10,000ft (3,048m), the other engines overheated and the port inner (No.2) engine burst into flames, and within seven minutes had parted company with the wing completely.

The pilot got out one radio message: 'One engine ablaze, trying to crash-land'. The aircraft almost immediately made a wheels-up landing on the desert near Meyadine, Syria, spun around and caught fire. Eight of the crew and seven passengers were killed. One of those aboard was Gene Roddenberry, a deadheading Pan Am pilot and the future creator of the cult television series *Star Trek*, who raised the alarm by following telephone lines the five miles into town.

When the Connie had left mainstream airline service, many were converted to freighters or to high-density seating configuration for various travel clubs or holiday resorts. Many of these 'non-sked' (non-scheduled) operators had mixed fleets of Connies and Super Connies with different engines and systems without the engineering and crew training backup enjoyed by the major airlines. Two accidents, in 1961 and 1964 to an Imperial Airways L-049E and a Paradise Airlines L-049, cost the lives of 74 army recruits and 81 resort customers (plus crews) respectively, and resulted in the revocation of the companies' operating certificates. Numerous operating irregularities were uncovered in both cases.

In Latin America, the situation was worse. Many small operators ran their Connies on the local registers (to be largely out of FAA control), until they literally fell out of the sky. It would be an exaggeration to say that the seabed around Puerto Rico and the Dominican Republic is paved with sunken Connies, but a fair number of them certainly met their ends in these waters. The poor safety record of the Dominican Connies led to their banning from US airspace in 1993.

Other Connie freighters, overloaded with meat, produce, tobacco or contraband failed to get airborne from jungle airstrips across Central and South America. Others still were expended in fighting budworm and other pests in Canada.

The Biafran Airlift of 1966–70 saw another seven Connies lost in crashes at various locations in West Africa and to enemy action. It is remarkable that more were not lost flying relief and arms into primitive jungle strips at night while sought by

Nigerian gunners, fighter planes and DC-3 bombers. At the end of the conflict, the survivors were abandoned and left to rot at various locations in Africa and southern Europe.

One of the most bizarre Connie incidents was the use of L-749A, C/N 2668 'CX-BGP', to bomb the presidential palace at Port Au Prince, Haiti, during a coup on 4 June 1969. Return fire struck the front of the Connie, blowing a hole through the nose and the cockpit roof. The damaged aircraft is thought to have landed on Grand Bahama where the crew unsuccessfully tried to escape by taxi. The damage was repaired, but after some more nefarious activities, the Connie is thought to have been deliberately burnt out in Colombia.

One of the last Constellation accidents took the life of famous Lockheed test pilot Herman 'Fish' Salmon. More known for testing experimental types such as the vertical take-off Lockheed XFV-1, which was nicknamed 'Salmon' after the only man brave enough to fly it, 'Fish' was co-pilot on the first flight of the L-1649 Starliner. After leaving Lockheed, he was involved in a number of operations involving Connies including a proposal to use an L-1049 mocked up as the 'supersonic' 'Condor' in an early 1970s disaster movie. This, perhaps thankfully for the moviegoer, never reached the big screen.

On 22 June 1980, Salmon was to fly an L-1049H belonging to Air Traders International from Columbus, Indiana, to Seattle, Washington, with a load of spare parts for the company's two Super Connies. Air Traders was a newly formed company planning to transport fish (of all things) from Alaska to the US West Coast. This was to be the aircraft's first flight after a long period of storage and a taxy test had nearly resulted in an accident two days before. On this day, an engine blew on the take-off run and the others lost power shortly after. The Super Connie struck a pole, flopped into a field and skidded into trees where it broke up and burned. Salmon, his daughter and one other person were killed, although five others escaped the wreck.

The crash was attributed to overloading, use of low-grade fuel and incorrect cowl flap settings. The crew was also said to have mishandled the emergency, not noticing the power loss on the three 'good' engines until it was too late.

The Connie's contribution to flight safety should not be forgotten — after service with TWA, the eighth Starliner was used in one of the first full-scale crash tests, conducted by the Flight Safety Foundation in 1964. Wired up with recording instruments and cameras, and filled with dummy passengers and crew, the propliner ran under its own power along a track at Deer Valley, Arizona, until it struck a series of obstacles, became airborne and crashed back into the desert. With the tanks filled with water rather than fuel, the instruments and film survived to reveal much useful data on the behaviour of various materials and structures such as seat mounts in a crash situation. The *in situ* wreck was then used again to test passenger evacuation times using live volunteers.

BELOW: Back in the days when men wore hats and women wore gloves to go flying, happy passengers disembark from Starliner N7301C *Star of Wyoming*. This was the second L-1649 built and the third to be lost in an accident. Leased to the Colombian airline Aerocondor, it crashed in thick fog at Bogota on 17 December 1966. 21 were killed and 39 survived. The crash was attributed to crew fatigue and the possible distraction of an unauthorised person in the cockpit. *Author's Collection*

ABOVE: Varig's L-1049G PP-VDA was the flagship of the Brazilian national airline when it was delivered in 1955. Two years later, on 16 August 1957, she was lost in the Caribbean when the No.4 propeller 'ran away' (overspeeded) and broke off, striking the No.3 engine. As the aircraft was on a three-engined ferry flight to New York with No.2 engine inoperative, there was no chance of maintaining height on only one powerplant and the aircraft was forced to ditch off the coast of the Dominican Republic. One of the 11 crew members aboard was drowned. *John Stroud Collection/The Aviation Picture Library*

BELOW: Qantas is rightly proud of its safety record, but the oft-misquoted claim that the Australian airline has never had an accident, is not quite true. VH-EAC *Southern Wave*, seen here at the small New South Wales town of Dubbo, crashed at Mauritius on 24 August 1960. while *en route* to Johannesburg via Cocos Island. The aircraft suffered an engine failure and overran the runway, breaking up and catching fire. Fortunately, all the passengers and crew were able to make a rapid escape with only six injuries. *Aeroplane*

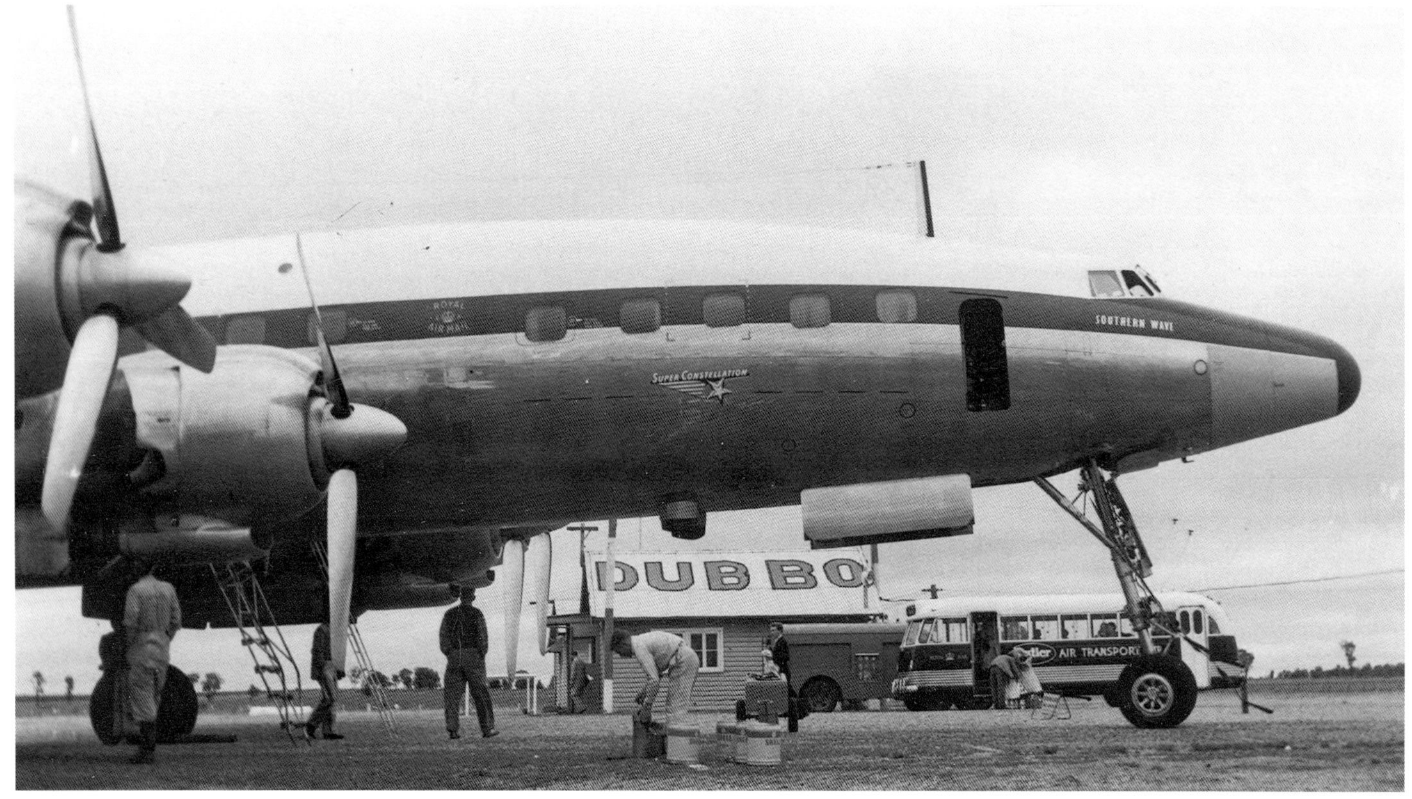

MILITARY LOSSES

Between them, the USAF and USN lost 35 C-121s and WVs in crashes, (about ten percent of military production) and a number of others in undercarriage collapses and ground fires. Many of the losses were a result of the high operational tempo of the Cold War, with its requirement to patrol the US coasts at all times. AEW Connies would fly in weather that kept their airliner cousins grounded and fly closer to the surface where there was far less margin for error in the case of engine failure. A couple simply disappeared.

One Navy aircraft was shot down by North Korean MiGs with the loss of all crew, others were damaged by Viet Cong mortars in Vietnam. At least two survived serious structural damage to return to their bases, testifying to the strength of the Connie airframe.

BELOW: This L-049, TWA's *Star of Cairo* was involved in the first fatal passenger accident when it crashed on an island in the Shannon River. 12 of the 23 mainly French and American occupants died when the aircraft hit the ground and exploded on approach to the Irish airport. The pilots were flying on instruments in darkness and cloud, but tragically the connections between the air data sensors and the altimeters were miswired and the aircraft was flown into the ground. *Michael Stroud Collection*

The tables below list every significant known accident to befall Constellations and Starliners. Note that many aircraft were returned to service after undercarriage collapses and other relatively minor accidents until the late 1960s, when the lack of heavy engineering support usually meant that a repairable aircraft was more often than not cannibalised for spares.

Dt.	Reg.	Model	c/n	Oper.	Pob/k.	Flightplan	Location	Summary
12.7.44	43-10311	C-69	1963	Lockheed	/0	—	Burbank?	Right landing gear collapsed during taxy run
29.3.46	NC86510	L-049	2034	TWA	/0	Washington	Washington DC	Landed with half flap, overran, struck small building
18.6.46	NC88858	L-049	2058	Pan Am	/0	New York–Gander	Willimantic, Conn	No.4 engine fire, engine fell off, aircraft made successful belly-landing
11.7.46	NC86513	L-049	2040	TWA	6/5	Training	Near Reading, PA	Inflight fire in wiring. Smoke filled cockpit, aircraft hit trees
24.9.46	NC88831	L-049	2031	Pan Am	/0	Shannon	Shannon, Ireland	Inadvertent gear retraction. Written off
12.10.46	N86512	L-049	2039	TWA	/0	Training	Wilmington, DE	Overran runway in light rain, hit cars on road, spun around and burst into flames
28.12.46	NC86505	L-1049	2026	TWA	/12	Paris–Shannon	Nr Shannon, Ireland	Altimeter miswired, flew low approach and crashed on small island in Shannon River
c1947	Unknown	L-049		TWA	/1	Gander–Azores	Mid-Atlantic	Navigator sucked out when astrodome failed
11.5.47	N86508	L-049	2029	TWA	4/4	Training	Delaware Bay, NJ	Lost control in left turn at 2,500ft. Recovered from spiral too low and struck sea
19.6.47	NC88845	L-049	2045	Pan Am	36/14	Karachi–Istanbul	Meyadine, Syria	No.1 engine failed, No.2 overheated, caught fire and fell off. Aircraft belly-landed on fire
26.7.47	N86511	L-049	2035	TWA	/0	Shannon	Shannon, Ireland	Starboard gear collapsed on heavy braking in wet. Repaired
18.11.47	N86507	L-049	2028	TWA	crew k.	Training	Newcastle, DE	Undershot, struck ditch, crashed and caught fire
21.1.48	N111A	L-649	2532	Eastern	25/20	Miami–Newark	Boston, MA	Diverted from Newark and La Guardia, landed 2,000ft short in poor weather. Hit snowbank. (*Other sources say no fatalities*)
7.2.48	NC112A	L-649	2533	Eastern	/1	NYC–W. Palm Bch	Nr Brunswick GA	No.3 propeller separated, steward killed by fragments, aircraft damaged in flapless landing
24.3.48	NC88833			Pan Am	/0	Dakar–Accra	Accra, Gold Coast	Nosegear failed to extend (poorly machined part). Made successful gear-up landing
15.4.48	NC88858	L-049	2058	Pan Am	31/30	Karachi–Shannon	Nr Shannon, Ireland	Making second instrument approach at night. Struck ground 2,380ft short of runway
13.7.48	RX-121	L-049	1968	LAPSA	/0	Zatec	Czechoslovakia	Hydraulic failure, wheels up landing. Repaired.
20.10.48	PH-TEN	L-049	2083	KLM	40/40	Amsterdam–P'wick	5 miles from Prestwick UK	Making 2nd attempt to land, struck power lines in fog. Famous KLM pilot Capt. K.D Parmintier killed
25.11.48	N90824	L-049	2086	TWA	23/0	Los Angeles	Los Angeles Airport	Ground fog caused pilot to land hard, blowing tyres and swerving off runway. Aircraft caught fire
30.1.49	NC86530	L-749	2528	Pan Am	/0	New York–London	Port Washington, NY	Collided with Cessna 140 NC76891, Cessna crew killed, Connie landed safely
23.6.49	PH-TER	L-749	2541	KLM	33/33	Cairo–Rome	Off Bari, Italy	Engine fire spread, dived into Bari Harbour
12.7.49	PH-TDF	L-749	2558	KLM	45/45	Delhi–Bombay	Near Bombay	Struck 800ft hill in monsoon rains while circling
28.10.49	F-BAZN	L-749	2546	Air France	48/48	Paris–Santa Maria	San Miguel Island Azores	Struck Redondo mountain in poor weather. Improper approach procedure
18.12.49	N86501	L-049	2022	TWA	/0	Training	Chicago Midway	Overran, crossed road into parking lot. Repaired
28.7.50	PP-PCG	L-1049	2062	Panair	50/50	Porte Alegre do Brasil	Porte Alegre, Brazil	Flew into power lines during a landing attempt
31.8.50	N6004C	L-749A	2636	TWA	55/55	Cairo–Rome	Nr Wadi Natrun Egypt	Fire in No.3 engine. Turned back but cr. in flames attempting belly-landing at night
10.10.50	N104A	L-749A	2521	Eastern	/0	Jacksonville, FL	Jacksonville Apt FL	Gear collapsed on landing. Repaired
3.11.50	VT-CQP	L-749	2506	Air India	48/48	Cairo–Geneva	Mont Blanc, France	Crashed in snowstorm 600ft below summit
18.11.50	N86511	L-049	2035	TWA	/0	Long Beach	Long Beach, CA	Overran in wet, hit rail line, right gear.collapsed. Repaired

Dt.	Reg.	Model	c/n	Oper.	Pob/K.	Flightplan	Location	Summary
19.3.51	N91202	L-749	2578	TWA	/0	Phoenix	Phoenix, AZ	Gear lever not fully down, gear-up landing. Repaired
22.6.51	N88846	L-049	2046	Pan Am	40/40	Accra–Monrovia	Nr Sanoyea, Liberia	Pilot descended while unsure of position, struck hill
19.7.51	N119A	L-749A	2616	Eastern	/0	?	Mt. Richmond, VA	Pilot feared structural failure in storm, belly landed. Repaired
23.3.52	PH-TFF	L-749A	2652	KLM	44/0	Karachi–Bangkok	Bangkok, Thailand	Prop blade on No.3 engine failed on base leg, fire broke out. Gear collapsed on landing
22.1.53	N38936	L-049	1962	Inter-continental	5/0	Training	Burbank, CA	Gear-up landing. Belly landed and caught fire
17.6.53	PP-PDA	L-1049	2066	Panair do Brasil	17/17	London–Sao Paulo	Sao Paulo, Brazil	Crashed on final approach in poor visibility at night
3.8.53	F-BAZS	L-749A	2628	Air France	42/4	Rome–Beirut	6 miles from Fethiye, Turkey	No.3 prop vibrated off, hit No.4. Aircraft ditched
1.9.53	F-BAZZ	L-749A	2674	Air France	42/42	Paris–Nice	Nr Barcelonette, Fr.	Crashed into Mt. Cemet during the approach
6.9.53	N6214C	L-1049	4014	Eastern/ N'west	32/0	Seattle–Chicago	McChord AFB, WA	No.3 prop oversped, No.4 engine overheated, left gear did not lock before landing at McChord AFB, aircraft swerved and caught fire
19.10.53	N119A	L-749A	2616	Eastern	27/2	NY–San Juan, PR	NY-Idlewild Airport	Flew into fog bank on take-off. Pilot disorientation led to crash on ground.
13.3.54	G-ALAM	L-749A	2554	BOAC	40/33	Sydney–Singapore	Singapore–Kallang	Crashed short of runway, hit wall, slid down runway and overturned. Pilot fatigue
3.8.54	F-BGNA	L-1049C	4510	Air France	37/0	Paris–New York	Nr Preston City, CT	Diverted to Boston in poor weather, ran out of fuel, belly-landed in field, caught fire
9.8.54	HK-163	L-749A	2664	AVIANCA	30/30	Lajes–Bermuda	Terceira Island, Azores	Flew opposite course to that ordered in poor weather, struck mountains
25.8.54	F-BAZI	L-749	2513	Air France	67/0	?	Gander	Overran runway and damaged beyond repair. Repaired using nose of c/n 1961, abandoned
5.9.54	PH-LKY	L-1049C	4509	KLM	56/28	Shannon–New York	Shannon River, Ireland	Gear re-extended, pilot mishandled actions, ditched in Shannon River
17.12.54	CF-TGG	L-1049E	4564	Trans Canada	23/0	Tampa–Toronto	Brampton, Ontario	Poor instrument approach, crash landed short of runway
23.2.55	N86509	L-049	2030	TWA	/0	Los Angeles–NY	NY, La Guardia	Skidded on wet runway, gear torn off in groundloop. Repaired
11.4.55	VT-DEP	L-749A	2666	Air India	19/16	Hong Kong–Jakarta	Sarawak, Indonesia	Incendiary bomb in starboard wheel well caused fire, hydraulic and electrical failure. Ditched.
16.6.55	PP-PDJ	L-149	2032	Panair do Brasil	24/16	Sao Paulo–Asuncion	Nr Asuncion, Paraguay	Descended too low on finals at night. Pilot fatigue suspected
27.7.55	4K-AKC	L-049	1968	El Al	58/58	Vienna–Tel Aviv	Nr Petrich, Bulgaria	Shot down by Bulgarian fighters after straying off course. Thunderstorms affected compass
25.9.55	EC-AIP	L-1049G	4552	Iberia	/0	Havana–Madrid	Kindley AB, Bermuda	Belly-landed on foam after gear failure. Repaired
17.12.55	F-BAZG	L-749A	2626	Air France	26/28	Algiers-	Algiers	Crashed on take-off and caught fire
21.12.55	N112A	L-749C	2533	Eastern	17/17	Miami–Jacksonville	Jacksonville FL	Crashed attempting go around in local fog
20.6.56	YV-C AMS	L-1049E	4561	LAV	74/74	New York–Caracas	Off Asbury Park NJ	No.2 propeller oversped. Vibration ruptured fuel tank, caused fire; crashed into Atlantic while attempting to return
30.6.56	N6324C	L-1049	4016	TWA	70/70	LA–Kansas City	Grand Canyon, AZ	Collided with United DC-7 N6902C. 58 killed on DC-7
15.7.56	PH-LKT	L-1049C	4504	KLM	68/58	Mokmer–Manilla	Nr Biak, Indonesia	Made low pass to give passengers a last glimpse of island. Struck sea and exploded
27.11.56	YV C-AMA	L-749	2560	LAV	25/25	NY–Maiquetia	Cevilla, Venezuela	Struck 6,700ft Mt. Naiguata. Followed incorrect approach procedures, also compass failure
15.1.57	N6018C	L-749A	2656	TWA	/0	—	Pittsburgh PA	Struck by Capital DC-3 on taxiway. Repaired
16.1.57	N91204	L-749	2580	TWA	/0	Louisville	Louisville, KY	Left gear retracted on landing roll. Repaired
7.2.57	N88855	L-149	2055	Pan Am	/0	Shreveport, LA	Jackson, MS	Struck ground on missed approach. Gear collapsed trying to land at Jackson. Repaired
14.2.57	PP-PDC	L-049	2056	Panair do Brasil	/0	Recife	Recife, Brazil	Nosegear collapsed, belly landed. Repaired
21.4.57	F-BGNE	L-1049C	4514	Air France	/1	Baghdad–Istanbul	Istanbul, Turkey	Passenger sucked out by explosive decompression

DT.	REG.	MODEL	C/N	OPER.	POB/K.	FLIGHTPLAN	LOCATION	SUMMARY
28.6.57	N6212C	L-1049	4012	Eastern	/0	—	Miami	Ground collision with DC-7 N808D, destroyed by fire
10.7.57	ET-T-35	C-121A	2608	Ethiopian A/l	20/0	K'toum–Addis Ab.	30 miles from Khartoum	Tyre exploded, No.2 engine caught fire, fell off, aircraft belly landed in field
16.8.57	PP-VDA	L-1049G	4610	Varig	11/1	Dom Rep–Miami	Nr Cabarete, DR	On ferry flight with No.2 engine out, No.4 prop flew off and struck No.3. Aircraft ditched
6.12.57	F-BHMK	L-1049G	4670	Air France	6/0	Training	Paris-Orly Airport	Crashed in flames making night practice landings in poor visibility
9.1.58	N6224C	L-1049C	4532	Eastern	/0	Training	Islip, NY	Hit snowbank on approach, wing ripped off. Repaired
2.6.58	XA-MEV	L-749A	2665	Aeronaves	45/45	G'ajra–Mexico City	Nr Guadalajara	Crashed.into La Latilla mountain after climbout. Crew failed to follow approved procedures
14.8.58	PH-LKM	L-1049H	4841	KLM	99/99	Shannon–Gander	100m w of Galway Bay	Possible propeller overspeed. Crashed in sea
9.9.58	N6920C	L-1049H	4822	Flying Tiger	8/8	Guam–Tachikawa	15 miles s-w Tokyo	Crashed into Mt. Oyama, Japan
14.10.58	YV-C-ANC	L-1049G	4575	LAV	23/23	Panama–Maracaibo	Venezuela	Descended too early at night, hit Mt. Alto del Cedro
10.11.58	N6503C	L-1049D	4165	Seaboard & Western	5/0	Training	Idlewild Airport, NY	Prop reversal on take-off, aircraft became uncontrollable, hit TCAL Viscount CF-TGL
15.11.58	VH-EAP	L-1049G	4680	Qantas	/0	San Francisco–Nadi	Nadi Airport, Fiji	Hit bank on landing, bounced, buckled airframe. Repaired
12.12.58	CF-TEZ	L-1049H	4851	TCAL	/0	Toronto	Toronto Malton	Hit trees on approach, made wheels-up landing
24.12.58	F-BAXX	L-749A	2527	Air France	28/0	Munich–Vienna	Nr Vienna Airport	Crew lost sight of ground on base leg, crashed 7,218ft short of runway
11.1.59	D-ALAK	L-1049G	4602	Lufthansa	39/36	Hamburg–Rio	Rio de Janeiro	Hit water descending in rain, crashed on beach. Crew fatigue a factor
17.1.59	N6234G	L-1049G	4659	Eastern	/0	Miami	Miami Airport	No.3 engine caught fire on take-off, right gear collapsed on landing, fire broke out. Repaired
12.5.59	N2735A	L-049	1978	Capital Airlines	44/2	Cleveland–Chicago	Charleston, WV	Landed too fast on wet runway. Pilot ground looped aircraft which slid over embankment and burned
25.6.59	N7121C	L-1049G	4648	TWA	0/0	—	Idlewild Airport, NY	Overpressurised in test, forward fuselage burst. Rebuilt
26.6.59	N7313C	L-1649A	1015	TWA	68/68	Milan–Paris	Nr Varese, Italy	Fuel tank vapour ignited by lightning, wing exploded
19.7.59	VT-DIN	L-1049G	4667	Air-India	46/0	Tokyo–Bombay	Bombay Santa Cruz	Incorrectly set altimeter, began overshoot too low in poor visibility, skidded into swamp, caught fire
14.10.59	VH-EAO	L-1049G	4679	Qantas	/0	San Francisco–NY	Lovelock Field, NV	No.4 prop feathered and fell off before emergency landing
24.11.59	N102R	L-1049H	4824	TWA	3/3	Chicago–LA	Chicago Midway	Hit building while turning on approach with No.2 engine out
3.1.60	N110A	L-749A	2531	Eastern	/0	Philadelphia	Philadelphia, PA	Right gear collapsed while taxying. Repaired but never re-entered service
21.1.60	HK-177	L-1049E	4556	AVIANCA	46/37	Miami–Montego Bay	Montego Bay, Jamaica	Oversteep approach, structural failure and fire. Crew fatigue a factor
13.2.60	N6229C	L-1049C	4537	Eastern	/0	Washington	Washington DC	Aborted t/o, groundlooped, left gear collapsed. Repaired
29.2.60	N7101C	L-1049G	4582	TWA	0/0	Chicago–Phoenix	Chicago-Midway	Maingear collapsed taxying on snow, damaged beyond repair
14.6.60	N1554V	L-749A	2555	Pacific Nthn A/l	14/14	Cordova–Anchorage	Mt. Gilbert, Alaska.	Poor navigation led to crash into mountain at 9,000ft. Air Defense Command radar failed to warn crew
24.8.60	VH-EAC	L-1049G	4606	Qantas	50/0	Mauritius–Cocos Is.	Plaisance, Mauritius	Aborted take-off, crashed in gully and caught fire
29.8.60	F-BHBC	L-1049G	4622	Air France	63/63	Paris–Dakar	Off Dakar, Senegal	Crashed into sea after landing attempt. Possible crew distraction, lightning strike or structural failure
8.11.60	N7125C	L-1049G	4652	Iberia	63/0	Barcelona	Barcelona	Left gear struck rubbish heap short of runway, aircraft veered left off runway and caught fire
16.12.60	N6907C	L-1049	4021	TWA	44/44	Columbus–NY	Staten Is., NY	Struck by United DC-8 N8013U in pattern, crashed in Staten Island. 84 in DC-8 and six on ground also killed

ABOVE: L-1049E YV-C-AMS of Venezuela's LAV was involved in a disasterous accident on 20 August 1956. About 90 minutes after taking off from New York the No. 2 propeller was oversped and could not be feathered. The vibrating engine probably cracked a fuel line causing a fire and the Super Connie crashed into the sea while trying to return, at about 1.30am. All 74 on board perished. *John Stroud Collection/The Aviation Picture Library*

DT.	REG.	MODEL	C/N	OPER.	POB/K.	FLIGHTPLAN	LOCATION	SUMMARY
26.1.61	PP-PDC	L-049	2056	Panair do Brasil	59/0		Belo Horizonte	Bello Horizonte, Brazil. Landed too far down wet runway, groundlooped and wound up in ditch
6.3.61	EC-AIP	L-1049G	4552	Iberia	36/0	Sao Paulo	Sao Paulo, Brazil	Caught by downward gust on approach, crashed and burned short of runway
10.5.61	F-BHBM	L-1649A	1027	Air France	78/78	Ft Lamy–Marseilles	Nr In Amenas, Libya	Bomb exploded, aircraft crashed, burned in Sahara
19.6.61	LV-GLH	L-1649A	1006	Tr. Atlantica Argentina	/0	Rio de Janeiro	Rio de Janeiro	Sheared off landing gear on abutment short of runway, slid down runway. Pilot error
20.6.61	N5595A	L-749A	2620	Int. A/c Services	/0	—	Oakland	Tail ripped off by runaway DC-7 N312A
3.8.61	N6220C	L-1049C	4528	Eastern	/0	—	NY Idlewild Airport	Undercarriage collapsed on landing, burned up
1.9.61	N86511	L-049	2035	TWA	78/78	Chicago–Las Vegas	Nr Hinsdale, Illinois	Missing elevator bolt caused full up deflection and stall. Crashed ten miles west of Midway airport
8.11.61	N2737A	L-049E	1976	Imperial A/w	79/77	B'timore–Col'bia SC	Nr Richmond, VA	Two engines failed, crew mishandled emergency, crashed into forest. Passengers were servicemen
11.11.61	HH-ABA	L-749A	2615	Air Haiti Int.	3/3	San Juan–Managua	East of Puerto Rico	Missing, no trace ever found. Documents invalid
3.3.62	PP-PCR	L-049	2060	Panair do Brasil	/0	Belo Horizonte	Rio-Galleo, Brazil	Nosegear would not lower, belly landing
15.3.62	N6911C	L-1049H	4804	Flying Tiger	7/1	Travis AFB–Adak	NAS Adak, Alaska	Drifted below glideslope and struck ground 328ft short, slewed off runway, caught fire
15.3.62	N6921C	L-1049H	4817	Flying Tiger	107/107	Guam–Clark AB	Pacific Ocean	Midair explosion seen, cause never determined nor wreckage found
20.3.62	HK-653	L-749A	2645	Avianca	/0	?	Bogota, Colombia	Gear failed to lower, belly-landed on foam. Repaired
14.4.62	N7115C	L-1049G	4596	TWA	/0	—	NY Idlewild	Nosewheel collapsed while being towed. Not repaired
26.4.62	N116A	L-749A	2611	FAA	6/5	training	Canton Island, Pacific	Undetected reversal of No.4 prop during go around
26.4.62	F-BAZE	L-749A	2624	Air Algérie	0/0	—	Algiers-Maison Blanche	Blown up by OAS terrorists on ground
28.5.62	N6213C	L-1049	4013	Eastern	/0	Wash'DC Idlewild	La Guardia, NY	Nose gear collapsed, substantial damage. Repaired
14.7.62	PP-PCF	L-049	2049	Panair do Brasil	/0	Rio-Galleo	Rio-Galleo, Brazil	Belly landing, not repaired
23.9.62	N6923C	L-1049H	4827	Flying Tiger	76/28	Gander–Rhein Main	560nm west of Shannon	Two engines failed, third accidently disabled by flight engineer, ditched
14.12.62	PP-PDE	L-049	2047	Panair do Brasil	50/50	Belem-Manaus	Parana de Eva, Brazil	Crashed six minutes from landing, cause undetermined
14.12.62	N6913C	L-1049H	4810	Flying Tiger	5/5	Chicago–Burbank	Burbank, CA	Pilot had heart attack, crashed on approach. Three on ground also killed

Dt.	Reg.	Model	c/n	Oper.	Pob/k.	Flightplan	Location	Summary
3.2.63	N9740C	L-1049H	4851	Slick Airways	5/2	Albuquerque–San Fr.	San Francisco	Struck approach lights, climbed but crashed left of runway
28.5.63	N189S	L-1049G	4541	Standard A/w	64/0	California–M'ttn KS	Manhattan KS	No.3 prop went into reverse pitch on approach, landed short and ripped gear off
1.3.64	N86504	L-049	2025	Paradise A/l	85/85	San Jose–Lk Tahoe	Nr Zephyr Cove, NV	Cr into mountain after missed approach in bad weather
9.3.64	N91209	L-749	2585	TWA	/0	Wash' DC–Baltimore	Boston, ME	Nosegear would not extend, landed on foam. Repaired
3.9.64	LV-GLI?	L-1649A	1008	FAA	0/0	—	Deer Valley, USA	Destroyed in safety tests
2.10.64	LX-IOK	L-749A	2562	Interocean	7/1	Dublin–Addis Ababa	Addis Ababa, Ethiopia	Veered off runway on landing. Attempted go-around with wrong blower setting
24.12.64	N6915C	L-1049H	4812	Flying Tiger	3/3	San Francisco–NY	San Bruno Mts, CA	Deviated from prescribed course after take-off in IFR conditions, hit mountains
5.5.65	EC-AIN	L-1049G	4550	Iberia Airlines	49/30	Madrid–Tenerife	Tenerife, Canary Islands	Struck grader and crashed during second landing attempt in adverse conditions
20.9.65	N9719C	L-1049E	4574	American Flyers	3/0	Ardmore	Ardmore, OK	Damaged beyond repair on landing
4.12.65	N6218C	L-1049C	4526	Eastern	54/4	Boston–Newark	Carmel, NY	Collision with TWA 707 N748TW, crash-landed on hill. Error by Connie crew, 707 landed safely
15.12.65	N6914C	L-1049H	4811	Flying Tiger	3/3	LA–Chicago	Nr Alamosa CA	Hit Blanca Pk due to navigation error at night/cloud
26.1.66	N7115C	L-1049G	4596	TWA	0/0	—	NY JFK Airport	Nosegear collapsed, aircraft written off
6.3.66	N6901C	L-1049	4015	LAPA	5/1	Lima–Asuncion	s-w of Callao, Peru	Engine failed, two feathered, ditched. Drug flight
8.3.66	G-ANTF	L-649	2504	ACE Freighters	/0	UK–Far East	Aden	Forced belly landing on MoD flight. Repaired
27.4.66	OB-R-771	L-749A	2521	Lansa	49/49	Lima–Cuzco	Tomas, Peru	Crashed into Mt. Talsua. Climb performance miscalculated
6.6.66	N86523	L-749A	2659	Pac Nthn A/l	/0	Kenai	Kenai, Alaska	Landing accident
15.8.66	N65	L-749A	2648	FAA	/0	Tachikawa	Tachikawa, Japan	Hydraulic failure, swerved on landing, struck ditches, gear collapsed
18.10.66	N6219C	L-1049C	4527	Eastern	/0	—	Miami	Damaged beyond repair
18.12.66	N7301C	L-1649A	1002	Aerocondor	59/17	Miami–Bogota	Bogota	Landed short in fog. Pilot distracted by unauthorised person in cockpit
17.4.67	N7777C	L-1049H	4803	Alaska Airlines	32/0	Kotzebue	Kotzebue, Alaska	Crew forgot to lower landing gear, belly landed
22.6.67	N5408V*	L-1049H	4849	Airlift Int.	7/7	Manila–Saigon	4 miles north of Saigon	Collided with RF-4C Phantom 65-0861, crashed. F-4 pilots ejected. *Also reported as N6936C
1968	N7324C	L-1649A	1030	Six T Ranch Inc	/0	Paramaribo	P'maribo (Surinam)	Struck trees on t/o, returned safely. Abandoned
1.68	'5T-TAC'	L-1049G	4645	Biafran Govt.	/0	Port Harcourt	Pt Harcourt, Nigeria	Crashed on approach in tight turn
30.3.68	HP-467	L-1049G	4678	RAPSA	3/3	Panama City	P'ma City, Panama	Crashed following No.3 engine fire
3.6.68	5T-TAC	L-1049H	4166	North Am A/c	0/0	Lisbon–Uli	Bissau, Guinea-Bissau	Blown up on ground

Left: Many non-scheduled operators found work for their Constellations undertaking military charter flights for the US government. One of these was Imperial Airlines who operated three L-049s on civil and military charter work from April 1960. Training and maintenance procedures were poor and the crew of N2737A seen here mishandled an emergency caused by improperly maintained fuel pumps on 8 November 1961. The aircraft crashed near Richmond, Virginia and all the passengers, 74 Army recruits on their way to Fort Jackson, South Carolina, and three of the five crew were killed. *Stephen Piercey Collection/ The Aviation Picture Library*

DT.	REG.	MODEL	C/N	OPER.	POB/K.	FLIGHTPLAN	LOCATION	SUMMARY
28.6.68	N8081H	L-1649A	1026	Willair Int.	/0	Stockton	Stockton, CA	Landed short, right gear collapsed. Not repaired
1.7.68	5T-TAG	L-1049G	4642	North Am A/c	4/4	Uli	Uli Airstrip, Nigeria	Struck treetops on approach, crashed
9.12.68	N7314C	L-1649A	1016	Fly by Night	104/0	Las Vegas	Las Vegas	Engine failed on take-off, gear collapsed trying to abort
26.3.69	N7311C	L-1649A	1013	Trans American	?	Colchane	Nr Isluga, Chile	Engine failed, wrong one feathered. Smuggling flight. Forced landing at 16,404ft
3.8.69	CF-NAJ	L-1049H	4828	CanRelief Air	4/4	Uli	Uli Airstrip, Nigeria	Flew into hillside on approach at night
4.8.69	N120A	L-749A	2617	Trans Southern	/0	Aracatuba	Aracatuba, Brazil	Crashed on take-off on tobacco smuggling flight
9.8.69	F-BGNC	L-1049G	4512	Catair	4/4	Doula,Cameroon	50 miles n-e of Douala	Crashed after starting ILS descent
28.11.69	5N-85H	L-749A	2662	Phoenix	'all killed'	Lisbon–Sao Tomé	Algeria–M'ccan border	Crashed after three engines failed
6.12.69	CF-NAM	L-1049H	4832	CanRelief Air	0/0	—	Uli, Nigeria	Damaged by bomb splinters. Never repaired
17.12.69	CF-NAK	L-1049H	4829	CanRelief Air	0/0	—	Uli Airstrip, Nigeria	Bombed by Nigerian aircraft
1.2.70	G-ANTF	L-749A	2504	Ace Freighters	0/0	ground	Coventry, UK	Damaged beyond repair
5.5.70	N174W	L-1049H	4636	North Slope	3/0	Fairbanks–Barrow	Barrow, AK	Hit snowbank on approach, causing structural failure
6.6.70	N8021	L-1049G	4673	Smugglers	5/0	La Rioja	La Rioja, Argentina	Gear collapsed on landing, fire broke out
0.0.71	N45515	L-1049H	4843	Unum Inc	0/0	—	Kingman, AZ	Wing exploded on ground
26.1.71	HI-129	L-749A	2523	Quisqueyena	/0	St Domingo–S Juan	Santo Domingo	Failed hijack to Cuba, crash landed at Santo Domingo. Repaired
20.10.71	N564E	L-1049H	4834	Balair Inc	4/4	St Domingo–Miami	Strait of Bahamas	Crashed in sea at night, possibly struck by lightning
29.5.72	PP-PDG	L-049	2037	Amazonense	14/14	R Branco–Cruizeiro	Cruizeiro do sul, Brz.	Refuelled from trucks, took off before fuel settled, two engines cut. Crashed attempting road landing
3.4.73	N6906C	L-1049	4020	A/c Airframe	/0	ground	Miami	Undercarriage collapsed while taxying. Not repaired
9.6.73	N173W	L-1049H	4674	A/c Spec'ties	3/3	crop spraying	Casey, Canada	Flaps retracted too soon, crashed into trees soon after t/o
5.8.73	N6202C	L-1049	4002	Happy Hour	8/0	Bahamas–Ft Laud.	Tamarac, FL	Fuel starvation, made wheels-up landing
24.9.73	N566E	L-1049H	4838	Nation of Islam	5/0	Gary	Gary Airport, IN	Failed to flare on landing, left gear collapsed, fire broke out
15.12.73	N6917C	L-1049H	4815	ANDES	3/3	Miami–Caracas	Nr Miami Apt	Over-rotated on t/o, stalled and crashed into houses
11.5.75	N45516	L-1049H	4840	A/c Spec'ties	6/6	Mesa–Kansas	Nr Mesa, AZ	Lost power on all four engines, struck trees and playhouse in forced landing
3.6.75	N6931C	L-1049H	4813	Sky Truck Int	/0	Guadeloupe–S Juan	Guadeloupe	Damaged during one-engine emergency landing, w/o
19.5.76	N468C	L-1049H	4846	F&B Livestock	3/0	Tegucigalpa–Miami	Blue Creek, Belize	No.1 prop ran away, came off and struck No.2. Left gear stuck partially up, aircraft ran off runway
22.10.77	N273R	L-749A	2650	Lanzair	0/0	ground	Lomé, Togo	Destroyed by fire
15.10.78	N6924C	L-1049H	4852	Smugglers	3/1	Riohacha	Riohacha, Colombia	Premature gear retraction on take-off
21.6.79	C-GXKS	L-749	2609	Beaver Airspray	4/0	Agricultural flight	Rivière du Loup, Que	Hydraulic failure on t/o, overran. Caught fire during dismantling
31.8.79	HI-260	L-049	2070	Quisqueyana	0/0	—	Santo Domingo	Damaged beyond repair by Hurricane David
3.10.79	N6695C	L-749	2671	Aero Hist Ass.	0/0	museum	Bradley Air Mus CT	Damaged beyond repair by tornado
22.6.80	N74CA	L-1049H	4850	Air Traders Int	3/8	Columbus– Seattle	1 mile from Columbus IN	Fire on Nno.2 engine, others overheated, crew mis-handled emergency. Pilot Herman 'Fish' Salmon
26.10.81	HI-328	L-749	2607	Aerolineas Argo	3/3	St. Thomas	St. Thomas, Virgin Islands	Performed turn to avoid aircraft, turned onto approach and struck the sea
1988	HI-422	L-749A	2667	Aerochago	?	?	Santo Domingo	Landing accident
5.4.90	HI-515CT	C-121S	4192	AMSA	3/1	S Juan-S Domingo	Off Levittown, PR	Unauthorised three-engined ferry flight. Two more engines failed, aircraft ditched
6.90	HI-532CT	C-121J	4155	Aerochago	0.0	Santo Domingo		Heavy landing. Not repaired
3.2.92	HI-542CT	L-1049H	4825	AMSA	0/0	—	Borinquen, PR	Struck by taxying DC-4 N74AF. Fire broke out
22.9.98	HI-548CT (C-121C)	L-1049	4202	Aerochago	0/0	—	Santo Domingo	Damaged when struck by C-46 blown into it by Hurricane 'Georges'. Broken up in early 1999

8 SURVIVORS

ABOVE: Few Constellations survive in Navy markings to remind the younger generation of the work and sacrifices of the Barrier Squadrons, the 'Hurricane Hunters' and 'Typhoon Trackers' and the 'Puckered Penguins' of the Antarctic. WV-2/EC-121K 143221 seen here is kept in the storage yard of the National Museum of Naval Aviation at Pensacola, Florida. *Author*

The number of surviving Constellations, Super Constellations and Starliners out of the 856 built is very low. The Connie is a big aircraft, hard to maintain and hard to keep indoors. A precise figure for survivors is difficult to quantify exactly as a number are in rarely-visited corners of the globe. The exact status of many could be the source of hours of debate with their owners, should they be located. Others are the pride and joy of museum creators and volunteers, and a smaller number still (currently five) are kept in an airworthy state.

Many of those not cared for by a museum or group are at the mercy of vandals, developers, airport authorities, scrapmen and the tropical weather. A depressing number of these aircraft, despite their many fans, continue to fall victim to various fates. The long-term Malta resident '5T-TAF', Kirkop's 'Super Constellation Bar', was destroyed by fire in May 1997. Arsonists have also accounted for several other Connie bars and discos over the years including '5N-83H' at Faro, Portugal. The tornado that struck the Bradley Air Museum in Connecticut in October 1979 numbered L-749, N6695C, among its victims, and others have been damaged by storms. One of the saddest losses was that of NC-121K, 141292, the very last Connie in US military service. Retired in 1982 to the Florence Air and Missile Museum in Florence, South Carolina, it could not be moved when the museum was forced to close (by a car park expansion) and was broken up in situ in 1998. Some parts at least could be salvaged to help other projects.

The fate of the Indian aircraft not slated for preservation is unclear. All nine surviving aircraft were extant in 1987, four at Goa, four at Poona (or Pune) and one at Santa Cruz. Various of these have been seen since, but the location of only one, IN 315

ABOVE: TWA's N90831 *Star of Switzerland* was the tenth Constellation built and is the oldest to survive. Today it is displayed in the preserving desert climate at the Pima Air & Space Museum having been extensively restored in the 1970s.
David Willis

(stored for the navy museum at Goa), can be confirmed at time of writing despite visits by enthusiasts to most Indian air bases.

Occasionally, however, there is good news of a kind. Two of the Biafran Airlift Super Connies have been confirmed as remaining where last parked on the South Atlantic island of Sao Tomé, although essentially in an unsalvageable state. The L-1049H at Borinquen in western Puerto Rico is still there, despite having vanished from most references and, most encouragingly, one of its sister ships is being readied to fly to Europe at the time of writing. A Swiss group called the Super Constellation Flyers is restoring C-121G/L-1049H HI-583CT, for passage to Europe and eventual presentation on the airshow circuit.

On the Starliner front, Maurice Roundy of Auburn, Maine, USA, owns three-quarters of the intact survivors. Technically, none of them are airworthy at present, although one has been made so for the purposes of a one-off ferry flight from Sanford, Florida, to join the others at Auburn. Maurice hopes that someone with the money and resources will acquire one of these magnificent aircraft from him and display it where it belongs, in flight.

The ranks of airworthy Connies have dwindled to a small but select bunch, all of which look like flying for many years to come. Currently they number five. Four are in the USA and one is in Australia. All are Super Connies except L-749, N494TW, based at Avra Valley, Arizona, with computer magnate and business jet developer Vern Raburn. This was the first C-121A accepted by the USAF and flew on the Berlin Airlift, and later served as a VIP transport. Acquired from the actor John Travolta in 1987, it was restored to its original configuration and colour scheme from its previous incarnation as a budworm sprayer, and is now frequently seen at airshows in the western US. The aircraft also undertook a successful European tour in 1998.

BELOW: At the end of the Biafran Airlift, Connies that had been so vital in relief work were abandoned all over west Africa and southern Europe. One of these was CS-TLC, one of several falsely registered '5T-TAF'. Sold at auction at Malta's Luqua Airport in 1972, it was towed to nearby Kirkop and turned into a restaurant/bar. Sadly it was later to fall victim to arsonists.
Stephen Piercey Collection/The Aviation Picture Library

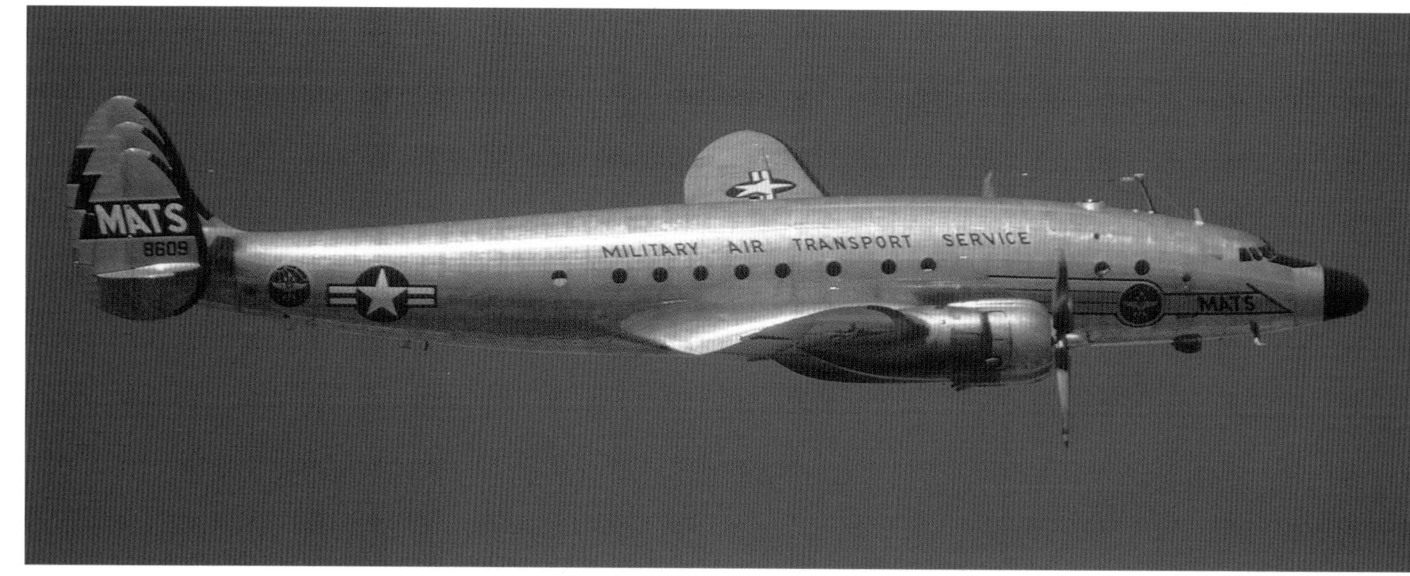

At Camarillo, near Oxnard, California, there are two airworthy Connies, both C-121s. C-121C, N73544, last used by the West Virginia Air National Guard and now owned by D. Benny Younesi's Constellation Historical Society, is in a military passenger configuration. Some unaccounted for hours in the aircraft's logbook suggest one final secret mission before the aircraft was made available for civilian purchase.

The other Camarillo Connie is the Global Aeronautical Foundation's N548GF, which retains the lower radome, tip tanks and internal equipment it carried when retired from the Air Force Reserve's 79th AEW and Control Squadron as an EC-121T in 1978. It is flown less frequently than N73544, partly because of the difficulty of acquiring qualified crew. According to the FAA, it is an EC-121, for which there is no type authorisation for crews and not a L-1049 (for which there is).The only purely civil Constellation still flying is L-1049H N6937C, based at Kansas City's Downtown Airport. Lovingly cared for by the Airline Historical Museum (better known as Save-A-Connie), this ex-Sky Truck International freighter and later Aircraft Specialties crop sprayer has now adopted full TWA colours and titles, as a tribute to the airline most associated with the Constellation.

Last but not least, The Historical Aircraft Restoration Society (HARS) at Mascot Airport, near Sydney, Australia, flies a C-121C in a pseudo-Qantas colour scheme. HARS has yet to convince Qantas that passengers will not complain about the age of the national carrier's equipment if the Super Connie is seen on the ramp in its full colours, and for the time being it wears, simply and evocatively, the word 'Connie' on its dolphin-like fuselage.

ABOVE: C-121A N749TW is the only 'regular' Constellation currently on the airshow circuit. It wears the MATS colours it had when it served in support of the Berlin Airlift, and visited Europe in 1998 to commemorate the 50th anniversary of that event. *Author*

BELOW: The only Connie in the UK is N7777G, an ex-KLM L-749. Its colourful career included touring with the Rolling Stones, drug running, cattle carrying and an abortive TV role. One thing it never did was to fly with TWA. It is only seen these days on the infrequent occasion of an open day at the Science Museum's outstation at Wroughton, near Swindon. *Author*

BELOW RIGHT: L-1049H HI-542T seen intact but forgotten at Borinquen, Puerto Rico in July 1999. *Author*

Model	c/n	Identity	Status	Location/owner/notes
L-049	1970	N90831	Display	Pima Air & Space Museum, Tucson, Arizona, TWA colours
L-049	2071	N86533	Restoration	Moved to 'Wings of a Dream' Museum, Brazil late 2000. Formerly bar at Ascuncion, Paraguay
L-049	2072	N9412H	Shop	Pilots shop, Greenwood Lake, New Jersey.
L-1049	2089	N2520B	Display	Santa Cruz, Bolivia. Former Pepsi hoarding, now grey and blue
L-749	2503	F-ZVMV	Stored	Musée de L'Air, Paris Le Bourget. Engine test bed configuration
L-649	2522	HI-332	Derelict	Last noted Agua Jira, Colombia (impounded)
L-749	2553	N7777G	Stored	Science Museum, Wroughton UK, TWA colours.
L-749A	2600	N608AS	Stored	Henry Oliver III. Tucson Ryan, Arizona. Reportedly for sale in airworthy state
L-749	2601	N494TW	Airworthy	The Constellation Group, Avra Valley, Arizona. The 'MATS Connie'
L-749A	2602	N9463	Stored	Columbine II Inc Santa Fe, New Mexico. Airworthy but not flown
C-121A	2603	HI-393	Unknown	Last noted with Aerochago Santo Domingo 1994
L-749A	2604	N749VR	Stored	Avra Valley, Arizona Dutch Constellation Group
C-121A	2605	N422NA	Display	Valle-Grand Canyon Airport, Arizona. Planes of Fame Museum, *'Bataan'*
C-121A	2606	48-0614	Display	Pima Air & Space Museum, Tucson, Arizona *'Columbine'*
L-749A	2613	N1206	Display	International Society of Vehicle Preservation. Salina, Kansas (reportedly for sale)
L-749A	2675	CN-CCN	Stored	Casablanca, Morocco Royal Air Maroc
L-1049H	4137	N105CF	Airworthy	Opa Locka, Florida For Super Constellation Flyers, Switzerland. Formerly HI-583CT
C-121J	4145	131644.	Derelict	Main fuselage still buried under snow at McMurdo Sound, Antarctica
VC-121E	4151	53-7885	Display	US Air Force Museum, Wright Patterson AFB, Ohio. *'Columbine III'*
EC-121S	4174	54-0155	Display	USAF History & Traditions Museum, Lackland AFB, Texas
C-121C	4175	N73544	Airworthy	Constellation Historical Society, Camarillo, California
C-121C	4176	VH-EAG	Airworthy	HARS, Mascot, NSW Australia in pseudo-Qantas colour scheme
C-121C	4196	N1104W	Stored	National Air and Space Museum Dulles Airport, Washington DC
C-121C	4199	54-0180	Display	Transport Aircraft Museum Charleston AFB, S. Carolina, marked as '40153'
EC-121T	4335	N4257L	Tech aid	Vocational Tech College, Helena Airport, Montana, marked as 52-3417
EC-121T	4336	N4257U	Display	Combat Air Museum Topeka-Forbes, Kansas, marked as 52-3418
EC-121T	4343	52-3425	Display	Peterson Air and Space Museum, Peterson AFB, Colorado
EC-121K	4347	137890	Display	Tinker AFB, Oklahoma, Marked as EC-121H 55-0552
EC-121H	4350	N51006	Stored	Minden Air Corp Yard, Tuscon. Marked as 30535
EC-121T	4363	N548GF	Airworthy	Camarillo, California Global Aeronautical Foundation
EC-121T	4369	53-0554	Display	Pima Air & Space Museum, Tucson, Arizona
EC-121D	4370	53-0555	Display	USAF Museum Wright-Patterson AFB, Ohio
NC-121K	4421	141297	Display	Museum of Aviation Warner-Robins AFB, Georgia
EC-121K	4433	141309	Display	McClellan Air Museum, McClellan AFB, California, marked as 54-0552
EC-121K	4435	141311	Display	Octave Chanute Aerospace Museum Rantoul, Illinois
EC-121K	4495	143221	Stored	National Museum of Naval Aviation, NAS Pensacola, Florida
L-1049C	4519	F-BRAD	Restoration	Under restoration for museum, Nantes, France, Air France colours
L-1049E	4544	CF-RNR	Bar	Mississauga Ontario (next to Pearson Airport). Formerly at Regal Constellation Hotel,Toronto
L-1049E	4557	N1005C	Stored	For Dover AFB Museum (ex Amelia's Bar, Penndel, Pennsylvania)
L-1049G	4604	D-ALIN	Display	Hermeskeil Museum, in Lufthansa colours
L-1049E	4614	IN315	Stored	Stored for Indian Naval Museum, Goa Dabolim
L-1049G	4626	F-BHBG	Bar	Outside Le Moulin disco, Quimper, Normandy, France
L-1049G	4671	F-BHML	Display	F.J. Strauss International Airport, Munich, in Lufthansa colours as 'D-ALAP'
L-1049G	4686	BG583	Believed stored	Indian Air Force Museum, Palam New Delhi.
L-1049G	4687	BG579	Believed stored	Pune, India
L-1049H	4825	HI-542T	Derelict	Rafael Hernandez Airport, Borinquen, Puerto Rico
L-1049H	4830	N6937C	Airworthy	Airline Historical Society, Kansas City Missouri in TWA colours
L-1049H	4831	CF-NAL	Derelict	Sao Tomé, Ex-Biafran airlift
L-1049H	4832	CF-NAM	Derelict	Sao Tomé, Ex-Biafran airlift
L-1049H	4846	N468C	Coop	Blue Creek, Belize. Fuselage only
L-1649A	1013	N7311C	Wreck	Up a mountain, Isluga, Chile
L-1649A	1018	N7316C	Stored	Maine Coast Airways at Auburn-Lewiston, Maine
L-1649A	1030	N8083H	Stored	Maine Coast Airways at Auburn-Lewiston, Maine
L-1649A	1038	N974R	Restoration	Sanford, Florida, by Maine Coast Airways. Set to return to air in 2001
L-1649A	1042	ZS-DVJ	Display	South African Airways

Notes:

The Greenwood Lake NJ Connie may be moved or restored as the state has bought the airport.

The prototype Starliner, formerly an amusement park attraction in Japan was moved to Nagoya in 1984 and seems to have subsequently been scrapped.

The Super Constellation Flyers hope to have their L 1049H based at Basle-Mulhouse in Switzerland sometime in 2001.

The Constellation near Faro, Portugal was burned out and only the wings survive.

In late 2000, the L-049 at Ascuncion was disassembled and transported to Brazil for the new aviation museum being set up by the airline TAM.R7V-1.

N4247K of World Fish and Agriculture Inc (also known as Winky's Flying Fish) was impounded in Manila, Philippines c1987 and may possibly still be there.

Most of the Indian Air Force and Navy Connies have not been reported for some time.

ABOVE: North of Los Angeles near the town of Oxnard is Camarillo, one of only a few places where more than one Constellation can be found togther. More remarkably, both of these aircraft fly — C-121C N73544 (left) belongs to the Constellation Historical Society and EC-121T N548GF to the Global Aeronautical Foundation. *Author*

LEFT: Despite its decrepit appearance, this L-1049H (N6922C) seen at Sanford Florida in 1988 was airworthy and flew on for several years more, latterly with AMSA, before it was abandoned in Puerto Rico after a ground accident. The aircraft wears the remnants of an Iberia paint scheme applied briefly for a TV commercial in 1980. *Austin J. Brown/The Aviation Picture Library*

BOTTOM: Seen in its glory days with Cubana, CU-P573 (c/n 4557) served with Seaboard & Western, BOAC, Eastern, Aerlinte and Capitol before becoming mounted atop a restaurant in Pendel, Pennsylvania in 1967. This veteran L-1049E is still there, serving as 'Amelia's Bar'. *John Stoud Collection/The Aviation Picture Library*

ABOVE RIGHT: Amazingly, all three of the VC-121 Connies that wore the '***Columbine***' name still exist. General Eisenhower's ***Columbine*** is preserved as seen here at the Pima Air & Space Museum in Arizona, ***Columbine II*** was restored from a battered wreck to airworthy condition in Arizona but has rarely flown since, and President Eisenhower's ***Columbine III*** is at the USAF Museum in Ohio. *David Willis*

CENTRE RIGHT: L-1049C F-BRAD, a Biafran Airlift veteran, has been displayed for many years on a roundabout at Nantes, France. It has recently been adopted by a group at the nearby airport and will undergo a full restoration soon. Several Connies were preserved like this in France, but have almost all been scrapped or burnt. *Michael Stroud*

BELOW RIGHT: The privately-owned museum at Hermeskeil, Germany has a large collection of aircraft. Among them are a full-scale replica Concorde, and L-1049G D-ALIN which arrived from Hamburg Airport in 1981. *Author*

USAF
AIR FORCE
8614

AIR FRANCE
SUPER CONSTELLATION

LUFTHANSA

9 Chronology

Chronological Milestones

7 June 1938	First flight Douglas DC-4E
10 July 1940	Contract signed
2 February 1942	First flight Douglas DC-4
9 January 1943	First flight prototype Constellation (c/n 1961)
17 April 1944	Record flight Burbank–Washington DC
4 August 1945	First Atlantic crossing (by USAAF)
14 October 1945	Award of Approved Type Certificate
15 November 1945	First delivery to TWA
3 February 1946	First commercial flight (New York–Bermuda, Pan Am)
5 February 1946	Inaugural New York–Paris flight, TWA
1 March 1946	Inaugural Los Angeles–New York flight, TWA
27 July 1949	First flight de Havilland Comet 1
29 September 1949	First flight Douglas DC-6
14 July 1950	First order for AEW (PO-2) Super Connies
13 October 1950	First flight L-1049 Super Constellation (c/n 1961S, NC25600)
10 February 1951	First flight Douglas DC-6B
29 April 1951	DC-6B enters service
17 December 1951	First commercial flight L-1049 Newark–Miami, Eastern Air Lines
17 February 1953	First flight L-1049C (c/n 4501)
18 May 1953	First flight Douglas DC-7
December 1953	First flight WV-2 (c/n 4304)
August 1954	First Flight L-1049D (c/n 4163)
7 December 1954	First flight L-1049G
20 December 1955	First flight Douglas DC-7B
27 May 1955	First flight Sud-Est Caravelle
20 September 1956	First flight L-1049H (c/n 4801, VH-EAM)
10 October 1956	First flight L-1649 (c/n 1001, N1649)
late May 1957	L-1649 Starliner enters service
20 December 1957	First flight Boeing 707-120
12 February 1958	Production ends. Last L-1649 rolled out
27 April 1958	First flight de Havilland Comet 4
6 April 1967	Last TWA passenger Constellation flight (749A, c/n 2670, N6020C)
11 May 1967	Last TWA freight flight (1649A, c/n 1017, N7315C)
1968	Last US scheduled passenger service — Alaskan Airlines
1978	Last USAF Connies retired
1982	Last USN Connie retired
1983	Indian Navy Constellations retired
1993	Last Dominican Connie freighters grounded

List of Sources

Documentary references

Johnson, Clarence L., *The Development of the Lockheed Constellation.* Paper, Lockheed Aircraft Corporation, Burbank, 1944

Hibbard, Hall L. and Johnson, Clarence L., *The First Constellation Decade.* Paper

Lockheed Aircraft Corporation, *Tentative Cost Analysis, Lockheed Constellation Model 149 or 749 Modified for Petroleum Exploration and Executive Transport Use.* Lockheed Report SLR/782 14/11/1947

Weather Radar Installation in TWA Constellations. Report date unknown

Consolidated Aircraft Corporation. Convair Report SE310 15.7.1958

Lockheed Model L-1049G General Performance Data. Untitled report on prototype Constellation (1944)

Summers, Wg Cdr M., *Report on Mock Up of Lockhead* (sic) *C-69B Constellation Airliner.* Wright Field, Ohio 24.6.1943

NEW SPEED TO SHORTEN THE DISTANCE

QUIET LUXURY TO MAKE THE TIME FLY

Largest, Roomiest Airliner in the World
Far Quieter for Greater Comfort • Wider Aisles
Larger Windows • Wider Seats
Finest Air Conditioning • Restful 5-Cabin Privacy
Congenial Starlight Lounge
Interior Design by Henry Dreyfuss
The Fastest Constellation Ever Built.

For all the speed, and quiet comfort, too, fly Super Constellations over every ocean and continent on these 19 leading airlines:

AIR FRANCE • AIR-INDIA INTERNATIONAL
AVIANCA • CUBANA • DEUTSCHE LUFTHANSA
EASTERN AIR LINES • IBERIA • KLM • LAV
NORTHWEST ORIENT AIRLINES • PAKISTAN INTERNATIONAL
QANTAS • SEABOARD & WESTERN • SLICK AIRWAYS
TAP • THAI AIRWAYS • TRANS-CANADA AIR LINES
TWA-TRANS WORLD AIRLINES • VARIG

LOCKHEED SUPER CONSTELLATION

Look to Lockheed for Leadership

LEFT: TWA and Lockheed worked together to promote the Super Constellation in the press. This typical advertisement from 1955 featured the lounge area as well as emphasising the speed of the new model. *John Stroud Collection/The Aviation Picture Library*

Books

Germain, Scott E., *Lockheed Constellation and Super Constellation*, Volume 1, Airliner Tech series. Specialty Press, North Branch, Minnesota, 1998

Ginter, Steve, *Lockheed C-121 Constellation, Naval Fighters No. 8*. Naval Fighters, 1983

Hardy, M. J., *The Lockheed Constellation*. David & Charles, Newton Abbot, 1973

Marson, Peter J., *The Lockheed Constellation Series*. Second ed. Air-Britain (Historians) Ltd, 1982

Pace, Steve, *Lockheed's Constellation, Enthusiast Color Series* Motorbooks International, Osecola, 1998

Robson, Graham, *Prop Perfection: Restored Propliners and Warbirds*. Airlife, Shrewsbury, 1997

Stringfellow, Curtis K. and Bowers, Peter M., *Lockheed Constellation*. Motorbooks International, Osceola, 1992

The Constellation Group, *MATS Constellation European Tour June to September 1998*. Brochure

Eastwood, *Piston Airliner Production List*

The Aviation Hobby Shop *(various editions)*

Magazines and Journals

Boesen, Victor, 'Evolution of the Constellation', *Skyways*, October 1945

Francillion, René J., 'Connies' in uniform, Lockheed's Constellation/Super Constellation Military Variants', *Wings of Fame* Volume 19. Aerospace Publishing, London, 2000

Hibbard, Hall, 'A Star is Born', *The Lockheed-Vega Aircraftsman*, January 1943

Sharma, Rajesh, 'Requiem for the Connie', *Vayu Aerospace Review* (India), 2.1987

Thoren, Rudy, 'How We Tested the Constellation', *The Lockheed Star*. Date unknown

'How to fly the Constellation' and 'Design Analysis of the Constellation', *Air News with Air Tech*, December 1945

Various issues of the following magazines were consulted:

Aeroplane Monthly/Aeroplane. IPC Media, London

FlyPast. Key Publishing, Stamford, Lincs

Flight, The Aeroplane, Aviation Week, Air Classics, Propliner, Naval Aviation News

INDEX